PRAISE FOR
BEYOND THE STETHOSCOPE

"Lucy Mayes has compiled an important and compelling book written with care and sensitivity. I read this book in a sitting and finished with a sense of optimism and thankfulness that the heart of healthcare is alive and well."

Dr Catherine Crock AM, Physician,
Chair & Founder, The Hush Foundation

"Great writers draw you into the story from the first page; Lucy Mayes is one of those. In a moving, heart-warming and inspiring tale, Lucy sets out to rescue her doctor husband Richard from impending burnout. Her method? Collecting stories from doctors who still love their work and who find ways to flourish in a broken system. The end result is a profound gift, not just for her husband, but for all who practice medicine. Lucy has the advantage of viewing medical practice from outside the profession, asking fresh questions and bringing deep humanity to her quest. Highly recommended, this book will save many doctors' careers and will be a great blessing for their patients too."

Dr Robin Youngson, Anaesthetist, Author and
Founder of Hearts in Healthcare

"It is hoped that many doctors and patients will read and be inspired by the wisdom and compassion of the doctors who have shared their insights in the pages of this book, *Beyond the Stethoscope.* Heaven knows we need it."

Dr Craig Hassed, General Practitioner, Lecturer and Author

"Wisdom is timeless and the re-discovery of it is always timely. This book is about the wisdom revealed by doctors on reflection of their experience. These stories make a chorus of voices that encourage the progressive integration of self and other, that is only effective when there is deeper awareness of the human condition and all of its connections. The physical, psychological and emotional dimensions of the co-dependent doctor–patient relationship are revealed to a point that is, at its least, transparent and tangible, and at its best, transcendent. I unreservedly recommend this compelling account of individual journeys to better medicine through the lives of a broad range of doctors, so ably and sympathetically presented by Lucy Mayes."

Mark R Newton, MD FRACP, Neurologist, Victoria

"There is one common thread that connects and ties these inspirational stories so generously shared by all – the Heart and Art of Medicine, and our compassion to heal and be healed."

Associate Professor Vicki Kotsirilos AM,
Holistic General Practitioner and Health Leader

"Doctors love their evidence-based medicine, but when we are talking about really difficult topics, the power of narrative trumps all the statistical evidence you could ever accumulate. These stories, and the conversations they will enable, are vital to the wellbeing and sustainability of our profession."

Dr Katie Moore, Paediatric Oncologist,
Monash Health

"This is a beautifully crafted piece of work that honours doctors, first and foremost, as people. Thanks goes to Lucy for tenaciously fighting for such an important group of stories, in this digital world, where connectedness is both easier and more distant than ever. Humans are fallible and imperfect by scientific standards, and doctors are no different; machines can out-science any human, any time. What machines cannot do is feel with their heart, trust in their gut, listen with compassion or hear with empathy. These qualities provide the true connection that modern patients and doctors so desperately crave, and provide the ultimate healing for all."

Dr Mark Nethercote, Consultant Paediatrician, Ballarat, Victoria and author of A Time For Grace.

"Lucy Mayes has travelled the world to bring us inspiring stories of doctors who have found ways to revolutionise healthcare by reuniting healing and spirituality. Their acts of love, compassion and kindness fill me with hope. They have found a way to put the 'care' back in healthcare. This is the 'new medicine' that will change the world, one empowered patient and one conscious health care provider at a time!"

Sharlene Crage, Wellness Coach

"Artistic story teller Lucy Mayes has spent eight years listening with doctors: communing, story catching, learning, celebrating, and mourning. *Beyond the Stethoscope* reveals varied experiences in medicine. Here are 'back stage' vulnerabilities of ordinary, extraordinary humans; oath-bound bearers and givers of state-of-the-art medical knowledge, who choose to pour out life daily. I am awed, as I was absorbed, reading this astonishing tapestry. To all you doctors who have shared life glimpses – the world's doctors whose stories are hidden – we patients are deeply grateful."

Carol McDonough, Victorian Honour Roll of Women

"Lucy Mayes has listened and breathed deeply with the many doctors who reveal their felt experience of a life dedicated to caring for others. The power of her book is to give their voices the space to breathe and be heard on their own terms."

Jinette de Gooijer, PhD, Socioanalyst

ABOUT THE AUTHOR

Lucy Mayes is a trained lawyer, social worker and company director. She works as a leadership, community and organisational development consultant, and story catcher. Her writing has been published in literary and academic journals and she is a sought-after speaker and facilitator. Lucy has served on several not-for-profit boards and has worked in leadership development for over twenty years. Her innovative work in leadership has led to her being awarded a Rotary Paul Harris Fellowship, and being Victorian runner up of the prestigious Australian Rural Women's Award in 2008, sponsored by the Rural Industries Research and Development Corporation.

Lucy lives in Central Victoria, Australia where she is a proud and passionate mother, wife and community member. Her interest in the medical profession stems from her role as 'doctor's wife,' and also from a former life practicing medical litigation law, and a lifetime interest in human systems and purpose at work.

www.lucymayes.com

BEYOND THE
STETHOSCOPE

Doctors' Stories of Reclaiming Hope, Heart, and Healing in Medicine

LUCY MAYES

Dear Caroline,

How delightful to have met a fellow warrior for the human spirit in medicine!

Keep up your important work.

♡ Lucy

Published in Australia by
Heart Works Press
Postal: PO Box 591, Castlemaine, VIC 3451
Email: lucy@mayes.net.au
Website: www.lucymayes.com

HEART WORKS PRESS

First published in Australia 2017

 A catalogue record for this book is available from the National Library of Australia

Author: Mayes, Lucy
Title: BEYOND THE STETHOSCOPE: Doctors' stories of reclaiming hope, heart and healing in medicine
ISBN-13:   978-0-6481827-2-6 (Createspace Paperback)
ISBN: 978-0-6481827-1-9 (eBook)

Cover artwork, layout and design by Anna Wilson Illustration & Design
Back cover photopgraph: Richard and Lucy Mayes, by Rosana Kersh photography
Printed by Ingram Spark
Typesetting by Nelly Murariu, PixBeeDesign.com
Editing by Meredith McGowan, Multi-Task Editing
Printed by Createspace

"Beyond the Stethoscope" is for:

Dr Richard Mayes and is an act of love.

Dr Santha Trail, a General Practitioner, mother, wife and friend. Santha died tragically and unexpectedly of a spontaneous coronary artery dissection during the writing of this book and I never had a chance to 'catch' her story. She was a deeply loved and respected member of, and contributor to my community, colleague of my husband's, and friend of mine and many. She was passionate about supporting nursing mothers, indigenous communities and about her young family.

All doctors, and those aspiring to be doctors, in all fields of endeavour who work way beyond the call of duty, with all the highs and lows, pressures, demands and rewards of your important work. May you be richly rewarded and deeply sustained by your giving, and by this book.

ACKNOWLEDGMENTS

This book is the product of the enormous generosity of spirit of those who have shared their very personal stories. Without these contributing doctors, clearly, there is no book. But without their ongoing support and enthusiasm for this project, there would also have never been a book. I am immensely moved, humbled and grateful for these doctors' willingness to share not only their reflections on their life, work and professional journeys, but also often their homes and hospitality.

I started by cautiously making cold contact with the names and contact details I found on the medical practitioner listing on the Australasian Integrative Medicine Association (AIMA). A small handful of people responded and reassured me that I had a project worth pursuing. The first few interviews were conducted eight years ago and led to referrals to friends and colleagues, and the ball started rolling from there. The greatest door was opened through the Balint Society of Australia and New Zealand, and led to a trip to New Zealand where I was generously hosted in the homes of a number of the contributing doctors, and introductions to more people I should talk to, rolled in. I had the most wonderful week and was deeply inspired by some of the good work happening there. A conference in Ireland for my work in community development – where I was again generously hosted by a doctor – led me to David Reilly and Vikram Patel, two enormously influential and respected health care reformists whose stories I was delighted to be able to include in this book. I could have stayed in the UK and followed more leads there, working my way into other nations and continents, but this was an unfunded, 'love' project, conducted alongside my paid work and my family responsibilities. I had to choose an end point.

There are also doctors who shared their stories with me and then chose to withdraw them, or whose stories could not be included in this work, due to editorial, ethical or legal constraints. I thank them for their time and sharing. To those of you who withdrew, I respect your choice to remain a silent contributor in the end. I thank you for your time and sharing. To those who were unsure that your stories would be of any use to anyone else, thank you for allowing me to fight hard to convince you to let me keep your stories.

I have done a number of 'story catching' projects through my work and without fail, I find that the act of actually giving people a space to be heard in their endeavours and passions can be almost as therapeutic as the end product. There were many times after numerous rejections from publishers, and being told that "doctors don't read books," when I thought those conversations might be the only product of this project. But contributors kept contacting me to see how I was faring, and encouraged me to keep going (Cath Crock in particular, thank-you). People would send news stories my way, showing me that the world wants to talk about this stuff. I also know through my work in leadership development that shared story is where the real gold of learning and change lies. In the end, I just had to honour these stories and give them to the world. My hope and intention is that they will make a positive difference to individuals, organisations and systems.

My mother, Margaret Rees-Jones was also writing a book through this journey. Her dogged pursuit of her goal and successful publication inspired me to keep going with this book. Her home by the beach also housed me when I needed to escape all other distractions and write / edit. My dear father, sister and mother-in-law (fellow long-suffering doctor's wife) also helped me in millions of ways, especially with the children, over the years that I was bringing this 'baby' into the world. My dear friend Carol McDonough has been supportive in many ways over many years but most particularly with some very persistent 'nudging' and long hours of listening. Also, Mark Slattery who generously edited, believed and championed in the early days; and Meredith McGowan, my editor and friend to the end, for whom nothing was too much trouble. Gordon Thompson and Julie Postance were invaluable supporters and advisors on the publishing process, and Catherine Deveney's "Gunna's writing workshop" was a much needed and enjoyable injection to get me over the line from 'gunna' to 'done.' My Monday morning coffee girls and Origini and your coffee – what would I do without the 'kitchen table wisdom' and the fabulous coffee that we share weekly? My thanks to each of you. To those beautiful children of mine, Angus and Sophie: you were my cheer squad; encouraging me to keep going, advising, listening, being OK with being ignored for a while, and throwing my: 'dreams can come true' rhetoric back at me when needed. Deepest gratitude and love to you both. May you follow your dreams too.

Most of all though, I want to thank my seemingly tireless husband, Richard Mayes, for not only letting me run away on several occasions to pursue this project, which felt at times like it had no end, but also for your generosity in letting me share your story – a sharing which did not sit comfortably. It has been hard work walking alongside you at times as you pursue your 'love-job' – as it has no doubt been hard as I pursue mine. At times, I watch you eaten up by our community and their health needs; at times, I see you sinking; and at times I want to scream and tell them all to leave you and us alone so I can steal you away to an easier life. (Did you see? One of the other doctor's wives in this book actually did that!) But then I see the power of the work that you do; and its meaning to you as a deep expression of who you are. I love, respect and back you all the way. It is immensely important work, and the greatest gift and service you and all the other amazing doctors do. The world is a better place for you and your efforts. Thank you for letting me share and celebrate that.

CONTENTS

FOREWORD

Associate Professor Craig Hassed[1]

Sometimes, in rare moments of great clarity and conviction, we find an idea bursting into the mind and, if someone is there to listen, straight out of the mouth. It is as if the idea came from somewhere else and yet we completely own it and it is perfectly suited to meet some pressing need that will not be denied. Such ideas have an irresistible emotive strength and a sense of destiny about them – it will come to pass. At such times head and heart speak as one and are ready to serve a purpose greater than ourselves.

It seems that Lucy Mayes experienced one such moment when she heard her doctor husband's despondency relating to his lived experience of modern healthcare. Despite great dedication and compassion for his patients, he felt ineffectual at times to meet their complex health and emotional needs. Modern medicine immersed doctors and patients in a system where spending quality time was valued less than the volume

---

1   Associate Professor Craig Hassed works at the Department of General Practice and is co-ordinator of mindfulness programmes at Monash University. His teaching, research and clinical interests include mindfulness-based stress management, mind–body medicine, meditation, health promotion, integrative medicine and medical ethics. Craig is regularly invited to speak and run courses in Australia and overseas in health, professional and educational contexts and has collaborated with a number of national and international universities helping them to integrate similar content. He was the founding president of the Australian Teachers of Meditation Association and is a regular media commentator. Craig also featured in the documentary, 'The Connection' (2014) and wrote the companion e-book, *The Mindfulness Manual*. He co-authored the free online Mindfulness course with Richard Chambers, in collaboration with Monash University and FutureLearn. He has authored and co-authored several books including: *The freedom trap: Reclaiming liberty and wellbeing*, Exisle Publishing, Wollombi, 2017; *Illuminating wisdom: Works of wisdom, works of art*, Exisle Publishing, Wollombi, 2017; *Mindful learning: Reduce stress and improve brain performance for learning*, Exisle Publishing, Wollombi, 2014; *Mindfulness for life* (co-authored with Stephen McKenzie, Exisle Publishing, Wollombi, 2012; *The essence of health*, Exisle Publishing, Wollombi, 2008; *Know thyself*, Michelle Anderson Publishing, Melbourne, 2006; and *New frontiers in medicine*, Michelle Anderson Publishing, Melbourne, 2001.

of clinical encounters. It had become a system where importance of healing had been eclipsed by complex and oftentimes toxic treatments. The emphasis on pharmaceuticals, surgery and tests had trumped prevention and healthy lifestyle change. It had become a system within which the doctor was trying to care for patients when they themselves were feeling stressed and burned out, and their emotional and physical reserves were often far lower than the patients'. Lucy was suddenly and irresistibly driven by two deep callings; one to uplift her husband and the other to ring out a clarion call to the wider community to rethink what kind of healthcare it really needs. It was at this moment that Lucy found herself spitting out the words: "You are not alone. There are plenty of doctors who think and work the way you do. They are powerful healers. They sustain themselves. I'm going to find them."

From that moment of clarity, resolve and compassion arose the idea for a book, one that would recount the stories and insights of doctors who care for and care about their patients every day – a book that would also shed a light on both the problems and potential solutions to the ills of modern medicine. Patients and doctors cannot be healthy, and compassion cannot sustain itself, if the system within which they live and work is unhealthy. Compassion for the suffering of others, which is the only true foundation upon which healthcare can be built, cannot flourish where powerful commercial interests have overtaken common sense and an ethos of care. It cannot meet their collective needs, no matter how well intentioned, if the whole philosophy upon which it is based is misguided. Consciously or unconsciously, doctors are indoctrinated into this philosophy from their first days of medical school and, consciously or unconsciously, patients have been indoctrinated into a superficial idea of what healthcare and healing really are. Why are we surprised that, despite great effort and expense, modern healthcare doesn't meet the needs for which it exists and that it has itself become an increasingly common cause of morbidity and mortality?

It is rare for a truly inspired thought not to come to fruition and *Beyond the Stethoscope* is the manifestation of Lucy's moment of inspiration. The stress, burnout and poor mental health of doctors who are meant to be healers is both a symptom and a sign of a wider malady within the healthcare system. The system cannot change unless the community wants and seeks out a different kind of healthcare – one where holism does not give way to reductionism, where mind and heart are not subsumed into materialism, where prevention is always better than cure, and where deep listening is more than just exchanging clinical information. One where healing is more than merely using a drug to manipulate blood lipid or glucose levels back into a 'normal range' or surgically removing a cancerous growth. Modern biomedicine is not 'wrong' it is just limited in its scope and, in terms of importance, oftentimes puts last things first and first things last. But for such a paradigm shift to take place in modern healthcare, patients have to demand something different and be prepared to put in the effort required to make it a reality. It can't be a top-down imposition from the doctor 'doing' healthcare to their patients – it has to be a partnership where they walk the path to healing together.

It is hoped that many doctors and patients will read and be inspired by the wisdom and compassion of the doctors who have shared their insights in the pages of this book, *Beyond the Stethoscope*. Heaven knows we need it.

INTRODUCTION

"A professional training often wounds us. It encourages us to repress certain parts of our human wholeness and focus ourselves more narrowly and cognitively on the grounds that this will make us more useful and effective ... Often parts we have repressed ... are human strengths – the heart, the soul, the intuition, aspects of ourselves that are our resources in times of stress and crisis and enable us to understand and strengthen others. Few people realize how repressive medical training can be ... every doctor can give you examples of falling away from wholeness."

Rachel Naomi Remen[2]

"How was your day hon?"

The question is almost on autopilot, and I expect no interesting reply tonight beyond the usual: "Yeah, not bad," as I roll over, turn my back on him, yawn and claim my side of the bed, on this humid Queensland night. I am almost asleep when the reply comes.

"Weird."

I roll back towards him. "What happened?" I ask.

There is often not much that my doctor husband can tell me about his day beyond the superficial, for fear of breaching confidentiality. And

2   Sala Horowitz, 'Healing patients and physicians: An interview with Rachel Naomi Remen MD, Pioneer in Mind-Body-Spirit Medicine,' *Alternative and Complementary Therapies*, June 2001, 7(3): pp. 149–153, p.149. https://doi.org/10.1089/107628001300303673. Retrieved 12/10/2017.

there is often not much understanding I can lend to some of the nuances of that day, and the depth of the weight he carries home with him from the various dramas, tragedies, diagnoses and pathologies he has encountered. In his day, he wrestles with patients and pharmaceuticals. In mine, at that time, I was wrestling with toddlers and traffic. They lend themselves to different kinds of exhaustion, and not ample possibility for connection at the end of the day.

He rolls towards me and has a go at translating his planet to mine:

> "I had this woman who came in today: she's in her sixties; she's struggling with depression and hormone imbalance coinciding with her menopausal symptoms, and she's come in for her script for a cholesterol lowering tablet."

Not as interesting as I had hoped. I calculate whether I can stay awake, and murmur to him that I am listening. He obviously needs to talk.

> "All she wanted was the script, but I found myself wanting to dig a little deeper at her whole hormonal picture, a lot of which could be managed with lifestyle changes. Just before we ended the consult she asked for another script – for her thyroid, another hormone area. It was suddenly so apparent to me what a mess we can make when we don't look at the body as a whole system. There is such pressure to put people on medications – which do save lives – but sometimes we end up effectively upsetting the whole system, putting them on one drug which leads to the need for another drug, and then another. It's almost as if by putting out one fire, we start another. This woman probably ended up feeling sicker, where a lifestyle intervention may have been all that was needed in the first place to lower the cholesterol and have her feeling well."

"What did you do?" I asked.

> "I didn't have time to talk to her about untangling the
> mess, casting doubt on her regular doctor, getting to
> the bottom of her symptoms. But I just suddenly had
> this flash of all the times I have done this to people.
> That is pretty much what we are trained and expected
> to do.
>
> I just thought *I can't do this anymore.*
>
> When I spend too long with patients trying to get to
> the bottom of things with them though, I get so far
> behind, my colleagues end up wearing the load. But
> I just can't do ten-minute medicine anymore."

Now I am awake and listening.

We had moved to Queensland, Australia from a small-town rural
practice in Victoria because he had been burning out. We had thought
that the sea change and a broader geographic practice area would help
him to restore the balance. It seemed though, that the burden of
medicine was for him something beyond the location of his practice.
And yet, the irony: this is a job he loves with passion. It is meaningful
work, which goes to the very core of who he is.

I had recently read an article in Australia's *GP Review* magazine
(they used to pile in tall, mostly unread towers on our breakfast table,
before they went online), entitled 'Enough is enough.' It told how studies
had shown that "more than half of Australia's general practitioners
have considered leaving the job because of workplace stress, and that
eight in ten have said their emotional health has suffered due to their
work."[3] "There's no doubting it: Australia's GPs are more stressed than
ever," cited the article. "So," it asked, "what's wrong with General Practice,
and what can be done?"[4]

---

3   *GP Review,* Sept 2009, vol. 13, no. 4, p. 17.
4   As above.

My husband was very close to becoming one of these statistics, if he wasn't already, and probably will be again.

We met at Uni. I have walked with him and watched his path to and through doctoring: from intuitive calling, to earnest study, through dogged training, then self-doubt, hope, exhaustion, hope, being overwhelmed, hope, and then to burnout, depression and disconnection: from himself; from us – his family; and from his patients. I could see it in the shuffle and stoop as he walked, in the mumble he had adopted, and in his words this night. He was sinking again.

I sat up. "You're an amazing doctor," I said. "Don't apologise that you want to spend longer with patients, that you want to go deeper than their presenting complaint, that you want to help them towards long-term wellness, not just short-term bandaids. The way you see it is the way it should be. That is what the patients want; that is the future of medicine; and that is what will sustain you." I was gripped by a ferocious certainty, and an urgency that he had to be bringing his craft to the world in the way that he instinctively knew how.

And in this moment of protectiveness and passion I spat out the words: "You are not alone. There are plenty of doctors who think and work the way you do. They are powerful healers. They sustain themselves. I'm going to go and find them."

And I did. Some of them. There are many, many more, and their ranks are growing. I found others too, who are working as significant and inspiring leaders in healthcare reform.

So began this book.

When we hear about the health system in the media, we most often hear that it is in 'crisis,' or at the very least, that it is unsustainable. Concerns include public hospital waiting lists; the ageing population; the burden of lifestyle illnesses of our times such as diabetes, mental illness and other chronic diseases; conveyor-belt medicine; the affordability of universal health care systems to the public purse; the affordability of private health insurance to the private purse; and therefore, the affordability and polarisation of care.

We have seen wonderful life-saving and life-enhancing technological advances in medicine in the last century, and with them raised expectations and costs. Our knowledge and understanding of the vastly complex system that is the human body has been part of this revolution and yet – through lifestyle choices and circumstances, environmental ignorance and blindness, politics and economics, and our very humanness – we continue despite all the advances, to get sicker. Our doctors are caught somewhere in the midst, and they, just like the system and the patients, are under pressure and struggling.

Dr Glenn Colquhoun, a general practitioner (GP), writer and poet, acknowledges the complexities of this in General Practice, in his contribution to this book: "We need to unload and repackage the model. The waiting room really does drive a lot … I've been at my current clinic for five or six years now and there are some patients I saw on the day I started and I'm still finding things out about them now, which I didn't in a million years know about them, and I'm embarrassed. But taking a full social and family history, which can be hugely revealing, is very inefficient and just not economic at all. In the long-term it has efficiencies but in the short term it means you get through a quarter of the patients. But, General Practice without that, you'd want to stab yourself in the eye, wouldn't you?"

At this time when the costs of health systems around the world are spiralling out of control, and our collective health is doing much the same; when the waiting room is, according to Dr Colqhoun, "like a siege mentality" and medical training and practice, according to a number of the interviewed doctors can be "brutal and dehumanising" – those at the front lines are a rich source of insight. The economists and government have had their say (put prices up and create tick boxes for doctors to follow),[5] the pharmaceutical industry has had its say (new drugs and drug regimes), the patients are having their say (walking at increasing numbers across the road to alternative and complementary medicines, or alternatively popping vast volumes of pills), and the doctors, those living the system daily, are mostly too busy and too tired to have their say.

There are powerful interests at play also, which became evident to me as I navigated the ethics and legalities of some of the stories that didn't make it to print. This is an issue that should be of significant concern to the profession – which voices are the powerful ones in these conversations, and which are lost. Professor Vikram Patel, an internationally renowned health care reformist says in his contribution to this book: "The tide is very much one of heavy professionalisation, a very close coterie between medicine and big business; particularly technology, biomedical equipment, and the pharmaceutical industry. What you see now is not only the disempowerment of the community, but also the conversion of health care from a social and public good to, essentially a business enterprise." An annual *Forbes* study into the most profitable industries in the world consistently ranks health technology as *the* most profitable business sector in the world, with Biotech, generic

5   Admittedly, this is simplistic! At the time of writing, the Medicare system (Australia's publicly funded universal healthcare system) was under review and in the opinion of some, under threat – but individual Members of Parliament were also earnestly concerned about the plight of the healthcare system and of doctors within it. One of the stories which didn't make it into this book led to a National Parliamentary Inquiry into health regulation in Australia – there is awareness of and action over the fact that things are not well with the health system. I have made a decision that a deeper exploration of these issues is not part of this book – it may be the next book!

and major pharmaceutical companies ranking among the top ten most profitable industries in the world.[6]

These are difficult issues; solutions are not obvious. Health and health systems are one of the 'wicked' issues of our times and the 'answers,' in my view, require us to suspend judgement, suspend knowing, suspend our 'fix-it' or siloed mindsets, and to have the challenging conversations. Like my husband's awareness in the above story that the drugs designed for, and effective in treating one symptom, can, without a big picture view of the whole, together combine to create more problems than they solve – we need to view the health system in the same way: broadly and holistically. I invite you to read these stories from your heart, not from your head. I believe that some of the answers to these deeply difficult issues lie in the messy not knowing; in the challenging of our world views; in popping ourselves out of our narrow lens; in reading between the lines; in finding the themes and threads; in being brave and challenging powerful structures and influences which do not serve the greater good; and in listening deeply to the people at the front lines of medicine.

Some, who have tried to speak up, have been knocked back into place. Some have given up trying and have found other paths – usually believing the failure is theirs. Some have found a way around the system, the training, the professional culture, the status quo, and the day-to-day challenges of their work, in order to provide a service that they believe to be healing, and which is fulfilling and sustainable for them to provide. Many have chosen to keep their heads down and remain voiceless. I heard sad, shocking and difficult stories which, due to legal, ethical and privacy considerations were either withdrawn by me, or by the person who shared them with me. These were stories of burnout; of the devastation of being sued; of institutional bullying; of having to leave the profession due to not

6   Liyan Chen, 'The most profitable industries in 2016' *Forbes*, Dec 21, 2015: https://www.forbes.com/sites/liyanchen/2015/12/21/the-most-profitable-industries-in-2016/#104488a05716. Retrieved 3/10/2017.

coping; and of the fear and actuality of damaging and disheartening professional investigations.

Cultural change is slow, and complex. The evolution of our understanding, and our preparedness to challenge science and systems threatens the ivory towers of those who have built status, careers and fortunes from particular ways of knowing, seeing, organising and thinking. Challenging industry, institutions and power structures requires sheer courage and determination. Challenging the status quo is in fact the first job of a scientist, and yet challenging the 'known' and embracing things we can't yet 'see' or measure (or which it is not lucrative to measure) is a difficult leap for many. Those who are awake to different ways of seeing and being are seen as renegades and pioneers. It is not easy to be an early adopter and leader of cultural change. You will meet some of the brave in these pages. Theirs are challenging, pioneering, heartening and sense-making calls for a new future for medicine.

We're not talking about what you might imagine to be radical diversions from the norm here – we are talking about well-evidenced approaches beyond the traditional personas and silos of medicine. For example, the simple fact that quality food is an essential tool in the preventative and healing toolkit (food guidelines are political); that our mind and body are inexorably connected; and that compassion and humanism are basic human rights, healing tools in and of themselves, and have a place in medicine. One of the book's contributors, anaesthetist Dr Robin Youngson who co-founded Hearts in Healthcare, describes his work in seeking to restore compassion in healthcare as "an underground movement, a counter-cultural change. It has to be underground," he says, "because we threaten the very grass roots on which orthodoxy stands." Another contributor, physician Dr Catherine Crock, Founder of the Australian Centre for Patient and Family Centred Care and The Hush Foundation rightly says: "It seems so ridiculous to me that patient-centred care is the work of crusaders. It's sort of embarrasing."

Despite my having argued that the barriers to a sustainable, 'healthy' health system are complex, one of the contributors to the book,

Dr Joan Campbell, who has been involved in advising on and creating Standards in New Zealand, sees it as relatively simple: "It's about patch protection and power. Nothing more, nothing less. We can blame the system for its complex multilayered structure, we can discuss different philosophical ideas like critical theory and postmodernist thought, yet at the end of the day, it's about many doctors still wanting to be in charge of the health team, still wanting to be the experts, and still protecting their specialty or guild. It's about some groups having the power to exclude others. It is often not about the public's health. It's that simple. It makes you want to weep." Professor Vikram Patel, in his contribution, would agree. He says: "The problem that I see facing healthcare around the world is the over-medicalisation of health problems, to the extent that we have effectively disempowered the entire world, except for those who are doctors and nurses ... Doctors are facing burnout because they are controlling and wanting to remain the fountain-head of knowledge."

It is clear that we need to tread gently and respectfully as this profession navigates the radical 'disruption' facing many industries around the world. I have made the decision, like many of the book's contributing doctors, to focus on building positive relationships and dialogue with the profession through the stories I have chosen to collect and share. I could have collected stories of devastation and extreme challenge. Instead, I have chosen to collate stories of hope, and palatable challenge – whilst not shying away from difficult conversations.

For those who are keen for 'the 10-step solution to burnout,' or the '12 keys to sustainable healthcare reform,' this is not your book. 'How to' appeals to scientific and intellectual minds (and certainly has its place), and so it is a risk to take the story telling angle. But in my work in leadership development, I hear more and more about the power of shared story to effect change, and to tackle the significant challenges of our times. I certainly see the power of shared story daily in my work on the ground, in delivering profound change through story based leadership training. This book is no scientifically produced, evidence-based dissertation on health care reform;[7] this is a heart and soul investigation of deep wounds and deep wisdom, told through story: that ancient art which binds us and humanises us. And, just like the ancient art of medicine, so too does shared story heal.

So, what happens when you put doctors into a safe space, put the words: *hope, heart* and *healing* in front of them, and turn the listening chair – which they so often occupy – the other way? What happens when you ask doctors what it is like to be in their shoes: the highs, the lows; how they make meaning in their work; how they sustain themselves; and what 'healing' looks like? Ask them: whether compassion can be taught; about their dreams for the future of medicine; and what, if any, advice they would give to junior doctors, or to patients? What happens when you sit, mostly in silence, and bear witness to the story of the doctor, as they do for so many day in, and day out?

Have you ever wondered when you sit and offload your concerns and pathologies to your doctor what it is like for them to be a critical partner in your life and wellbeing?

The wisdom that speaks from these doctors, about health and healing, but also about life in general, can perhaps only be held by those who hear and see all the reaches of the human condition – in all its variations – approximately thirty times a day.

Behind the scenes of the 'health system,' beyond the stethoscope, are human beings doing their best to keep us all ticking along for as long as possible. What about their wellbeing?

Have you ever wondered when you sit and offload your concerns and pathologies to your doctor what it is like for them to be a critical partner in your life and wellbeing, and that of scores of others, day in and day out? Those people we hold up on pedestals, needing them in

---

7   Others have written these books, see 'Further Reading'.

our time of illness to be all-knowing, all-fixing, infallible – non-human, really. And yet, while needing them to never make a mistake, to not be having a tired day or a midlife crisis in the background, we call for them to see our humanism, and to meet it with theirs.

Amid galloping technological advancements, political pressures, incentives to implement complicated public health campaigns and increased public expectations for quick fixes – combined with the patient's new status as an internet-informed, claim-capable and demanding consumer of medicine – doctors are having to maintain themselves, their knowledge, their personal and professional boundaries, and some semblance of control (and some modicum of professional satisfaction).

One of this book's contributors describes the current landscape as factory style, conveyor-belt medicine. Demand is seemingly insatiable. The Medicare system and its equivalents, along with the corporatisation of medical services, incentivises quick consultations and instant solutions. Doctors have to watch their back and cover their tracks at all times for fear of being sued for making a mistake. There is enough fear built into the emotional pressure cooker of

None of these doctors signed up to be factory workers.

making a high-stakes mistake without the added legal burden of more recent times. Hospital based medicine is led by non-medical managers and is all about the bottom line. It is not hard to see how a doctor who most likely has entered the profession with the desire to help people heal, who has taken an oath to do just that, who has studied and trained for between six to ten years to be entrusted to the task, who intuitively understands (although possibly hasn't been trained in) the socio-psycho complexity of illness, might be left feeling a little bereft.

None of these doctors signed up to be factory workers. Some might say: "But they get paid well to do it." In fact, they're not – especially the ones at the coal face: general practitioners. I don't know of many high demand, high risk, high responsibility, high overheads (including ever increasing insurances), emotionally, physically and intellectually demanding jobs where your pay is determined by the government; where it crawls up in line with the CPI[8]; where it never increases more than that, despite your growing experience and expertise; and where the more time you take to care, the less money you earn. While specialists can and do charge a significant gap to cover the difference; GPs, as the front door of medicine, are under pressure, both as a business choice and as a moral choice, to keep their costs accessible to the public. At the time of writing the Australian Medicare benefits rebate scheme was frozen, meaning that rising costs of service delivery will not be matched by government funded returns, leaving medical businesses and practitioners even more financially exposed.

"How was your day?" I ask my husband, most days. "Yeah," he replies sometimes, in a voice tight with exhaustion, "people are just really sick at the moment." *Yes*, I think to myself, *that is your job, get used to it. God*, I think, *that is your job. That's full on.* You go in wanting to help people, fix their ills; they go in there expecting you to, and quite often you can't. Or perhaps our own human-ness can only handle a certain load of complex and urgent human need and suffering.

"We are under siege," writes Doctor Kerryn Phelps, "like never before."[9] Doctor Phelps, former President of the Australian Medical Association (AMA) and of the Australian Integrative Medical Association (AIMA), believes that it is the policies, pressures and paperwork which are conspiring to force doctors to more closely examine their careers, their lifestyle and their options and that these mounting pressures are "an unprecedented threat to the health of the doctor."[10] The stories in this book suggest there is more to it than the burden of paperwork. Another

---

8   Consumer Price Index.
9   K. Phelps, 'Health and wellbeing of doctors and medical students,' *Australian Medical Association Position Statement on Doctors' Health*, 2011, Cited on Medical Renaissance website: http://www.medicalrenaissance.com/. Retrieved August 2012.
10   As above.

common thread is that without sufficient time to care to the full degree of one's professional knowledge and humanity, and without institutional support for the doctor's own human journey and needs, the burden of the 'siege' is too weighty for many.

A quarter of all doctors surveyed had had thoughts of suicide in the past, and the actual rate of suicide amongst doctors was found to be three times the national average.

Medical commentator Dr Atul Gawende has said that "the doctor's plight is inexorably tied up in that of their patient."[11] You could look at it the other way too: the patient's plight is inexorably tied up in that of their doctor's. Even if we have no sympathy for the predicament of the doctor, we can at least have some concern about the impact of the doctor's wellbeing on the quality of their medicine.

Medical representative bodies are rightly concerned, and recent figures on the mental health of our doctors leave no room for complacency or denial. A recent Australian study surveyed 50,000 practicing doctors and medical students about their health and wellbeing.[12] The results were shocking. A quarter of all doctors surveyed had had thoughts of suicide in the past, and the actual rate of suicide amongst doctors was found to be three times the national average. The researchers postulated that the statistics could be even higher and that suicide as a cause of death is quite possibly under reported by sympathetic colleagues. Medical students, junior doctors and female doctors are at particular risk.

The stories in this book tell of the many complex layers behind these statistics.

---

11   *How do we heal medicine? Ted Talk, 2012:* https://www.ted.com/talks/atul_gawande_how_do_we_heal_medicine. Retrieved 20/08/2013.
12   *National mental health survey of doctors and medical students,* Beyondblue, Australia, 2013: https://www.beyondblue.org.au/docs/default-source/research-project-files/bl1132-report---nmhdmss-full-report_web. Retrieved 12/10/2017.

To simplify, the doctors' stories identify two levels of responsibility for these increasingly unsustainable realities of medical practice. The first is systems, institutional and cultural reform. The second is the personal journey and growth of the doctor. A consistent theme in the stories is that finding joy and delivering satisfying and effective medicine is to a degree the work of the doctor's mindset and personal journey. Many have shared that walking that sometimes difficult path of vulnerability and true self-awareness is essential in reclaiming the parts of ourselves that, according to Dr Rachel Remen in the opening quote, and echoed by the book's contributors, have been repressed through the training, culture and realities of the job. She describes these as: "our human strengths – the heart, the soul, the intuition, aspects of ourselves that are our resources in times of stress and crisis and enable us to understand and strengthen others."[13] When these resources become unearthed again, the healing that becomes available is two-way. As the well-known Biblical proverb encourages: "Physician, heal yourself."[14]

A significant and welcome addition was recently made to the internationally regarded and adopted doctors' oath, the Declaration of Geneva, to include a requirement for "physicians to attend to their own health, well-being and abilities in order to provide care of the highest standard."[15] The Declaration of Geneva is a modern version of the ancient Hippocratic Oath and is a core ethical document for the profession internationally. It was first adopted by the World Medical Association in 1948 and has only been updated a handful of times since that time, and only after significant consideration and consultation.[16] As noted above, the stories in this book identify medical culture and systems as part of the problem impacting on doctor's health, and the

13   Sala Horowitz, 'Healing patients and physicians: An interview with Rachel Naomi Remen MD, Pioneer in Mind-Body-Spirit Medicine,' *Alternative and Complementary Therapies*, June 2001, 7(3): 149-153, p.149. https://doi.org/10.1089/107628001300303673. Retrieved 12/10/2017.
14   Luke 4:23.
15   World Medical Association Media Release, *Modern physician's pledge approved by World Medical Association*, 14 October 2017: https://www.wma.net/news-post/modern-physicians-pledge-approved-by-world-medical-association/. Retrieved 17/10/2017.
16   As above.

changes to the code go some way towards addressing this, with another potentially powerful addition which includes a reciprocal requirement of respect between teachers, colleagues and students, as distinct from the previous version where students were required to respect their teachers but there was no reciprocity.[17] *Australian Doctor* Magazine notes that these changes were largely due to a successful campaign by Australian and New Zealand doctors.[18]

The doctors whose stories make up this book share their personal journeys in medicine with vulnerability, and in some instances with considerable soul-searching over the balance between privacy, fear of judgment, and a commitment to sharing for the public good. They use language such as love, compassion and intimacy, which is likely to be uncomfortable, and certainly unmeasurable, to policy makers, economists and those pulling the strings in the delivery of medicine. To those actually doing the delivery of medicine though, these stories may feel like a welcome mirror. To those of us on the receiving end of medicine, it will come as a relief to know that so many doctors out there are earnestly interested in big-picture wellbeing: they see us as a human being first and a conglomeration of cells second. Despite the grim picture I have painted, these stories are hope-filled, and the practitioners are uplifted, humbled and deeply fulfilled by the joy and integrity of what they do.

Finding a balance between humanism and science in medicine makes sense. For patients don't just come with their bodies. They come with their emotions, their mindsets, their list of internet solutions, their hurts, their hopes, their fears, their needs – and the effects of the profoundly complex mix of life and living, of their eating, their doing and their relating. They come with their own unique balance of physiology and psychology. As one of the contributing doctors says: "There's no cook-book."

---

17   As above.
18   O'Rourke, G. 'I will attend to my health: historic changes to doctors' oath,' *Australian Doctor,* online, 17 October 2017: https://www.australiandoctor.com.au/news/i-will-attend-my-health-historic-change-doctors-oath. Retrieved 17/10/2017.

Medicine is delivered in turn by unique and complex human beings with their own set of needs, stories, hopes and fears. "My medicine is much more about art than it is about science," says Dr Glenn Colquhoun. "Our medicine becomes who we're connected to, what we care about, what we carry and haven't dealt with, and our sense of spirituality in the greater context. Those aspects of ourselves necessarily become much more a part of the conversation, although they remain unspoken. These parts of ourselves and our relationships can be a good part of the consultation. But we're slapped over the fingers all the time as doctors for bringing our subjectivity to the consultation. As if we don't? I mean, really? We just need to learn the power of our own well examined subjectivity."

The Stethoscope: one end attached to a pair of ears, the other connecting them to a heart, chest and lungs; a fundamental, 200-year-old, relatively simple tool in the practice of medicine; a routine checking device that immediately forces intimacy into the exchange between the listener and the bearer. The listener requires a broad base of knowledge to read important information into the messages that the heart and chest emit. The bearer requires a degree of vulnerability and trust to raise their shirt and allow these key organs to tell their story.

Stethoscopes are seen as symbols of the doctor's profession, indeed as an icon of perceived trustworthiness. Doctors are often seen or depicted with a stethoscope hanging around their neck. One medical commentator writes: "The stethoscope best symbolises the practice of medicine. Whether absentmindedly worn around the neck like an amulet or coiled gunslinger-style in the pocket, ever ready for the quick draw, the stethoscope is much more than a tool that allows us to eavesdrop on the workings of the body. Indeed, it embodies the essence of doctoring: using science and technology in concert with the human skill of listening to determine what ails a patient."[19]

The stories in this book place great importance on that very 'human skill of listening.' Not because it is the most important skill in the doctor's toolbox, but because it is not as often formally recognised or acknowledged for its fundamental role.

"The most important thing that doctors can do for their patients is listen to them," says immunologist and founder of Auckland University of Technology's MindBody Medicine courses, Dr Brian Broom, in his contribution to this book. "Listen to them at the beginning and listen to them at the end, and find out who they are," he says. "If you fail to listen to them beyond listening for diagnosis and treatment, without listening to them as a human being, you will miss something." This book is an invitation to do the same – to slow the pace of our doing, and of our grasping for fast and linear solutions. As doctor and writer Rachel Naomi Remen writes in her book *Kitchen table wisdom*: "Everybody is a story. When I was a child, people sat around kitchen tables and told their stories. We don't do that so much anymore. Sitting around the table telling stories is not just a way of passing time. It is the way wisdom gets passed along. The stuff that helps us to live a life worth remembering. Despite the awesome powers of technology many of us still do not live very well. We may need to listen to each other's stories again."[20] Aboriginal Australians well know the healing power of listening in stillness – they call it 'Dadirri.' I invite you to make yourself a cuppa and participate in the hopeful, healing conversation woven by the stories in these pages. As Dr Katie Moore, Paediatric Oncologist and contributor to this book says: "Doctors love their evidence-based medicine, but when we are talking about really difficult topics, the power of narrative trumps all the statistical evidence you could ever accumulate. These stories, and the conversations they will enable, are vital to the wellbeing and sustainability of our profession."

19   U Schuklenk, 'Medical professionalism and ideological symbols in doctors' rooms', *J Med Ethics*. 2006 Jan; 32(1):1-2.
20   RN Remen, *Kitchen table wisdom: Stories that heal*, Riverhead Books, New York, 1996, 2006 (10th Anniversary Edition), p. xxxvii.

There is a field of therapy for people experiencing illness known as narrative medicine, which is a way of using people's narratives of illness; their individual stories and meaning making, as a way to promote healing. Narrative medicine aims not only to validate the experience of the patient, but also to encourage creativity and self-reflection in the doctor.[21] In a private letter of support to surgeon Dr Sharad Paul, one of the book's contributors, about the power of narrative medicine, Dr Harald Kitler from the Medical University of Vienna, Department of Dermatology Medicine writes: "Medicine as a discipline cares as much about mankind as it cares about individuals. Medical history dissolves into individual stories. Each patient history is a unique narrative. Patients, like mankind, can be out of joint too if the narrative is missing. The famous case histories of Sigmund Freud and the novels and plays of his contemporary physician-literate Arthur Schnitzler pay tribute to the close relationship of narrative medicine and illness coping."

"The times that we call 'postmodern' do not care too much about stories," he continues. "We zap through our lives as we change TV-channels but we rarely watch a movie from the beginning to the end. We are highly connected but we fail to see the common thread behind short messages and headlines. We surf the internet for hours but we never arrive on the last page. Physicians take the personal history but they have no time to relate to personal stories. Our postmodern life keeps us busy but we do not make ends meet. We are, however, addicted to coherence. Nobody knows this better than patients who are seriously ill. Their first question almost always is: "Why and how?" The next question usually is: "How will it end?" Especially when it comes to serious disabling illness or death, we urgently need a coherent story, a personal narrative, which in the usual jargon is called 'meaning.' We need somebody who creates coherence if we are 'out of joint' and if we get stuck for the right word we need somebody to tell our story."[22] I believe the medical system also urgently needs a coherent story, a 'personal' narrative, and a deeper connection with 'meaning.' Maybe

21   From Wikipedia: https://en.wikipedia.org/wiki/Narrative_medicine. Retrieved 29/09/2017.
22   Private correspondence from Dr Kittler to Dr Sharad for the purpose of public commendation of Dr Paul's work, written on 26 May 2015, shared with permission.

the policy makers and powers that be in medicine are 'stuck for the right words,' maybe they need somebody from outside the system to help them to tell their story. This book is my attempt to possibly offer some coherence to a system that is 'out of joint,' by and for the humans who make up that system. At the very least, this book is an offering to my husband and others like him, of whom there are many: *See, I told you. You are not alone.*

It felt to me, as I travelled around Australia, New Zealand and beyond, seeking out doctors and their stories, that I became a kind of curator of the art of human story. My original intention in 'catching' these stories was to draw out themes, weave together some kind of social commentary about the big picture of sustainable medicine, and to speculate on the future of medicine. And yet as I tried to work my craft with the threads, I felt I was denying them the purity of their context and of their narrative. It became clear to me that, like a curator of art, it was not my job to comment: it was merely my job to hang these stories in the gallery of this book, and to invite you to come along and respond according to your own circumstances, and make your own meaning from them.

"Breathe deeply please," says the medical practitioner, when listening to a heart and chest through a stethoscope. May we be reminded of our power when we breathe deeply, feel deeply, connect deeply and listen deeply: of our power when we share our stories.

*Please note that the stories that appear within are edited transcripts of conversations, not written responses, and that the language is, accordingly, conversational.

1 | LET'S TALK HONESTLY

DR NINA SAWICKI

General Practitioner, with an interest in qualitative research methods and congenital hearing loss.

Wellington, New Zealand

Let's start by talking honestly about what being a doctor is really like. What it's like on a day-to-day basis in terms of how it impacts on you – there's physical fatigue, there's psychological fatigue and there's also a deeper, kind of spiritual fatigue.

Is it reasonable to ask one human being to see so much pain in a structured job which doesn't actually allow you to even acknowledge that the pain is there, because you've got to make diagnoses, write scripts, have performance indicators and stay at 'arm's-length'? We're not going to get anywhere unless we get doctors together to really talk.

> *Is it reasonable to ask one human being to see so much pain in a structured job which doesn't actually allow you to even acknowledge that the pain is there, because you've got to make diagnoses, write scripts, have performance indicators and stay at 'arm's-length'?*

There are expectations of what are good outputs in medicine – they are things like getting your screening rate up, immunising children, and getting diabetics on the drugs that the research tells us they'll do better on. I don't think anyone's got any issues with measuring a doctor's performance in this way, but it's all become so driven, as if there is a standard recipe for everyone and every condition. But the fact that there is a human being somewhere in that recipe who is cooking – no one is talking about that. So the person *may* have a better life if they take this drug, but they may have good reasons not to want to take it, and it is not our job to force it on them. It is our job to develop a relationship so that they can come to us with trust. I just see so many tensions bouncing around in there.

In a well-educated, literate, unharmed, undamaged population, the outputs model of medicine is much more achievable. But not when you're dealing with the sorts of people who I see, who have been abandoned, neglected or abused by their parents; many of whom have chronic conditions. We call some of these illnesses 'acceptable illnesses,' but our behaviour doesn't represent that. We treat them as if they are somehow being naughty, and need to pull their socks up. I think that is really the attitude of the medical profession towards these people – nobody really wants to look after them.

Often the people I see have led incredibly broken lives. I have seen the Third World in Wellington. I kind of knew it existed but that was only intellectual. I see people whose lives are shattered. For example, last week I saw a woman who was forty-seven. She was a heavy smoker – she came in drunk, and she looked like she was closer to seventy. She had lost a partner through murder but it had never been taken through the justice system, for a number of reasons. She'd been diagnosed with severe emphysema – she had about a quarter of her lung function. I raised the issue of smoking because it is never too late, but she looked me in the eye and said: "Well, I'm dying – you know – I'm dying, what the fuck?" Where do you start your smoking cessation programme? Do I put in the task bar: "I've done smoking education, I've done motivational support, discussed prescription drugs?" I would have ticked all the little boxes that the auditors from the government like to see that we've ticked to show that we are good GPs. But, I'm listening to a woman whose lungs, and probably her soul, are a third of what they could be. People like her need care more than the people who will eventually stop smoking, who will use the patches – for whom we can tick all the boxes. That's not all that hard, but these people we see here – they are so broken that just trying to develop a relationship with them is a mission in its own right. Until you've got that relationship, how can you expect them to listen to what you say? And you can't have a relationship with them, I believe, unless the patient believes that you understand their pain, or their past. There's nowhere to move – if you don't have that, it's all hot air. The people here are often suffering through circumstances which are beyond their control. Even if they were to blame, you can't judge people for the source of their pain.

I don't know how sustainable doing this kind of work is. I've seen three people this morning so far. The first had nursed a partner with prostate cancer at forty-five; she'd been sexually abused; she had someone crowbarred on her lawn a month earlier – she's in protective housing as a victim of domestic violence so she's been relocated to this area with some unsavoury characters around her – she had a paedophile across her lawn; she's got children at home; she's looking after her aunty who was a victim of the Christchurch earthquake, and she's come to me today because she's realised that maybe she's depressed! You don't want to think: *Yep, what's the next drama?* Once you get like that, you shouldn't be in the job. But how can you see patient, after patient like this? The next patient was a young man of thirty-five, had been unemployed for eighteen months; both parents are dead; no partner, no children; maybe a couple of friends. He has Asperger's syndrome so science tells us he's going to have some challenges. He asked for help; help didn't come. He got too stressed at work so gave it up. He smokes a bit of cannabis. You don't have to know much about medicine and health to know that his future's not looking rosy.

Human pain, human suffering and human misery have to be married with medicine and science. Having the science isn't enough, and having a heart isn't enough – you somehow have to marry the two.

You can see maybe one or two people a day like that but because this clinic has been set up to look after people that others won't look after. We see them day in and day out. I don't know what the answer is.

Human pain, human suffering and human misery have to be married with medicine and science. Having the science isn't enough, and having a heart isn't enough – you somehow have to marry the two.

I don't think the funders, the policy makers and the medical trainers – who tend to be academics who have gone through hospital hierarchy – get it. It's almost like the elephant in the room; people can see it but they're not talking about it.

If you name something, it loses a lot of power and fear. Sometimes we imagine that something is worse than it actually is if we ask or find out more about it. I remember reading that opiate use in older Australians is going up. Australia is one of the wealthier nations in the world and has got one of the highest standards of living. I don't know what is going on there, but the abuse of drugs is not getting to be less of a problem, so what is sitting there is maybe a blend of biology, susceptibility and hurt. Why would you use drugs that destroy you if you're not hurting?

I work part-time in a very high-income practice three mornings a week, which is an interesting contrast. When I came and worked here, I was starting to feel tired of wealthy parents bringing their children in with a sore throat, or "they've been a bit faint, could you do an eye test," or "I need to be back at work because I've got an important meeting and you're making me late for it." I just felt – *this is not real.*

I suppose a couple of personal things have had an impact on why I became a doctor, and perhaps why I work in this environment. My father was a holocaust survivor: he went to Siberia as a young man and survived it as a bit of luck, but was totally bereft – he lost his family, everything. He was eventually reunited with the remaining part of his family in another country, but was completely dislocated. I guess I kind of know that you can live through seeing a lot of trauma and you just get through it, you just keep going. A driving issue for him was that we had a duty to do something worthwhile with our lives. When I expressed, at about sixteen, that I might like to be a doctor, his comment was: "You'd never be able to doubt what you've done with your life." That counts for a lot. You can make money, become famous, have a nice life, but actually doing something worthwhile matters.

My mother had very severe mental illness. She had very severe and frequent bouts of depression and she eventually suicided. She had many attempts in her life. I kind of sensed that somehow the system failed her. Admittedly psychiatric care has improved because we've got better science and better drugs; but the system didn't serve her in a lot of other very basic ways that didn't have anything to do with drugs. They had to do with bringing things out in the open and supporting her rather than incarcerating her, and thinking about what it all meant for her family. Although this all sounds negative, I'm actually a positive person. I actually think most people want to do good, but circumstances may have not enabled them to.

I sustain myself with mountaineering. I've always loved the outdoors and my husband and I have done a lot of tramping. We've got two daughters, then a seven-year gap, and our son. He's profoundly deaf; he's got a double bionic ear. I had a pretty rough time when he was little because cochlear implants were still untested; there were ethical issues and technical issues. Anyway, he was implanted and when I wasn't working I pretty much devoted my time to giving him language. He's on his way now; he's on his journey. He speaks well, but he's got issues to deal with. Being a teenager and being deaf and not being sports mad is not an easy place to be for a boy in New Zealand. He's a pretty grounded kid; he's starting to withdraw a bit from me. So now it is time that I can do a bit more for myself. My husband suggested I do a mountain skills course

A lot of people have written about the psychological make up of doctors. Apparently we have low self-esteem and want to solve all the problems of the world.

and I fell in love with it. Getting into the alpine environment, into the wilderness and concentrating on food, shelter and warmth – the basics – is very grounding. If you're warm, sheltered, and your belly's full, life's pretty sweet. I'm also fed by just the incredible physical beauty and the amazing supportive, encouraging people I've met. I've often wanted to write, but at the moment it's not really an option. Maybe at the age of sixty I'll get my pen out!

A lot of people have written about the psychological make up of doctors. Apparently we have low self-esteem and want to solve all the problems of the world. I think that as doctors – indeed as humans – it is helpful for us to accept that there is pain in the world and we'll never completely avoid it. Even if we're all wealthy, and all have enough to eat – there will be other problems in the world. I think just acknowledging that pain is part of life; somehow it takes the sting out of it. The perception that you're not going to face challenges in life is an erroneous one. Life is full of challenges. I think once you accept that, it doesn't feel so bad.

I grew up with Roman Catholicism – I don't relate to it now. I think I'm probably much more aligned with a Buddhist way of thinking: mindfulness; working with the here and now, and what faces you in this moment; trying not to let the future overwhelm you or let the past drag you back. I also like Stephanie Dowrick's books. *Forgiveness and other acts of love* would be one of my favourite books. We don't need to hurt each other. You don't make your pain better by hurting other people. Nobody wins.

We've got some science and strategies around reducing mental and physical pain but there are, and I think there will always be, lots of people out there hurting. History tells us that people will probably continue to keep hurting each other, whether physically or psychologically or through other means. Humans have been around long enough for us to realise that somehow, we all own this.

I let patients who are facing all sorts of difficulties know that they are not alone. Not to minimise the way they are feeling, but just to let them know that other people have experienced similar things and have got through. I try to be compassionate and to find solutions that work for everyone.

As a doctor, it is very easy to let quantitative science take over, but quantitative and qualitative science are not mutually exclusive – they are complementary, and they answer different questions about the problem of human life. A drug trial, for example, can tell us which women should have treatment for breast cancer, and the survival rates, but it's not going to tell us what it is like to have breast cancer. They're different questions. I think the medical community is accepting now that both ways of looking at human illness are valid, and that these two perspectives need to be talking to each other, rather than past each other.

You don't need to be super bright to be a doctor. I think you need to be a bit compulsive, a bit obsessive and a bit of a plodder. A lot of what we do may appear mundane, but there's nothing mundane about people. Even if they've just come in with a bit of tummy pain, at the end of fifteen minutes you can tell them: "I think you're constipated, this is what you should do" – that's an exciting problem to solve. They don't have some interesting, complicated diagnosis, but you've helped them on their journey, and there's science around diagnosing constipation. If you don't like working with people, and you're more passionate about using your brain scientifically, then clinical medicine is probably not right for you. I never find it mundane, but the problems people present with may not be very sexy. You deal with what comes through the door. It is never not a challenge.

I might see three people in one morning, and I would do far more work than if I saw 20. It's not actually about the number of patients you see, it's about what you do with them. That's not really acknowledged.

It is interesting this whole issue of holistic medicine and 'alternative' therapies, because, being holistic isn't about whether you use mainstream medicine or complementary medicine. It is about seeing that you have a person in the room, for whom conventional medicine has some value, and so does some alternative therapy. There's no cookbook. Everybody comes with different expectations. I've heard some horror stories of people who have been to alternative therapists who have been very prescriptive, not been at all holistic, not made eye contact, and not actually asked: "Are you hurting? Is anything else going on in your life?" I've had one woman who actually went bankrupt because she was spending $20,000 per year on her therapies. She was very vulnerable and the practitioner that she was seeing did not even consider that she might not be able to afford this therapy that she was being told she had to have.

If I were in charge of health care reform, I would suggest that we have an afternoon nap, drink milk, have a cookie at three and hold hands. That would be a good start. We might actually start talking nicely and listening to each other.

If I could give advice to patients I would say: "Choose a doctor who smiles at you, looks at you in the eye, and can laugh!" Do they ask you open questions? And do they ask you the basic things like: "Are you getting enough to eat? Is your house warm? Are you sleeping? Do you have someone who loves you?" These are basic but important questions – fundamental to being a well person. If your doctor doesn't ask you that, then you've got to wonder if you're on the same page.

If I were in charge of health care reform, I would suggest that we have an afternoon nap, drink milk, have a cookie at three and hold hands. That would be a good start. We might actually start talking nicely and listening to each other.

One of my underlying concerns in modern medicine is the commercial commodification of health and people's health data. One of our fundamental responsibilities as doctors is to avoid harm and to investigate, prescribe and treat in such a way that we are confident that we are adding value to people's lives. I believe that this must always involve shared decision making, which is not really appreciated by our funders. There are a lot of prominent people in positions of power in relation to health who like the sound of their own voice. I would not like to be a manager – it is not something I have any aspirations to do. But when I see bad management and dysfunctional systems, I think: *I've got to do something.* There are a lot of opportunities to go to the relevant departments to point out some of the anomalies with what they are expecting us to do, which are not do-able. We need to start biting off manageable pieces and get some dialogue going. It's a bit like mountain climbing: getting to a summit is just very mundane – one foot in front of the other – just keeping on going. It is a lot of hard work but there is some thrill about plodding. When you look at a peak or squeeze through a bit of glacier, you don't say: "I'm going to get to the top," you just work on the bit in front of you. You say: "We've got the right equipment, we've got a good group of people, we're all looking after each other." All you can do is go with an open mind. If you get to the top, great: if you don't, well, you still had a good day out in the hills.

If I feel I have been able to create an environment where people feel heard, I feel I have succeeded. If someone opens up in real trust, sensing that you have their best wishes at heart, you may not always make the right decisions for them, but if they go out of the room feeling listened to, feeling heard, then that gives me a real buzz. Because I know what it feels like to be heard. Being listened to is one of the most amazing experiences of being human. When you've experienced being deeply listened to, it is quite powerful. You can never ever doubt the value, the inherent goodness of one human being trying to understand the life of another human being.

2 | DON'T FIX THE DEAD WOOD

DR DAVID REILLY

Consultant Physician, Researcher, Teacher, and pioneer of a more humane holistic and wellness-enabling health care. Dr Reilly was former head of the NHS1 National Centre for Integrative Care in Scotland, and National Clinical Lead for Integrative Care for the Scottish Government. He has made extensive international contributions and now directs TheWEL Organisation.

Scotland

To enter a professional walk of life is to enter a culture and a tradition. To enter medical training is to enter a virtual tribal-initiation. In 1973 as a keen young man interested in the wonders of life, healing and science, I entered medical training expecting to be guided into a rich exploration of the known and unknown of all this. Now while I remain deeply grateful for my training, and my teachers, and the transmission of rich cultural learning – the truth is I soon became dismayed at the weight of dogma underpinning the culture. I felt there was too often a lack of real open scientific enquiry, especially with regards to natural healing process and human relationships in care. I also grew deeply troubled by a stream of dehumanisation running through the centre of medical care – so much so that I almost left in my penultimate year.

---

1   National Health Service, the organisation responsible for publicly funded health services in the United Kingdom.

In classical determined-young-man fashion, I decided to stay and change the situation. It took more than twenty years, but I was never bored. I so loved being a doctor, even though the pressures in truth were damaging to my health. Instinctively following the old proverb that 'the wise man awaits his moment,' I knew that any change I could seed would best come after I had learned well and deeply within and from the system. So I worked hard, developed a good academic track record, and built my skills. But I never lost my perception that there was a better way. Traditional Shamans have at least a twenty-odd year apprenticeship, and medicine echoed these ancient roots in my twenty-one year path to be an NHS Consultant. On route, I knew that my job would be to bridge different worlds and I studied the craft of being a change agent almost as a second parallel vocation. In change, you don't want to run until you have the lay of the land. Early on, when asked what I would specialise in, I used to say "wholism," a word I coined for myself as a buffer against over-narrowing my view: later I'd discover that of course the term had already been coined by Jan Schmidt, of South Africa.

I loved acute medicine. It can be so satisfyingly effective, indeed life-saving, with fantastic drugs and surgery evolved through time and science. However, perhaps because of this evident effectiveness of drugs, my later exposure to grassroots medicine as a general practitioner in 1983 came as shock: there I saw how ineffective drugs would be in the emerging life-style epidemics – like stress, obesity, diabetes, heart disease and much more. Yes, drugs might usefully palliate and help slow progress, but they – and their conjoined 'fix-it' map of illness – will not yield the answers we needed to transform or prevent these epidemics. So I found myself with one foot in and one foot out of the current models of care – which spawned something of an anthropological approach in me – quietly moving amongst the care tribes, watching, and wondering as I went.

My first evident step off the medical-consensus map came a few weeks into my first year in General Practice. If given a safe space, my patients with chronic problems told me of their visits to alternative-medicine practitioners – echoing my curiosity and my reading of a world-wide rise in such demand. So I did an anonymous survey among my fellow GP trainees. It turned out that most of them shared an unspoken interest – and one in three had used some form of non-conventional care for themselves. Published in the *British Medical Journal*, this sparked real reaction, and was cited as the reason for the British Medical Association's first formal enquiry into this area.

So I went looking. Among the numerous areas I explored I found many good people giving good care (and often they were people disillusioned with their conventional medical training), and some radical knowledge and observations missing in the orthodox world. Yet, I also found the same sorts of tribalism, dogma, quasi-science and dysfunction I had seen in the mainstream. It seems to be a human thing. Also, an overspecialised view was common, with a very curious parallel in the complementary and alternative medicine field to the examinations and multiple diagnoses of Western mainstream medicine. Everybody's got something to fix. Therapists usually have their 'specialist' perspectives, within their own often narrow framework, while calling themselves holistic, indeed more-holistic-than-thou.

In examining this parallel world of other approaches to care, I visited what was then the Glasgow Homeopathic Hospital. I was impressed that it functioned like an island in the medical ocean that had a much greater emphasis on a person-centred approach (as its now called – there was no such discussion at the time). Indeed, I realised this hospital was misnamed. While identifying itself with the homeopathy used there, I saw it as a nascent and unnamed model of a more whole-person approach, which also blended orthodox and complementary treatments. For example, their emphasis on good nutrition, so lacking in the other hospitals in the city, chimed with my long-standing interest. I decided to work there for a while and explore. My colleagues told me this would be a career-ending move.

Over this time I introduced mind–body approaches and explored acupuncture. I was however so sceptical about homoeopathy – not its impressive consultations, but its dilute remedies – that I declined to use it clinically. Instead, I decide to put it to scientific tests. The subsequent four randomised double-blind placebo[2] controlled trials of homeopathy vs placebo, that I led with Morag Taylor and teams from Glasgow University, were published in *The Lancet* and *British Medical Journal*; and taken together, they added scientific weight to their very controversial conclusion that homeopathic medicines were not just working by their evident placebo action. I concluded that homoeopathy works, or the trial does not. The resultant waves of debate descended, in my view, into scientism and fundamentalism – on both sides of the fence – as two communities (well, more like tribes) came into conflict. This (on-going) battle of meta-analyses, a priori dismals and canonical pronouncements was over simplified, almost tabloid-ish. I realised this was not science; this was a cultural process. I decided it would not be fruitful for me to devote further research-time to this arena. I had come at this topic from my pre-existing enquiry into natural healing, and therefore placebo research. I decided to now concentrate on that core path.

Firstly, however, after I then returned to Glasgow University Department of Medicine as a clinical research fellow, I needed to finish and close my enquiry into CAM (as I labelled Complementary and Alternative Medicines – to side step the sterile debates of: "Is it one or is it the other?"). I published my findings in the report: 'Developing Integrated Medicine.'[3] In introducing the term integrated (indicating systems working in co-operation) I wanted to distinguish this from an *integrative* approach, and highlight the latter as the greater need –

2   A placebo is a substance or treatment with no active therapeutic effect. A placebo may be given to a person in order to deceive the recipient into thinking that it is an active treatment. In drug testing and medical research, a placebo can be made to resemble an active medication or therapy so that it functions as a 'control'; this is to prevent the recipient(s) and / or others from knowing (with their consent) whether a treatment is active or inactive, as expectations about whether a treatment will work or not can influence results. From Wikipedia: https://en.wikipedia.org/wiki/Placebo. Retrieved 1/10/2017.
3   D. Reilly and T. M. A. 'Developing Integrated Medicine,' report of the RCCM Fellowship in Complementary Medicine, The University of Glasgow 1987–90' *Complementary Therapies in Medicine* 1(Supplement 1), 1993, pp. 1–50.

care that fosters more coherence within a person and / or their care.
I regret that in some countries the term integrative is being used as a
synonym for integrated CAM. This search for a more integrative and
healing approach was now to become my life's work.

I recall a pivotal consultation that
moved me on from my CAM enquiry.
I had established a research clinic within
the Pain Relief clinic at the university,
and would see people only if the excellent
care of my colleagues had failed to
adequately progress the situation. I
began by asking would CAM take the

*My transition from
Descartes's watchmaker
to a gardener of human
recovery had begun.*

person further? The answer came as: well, sometimes – but overall,
not enough; not for the individual, and certainly not as the answer
to the modern epidemics. I had a consultation with one particular
lady which reflected my growing experience in creating a 'therapeutic
encounter.' I asked her, "In view of our meeting, how would you feel
if I did not prescribe anything?" She said, "That would be great,
everyone just wants to prescribe, or do things to me." Four weeks
later she came back to report she was quite transformed. Together
we could then explore this natural healing reaction. Together we
realised that if we had prescribed or used a treatment, we would be
attributing her marked positive change to the intervention. Instead,
we were set free to discover her innate healing capacity and how we
might now build on it. My transition from Descartes's watchmaker
to a gardener of human recovery had begun. Not prescribing, while
supporting recovery, became my default path when safe to do so. I
realised I had been trained to see the broken-ness in people. The
shift I made was towards seeing their wholeness, their inherent, if
latent strength. Perhaps more critically, I came to see afresh that
their strength is *life's* strength, present in us all. How might it be
released and supported becomes the question. This moved me away
from the fix-it model, with me as the one with the supposed answers.
It became clear that the job of opening the doors to inherent healing
change could be unlocked by transformed self-care. That in turn

called for the activation of compassion towards one's life. I nick-named it 'self-gardening'.

This shift in my perception was reinforced shortly afterwards. A young woman come to me at the end of the road after many years of a chronic bladder condition for which no cause or solution could be found. Andrea had the appointment card to have her bladder surgically removed. I suggested hypnotherapy as I was seeing remarkable healing changes from working in this way – but her response stumped me: "I don't do hypnotherapy." I felt that toolkit close. It's funny how areas you study first expand you – but then they can capture you on their map, within their boundaries. She pushed me off the map. In a moment of simple inspiration I asked: "Do you daydream?" Her response was: "All the time." "Ok. Let's just daydream together." We had a keenly focussed, eyes-open, therapeutic creative exploration. Within two days she recovered completely.[4] It was a gift to me, that pushed me off my modality-thinking, and into new exploration. I so valued the mind–body learning that hypno-analysis brought me, but Andrea pushed me further to confront that all the remarkable phenomena I had seen in 'altered states' were there and potentially active during any encounter – even if one or both participants were not conscious of this. I let the ritual go and came to rest on the study of the power for good and harm in ordinary encounter. I saw it for what it was, or could be: a 'therapeutic encounter.'

I continued to develop myself, my practice and my teaching around this fulcrum of 'therapeutic encounter' – exploring the consultation itself as a vehicle of change and healing, not just an algorithm towards diagnosis and treatment. Over twenty years I video-taped hundreds of hours of consultations – studying the remarkable things that happen when people are fully present with each other, bringing care, commitment and skill to achieving change. Critically, this is not psychotherapy or counselling, it is an active practical process with central focus on the release of life's innate

---

4   I tell the story of her recovery in a TEDx talk https://www.youtube.com/watch?v=LUFgxkBPh4Y.

capacities for healing, and wellbeing. Please bear in mind here the caveat of context: this study is in those (many) situations when no harm will come if therapies are withheld for now.

This work grew into what came to be known as The Healing Shift Enquiry. I had begun by seeing what I could learn from discrete areas of knowledge and practice: like hypno-analysis, the placebo literature, psychoneuroimmunology, the wisdom traditions and mind–body systems, meditation – and more recently enriched by what neuroimaging and knowledge of brain plasticity brings. Gradually this synthesised and led to mapping the common ground these all shared; then working out from there to build a new model of care. I asked then, as I do now: What is healing? What can it do and not do? How can we support natural capacities for recovery and wholeness, and how do we unwittingly roadblock this?

Such enquiry leads naturally into our inner world, our inner life. That's where suffering lives and is experienced, where meaning and its loss are formed, and that's where the wellspring of peace and happiness we all want is to be tapped. That connection to source sets the conditions for healing. Good science has established that the more happiness (as opposed to short-term reward and pleasure) and its corollary of less stress, the healthier we will be, the less illness we are likely to have, the better our recovery, the longer our life and its quality. But I'd emphasise that we will still get stressed, sick, age and die – we are talking here about working within the boundaries of the leeway that's available to us. These principles of healing care can of course also be employed along with medical interventions – in a personal and biological synergy.

Some years on, I decided to return to the homoeopathic hospital and lead its natural transition into something that would further seed and embody a better approach to health care, something that would better match the contemporary challenges of the long-term conditions and epidemics we were seeing more of.

In 1999 Prince Charles opened the new award-winning building. In leading that building project I set the vision of creating a place 'of beauty and healing'; a model of a healing environment. By staff vote, and with Scottish Government approval, it was then re-named the National Health Service Centre for Integrative Care. This name was chosen to signal that it was not about different treatments – orthodox or complementary – but about integrative care that took as its foundation a conscious application of therapeutic relationship aimed at supporting human healing capacity, and so emergent coherence, wholeness and wellbeing. We evolved award winning new models of care and research. My hope was that the ideas burning within the unit's candle might help spread a fire of change.

By this stage I was travelling the world and was privileged to share some of what was being learned. This became part of an international discourse that is exploring more person-centred care and research, helping to counter the imbalanced emphasis on just objective measures, and our stubborn attribution of outcomes to our favoured modalities and intervention – while missing the human potential for recovery and flourishing.

As the century turned, my practice was cited by the Public Health Institute of Scotland as the spark of the needed 'Fifth Wave' of Public Health thinking.[5] I then partnered with Phil Hanlon, Glasgow's Professor of Public Health who led the Fifth Wave enquiry, and the sister 'afternow. co.uk' project. Phil's pioneering work considered the cultural influences on wellbeing. We tagged it as: his team was studying the needed changes

---

5   "The UK has seen several phases of public health improvement since the Industrial Revolution, and ... each of these can be linked to major shifts in thinking about the nature of society and health itself. ... The first wave is associated with great public works and other developments arising from social responses to the profound disruptions which followed the Industrial Revolution. The second wave saw the emergence of medicine as science. The third wave involved the redesign of our social institutions during the 20th Century and gave birth to the welfare state. The fourth wave has been dominated by efforts to combat disease risk factors and the emergence of systems thinking. It is suggested that a fifth wave of public health development is now needed; one that tackles the complex challenges of obesity, inequality and loss of wellbeing, together with the broader problems of exponential growth in population, money creation and energy usage." Excerpt from: 'Making the case for a 'fifth wave' in public health,' *Public Health*, 2011 Jan;125(1):30–6. doi: 10.1016/j.puhe.2010.09.004. Hanlon P, Carlisle S, Hannah M, Reilly D, Lyon **A**.

'from the outside in'; while my team studied 'the inside out.'

Phil sat in on a consultation with me – it was a man with chronic pain coming back two days after a first consultation, and he was keen to describe a huge resultant shift in his perspective and wellbeing. Afterwards, Phil asked the wonderful question: "How can we take what we have just seen and scale it to the level of a nation?" This still-unanswered clamant question concerns us all: How are we to protect our children from the epidemics of degenerative disease and distress; and can we help turnaround the situation for the high percentage of adults now affected? This won't be through pills.

How are we to protect our children from the epidemics of degenerative disease and distress; and can we help turnaround the situation for the high percentage of adults now affected? This won't be through pills.

In 2004, through the charity-based department supporting my work, we launched a pilot evaluation of TheWEL Course,[6] a programme I had been writing over the years which aimed to apply the principles learned in one-to-one encounters, into a group situation. The research showed very positive changes in the participants – in wellbeing, symptoms, in quality of daily living, and, in later studies, on blood markers that correlate to the epidemics (like high fasting insulin levels that harbour later diabetes). I then delivered this model for the NHS, and later the Scottish Government gave support for further evaluation and experimental spread to primary care. By then I was their National Clinical Lead for Integrative Care and so was able to input to shifts in government policy towards a more person-centred and compassion-based approach.

---

6   WEL stands for Wellness, Enhancement, Learning. "Participants learn to activate a self-sustaining and growing improvement in their self-care. Guided into a self-enquiry, people develop a shift to a new awareness of their health and wellbeing that challenges and changes their self-care." From: http://thewel.org/theWEL/Home.html. Retrieved 12/10/2017.

TheWEL programmes expanded in 2010 with a StaffWEL version. Both are a twenty-hour immersion course at intervals over ten weeks. At entry, we found the staff to be no healthier for the most part than the patients and clients who come to them to ask how they might flourish in the modern world. Truth is, the staff mostly don't know. They were trained in disease screening and treatment – not wellness enhancement and recovery. The results are very encouraging with major impacts on staff welfare and influence into their clinical practice. Activated practitioners activate others. You help people change their lives in this way not just with a short burst of enthusiasm, but with work that shifts the inner maps that run our lives. By exploring what it takes to shift their *own* self-care, staff learn to help others with long-term conditions and poor wellbeing. Although it is not group psychotherapy, and people can use it as private space, I do read out people's anonymous comments on what they are struggling with. That neutralises the ego in the space, as we realise we are all in this together, sharing the struggles of modernity. From this acknowledged 'old story' we seed a new story: If we start to work in 'Fifth Wave' way – in nurturing support of wellness enhancement – the evidence shows that transformation is very possible, and useful degrees of improved wellbeing are all but inevitable. To make such statements without evidence would be irresponsible. The research results are available at www.thewel.org.

"We're not in an era of change, we're in a change of era."

We must and we can turn around the modern epidemics. This won't be so much about fixing the dead wood of old ideas, but going for new growth. As my colleague Andrew Lyon says: "We're not in an era of change, we're in a change of era." It will be built on great community ideas and actions, with environmental improvements. But it will rest on a foundation of supporting individual people's own innate strengths – the ones that the nurtured life and so the flourishing life, embodies and guides.

In 2016, thirty-eight years after entry to medical school, I left the NHS and the formal role of doctor – full of gratitude for having been a doctor and part of individual's, and collective, healing change. I now begin to flow anew into the adventure of sharing my on-going learning more widely.

Maybe it's an artist's healing mission to be tuning in to, and giving voice to the as yet un-voiced; to be part of the release of lives restricted. In a way, I feel that's my path. It's been a long and challenging one at times – but as Zen says: 'If you meet a rock, become water.'

3 | A 65,000-YEAR-LONG RANDOMISED CONTROLLED TRIAL, UNPUBLISHED

DR MARK WENITONG

*Kabi Kabi man, originally from South Queensland.
One of Australia's first Aboriginal Doctors; Senior
Medical Advisor, Apunipima Cape York Health Council;
past President and founder of the Australian Indigenous
Doctors' Association.*

Cairns, Australia

As a brand new Aboriginal doctor I was interviewed in the first week of my internship by ABC National Television about Aboriginal and Torres Strait Islander health. "And Dr Wenitong," they said:

"How are you as an Aboriginal doctor going to fix Aboriginal and Torres Strait Islander health in Australia?" *Well*, I thought: *Before lunch I would start with the Northern Territory, and then maybe fix Western Australia after?*

But what I really said was: "As an intern, all I really want to do this week is not kill anyone. If I can do that, I'll be pretty happy for a start."

This journey has not been easy, but looking back I have learned some useful things – especially about hope, life, death, sex, love, spirituality, stress – just the usual human conditions.

A Canadian Aboriginal Elder, and professor of medicine started a dinner talk that I was attending with this quote: "As a researcher, if I write a paper and two other people believe in it, it becomes truth. But as an Aboriginal Elder, for something to be 'truth', it has to resonate with Creator, spirituality, nature, lore and customs, relationships and our community."

Aboriginal and Torres Strait Islander knowledge teaches us that the practitioner's life is as important as anyone's, and hence their humanity and wellness should be preserved and supported as well.

Medicine, I'm pretty sure, was a different context for me than many other medical students. But one thing that has become more obvious is the evolution of Aboriginal and Torres Strait Islander cultural healing and wellbeing practice and its relationship to current and future best medical practice. As I watch the increasing numbers of young (and some not so young) doctors self-harming, it reminds me of how human we all are, and how much we in medicine should embrace that humanity and not try to minimise it.

This is a much more Indigenous way of practicing. It seems that medical school taught us how to save everyone's lives but ours. I wrote a poem about this called: "I have a pulse, just no heart-beat," which was so bad I can't share it with you without at least a small dose of Ondansetron.

One of the concepts we developed early at one of the medical school's Aboriginal and Torres Strait Islander units I worked at, was that we wanted to support every Aboriginal and Torres Strait Islander medical student to fulfil their potential as a human first, then as an Aboriginal and Torres Strait Islander person second, and then finally, to do well at medical school. Our medical students' lives should be an inherent part of the courses we teach.

Aboriginal and Torres Strait Islander knowledge teaches us that the practitioner's life is as important as anyone's, and hence their humanity and wellness should be preserved and supported as well.

Indeed, it is this humanity that ensures we can really communicate well with patients. When an Elder is teaching a younger person in the bush, the Elder is responsible for the younger person's life. I think this is the same for many medical colleagues who care about their students in this way, but I don't think this is well supported by us at an institutional level. In some ways, our younger medical graduates are learning survival skills, when they should be learning life success skills.

I'm one of those older practitioners who sometimes finds myself reminiscing about how tough things were back in the day: "... never even 'ad a scalpel for surgery in them days, just a plastic fork which were broke as well. Got one fork at the start of the week and one in the middle ... 'ad to last till the last operation ..." But of course, things are tough in different ways these days. Young doctors are now part of a new tech-savvy, highly mobile world influenced by contemporary media, business and social norms. These influences drive pressures in current graduates that we didn't have to put up with. If you fail anything, or anything goes south on you in training nowadays, the rest of your cohort will know within minutes. Relationships and families seem to be different too.

There is a star studded public love affair with doctors in TV media. Those Hollywood doctors are better looking and seem smarter than most docs I know. There seems to be a larger fear not just of failure, but of failing to achieve potential, than previously. Training still seems to not want to acknowledge human *failings* – like the need to be loved, the need for comfort, being acknowledged, feeling supported – which are not really failings at all.

This is where there is likely a strong connection between keeping our humanity and a strong sense of hope for success and happiness at a professional level. I think we are guilty of making being a *human practitioner* subordinate to *professional, evidence-based, state-of-the-art practitioner with a modern business management practice*. To do this, though, we have left the medical student or new registrar basically at the mercy of fate, rather than their shared humanity to succour them when times are hard.

We need both of course.

I am not talking about a bunch of wimps here, but very intelligent people, some of whom are really struggling with the daily realities of life, such as depression or anxiety and relationship issues – on top of the stress, death and dying in the health sector. Doctors have already proven themselves to be highly resilient people through their studies, but there are life circumstances you are not meant to be resilient to.

Don't get me wrong, this is a great and noble profession with real dignity, and a history of trying to do the right thing. But the increasing business model placed over the profession throws more docs under busses; it puts levers and pressures on doctors in the worst ways. Not only should you do good, but you should be rich as well, and famous! So society develops this newer health system with external economic, social and media drivers, which push a system that doesn't seem to value the humanity of the carers.

The pressure is on the doctor to be rich, incredibly smart, good looking, never complain, always able to take on more work, be across all the training information, be mistake free, knowing what you want, and be completely superhuman and an excellent partner and parent at the same time! Unfortunately, I know some doctors who appear this good, and that's just not helpful! Within the profession, we must have started believing we were all stars in a re-run of 'Grey's Anatomy'![1] We seem to have bought into both lifestyle and professional approaches that have belittled our real reason for being doctors; our humanity.

You can't treat people truly, without humanity. Well, let's face it, you can't even be a real person without humanity. The part of humanity that bleeds; the part that cries when there is sad news; the part that has empathy for the patient who has just been diagnosed with a terminal illness; the part that sees that life *is* actually very unfair to some people; the part that makes *us* a patient. That is the part that knows that you are human too, and it makes us a better doctor.

---

1   'Grey's Anatomy' is an American television series based on the lives of junior doctors, and first aired in 2005.

One of the things that anchors me in medicine is the long line of traditional medical practitioners of my ancestors, and my ability to see that important things in health from 65,000 years ago, stay relevant right now in contemporary health practice. Aboriginal and Torres Strait Islander health and wellbeing approaches have always been holistic, in the sense that all of the experiences of our patients are relevant to what they are going through, at all the times they are experienced. This is basic good practice. For example, if we are treating a patient for chronic pain and have never explored depression, sexual function and financial worries with them, we are probably not as holistic a doctor as we thought we were.

In an indigenous context, we take environment, relationships with land, creator / creation, law / lore, dance, food, as all playing a role in a person's experience of illness.

In an indigenous context, we take environment, relationships with land, creator / creation, law / lore, dance, food, as all playing a role in a person's experience of illness.

Taking into account the patient's everyday life is based on listening, really, just listening. Then application of a management regime in the context of the patient. Indigenous knowledge tells me that it's always about the patient and what their experience of life is, not just the medicine. The answer to whether your management regime was a success is probably seen more by the look on the patient's face, than in the blood tests. Also, relationships matter more than anything else, and that includes their relationship with you, their doctor. When our traditional healers work, they sometimes do so by healing community disharmony or relationship disharmony, and physical health then gets better. (Ref. A 65,000-year-long randomised controlled trial, unpublished.)

I was involved in a hospital consult earlier this year, and the treating consultant finished up with this great summary of where things were at, and the 'plan' for the future. I noticed the patient's face getting redder and asked what the problem was. As a doctor, the 'plan' looked tight. I would have walked away as that consultant going *yeah, good plan bro,'* to myself! The patient said to me: "That is the stupidest bloody plan I've ever heard." I thought about all the patients that had probably said that to my back as soon as I walked off. Medical training teaches us a lot about 'how' to be the doctor who always has an answer – evidence based of course – but not how to actually help people. There is a very big difference, which we stay blind to sometimes.

I was recently a patient on a Coronary Care Unit and the difference between an experienced cardiac nurse wanting to share good advice based on great knowledge and experience, versus the one just doing the job of taking observations was extreme. Great practitioners tend to be listeners, and via their shared humanity can translate important clinical information into a story the patient can understand and relate to. This is where I think there is a richness of practice – where humanity and medicine intersect.

Some things that could have been seen as 'un-professional' in the past, I see to be maybe even *more* professional. For example, being relational, in the right context. Allowing patients to know about you a bit more, or allowing patients to know you have no idea what the hell that weird disease is that they found on Google.

I'm both a health practitioner and a user of the system (I hesitate to say end-user in a health setting, but I guess we all are). So as well as getting three new chronic diseases for my recent birthday, I had a good friend take his own life. I'm not sure about the mental health system's ability to engage in anything less that total psychosis, so 'soft touch' mental health services or what we would call social-emotional wellbeing is harder to access. Issues of depression, loss, grief, are basic blocks to a person's wellbeing, and these are challenging to access both as a patient and as a doctor.

Working in Aboriginal and Torres Strait Islander communities, where death, dying and grief are very common, is of course emotionally draining – even more so when it's your relatives. Being able to self-care is important, as is reaching out to your friends and colleagues when they may be struggling. It doesn't matter how senior, we all struggle at times, and all of us appreciate support. Staying human is allowing that support.

Arguably the most challenging time in my career was responding to the deaths of eight children who were murdered in their sleep one night. While the family counselling and outreaches were challenging, seeing eight small coffins on the stage at the funeral was just hard to come to terms with. This of course infected my family

You're going to need to pack your humanity for this journey … the thing that makes us better doctors may be the thing that saves us.

life, and it took another twelve months to really get over the darkness. Even with regular debriefs and professional peers who I reached out to, it still took time to work through. I've never had a medical mate say 'no' to giving me some emotional support, but that may be the quality of my friends, and the fact that some in the mental health area already thought that I needed their help? Our profession needs to talk more. Your colleagues and friends will listen.

My advice to younger and student doctors is this: chillax.[2] I didn't have to solve Aboriginal and Torres Strait Islander health in my first six weeks, and you don't have to be a super cool, groovy doc who knows all things. People still ask me when I'm going to solve the Aboriginal and Torres Strait Islander health problem, and I keep being happy I never killed anyone this week. You're just a person on one of the most exciting journeys you will ever take. You will need to be forgiving of yourself. Stay humble or medicine will humble you. Change the parts of the system you can, and don't sweat that parts you can't. And remember, you are just a person. Treasure your close friends and don't neglect family; you will need them both. You're going to need to pack your humanity for this journey … the thing that makes us better doctors may be the thing that saves us.

---

2 An Australian colloquialism meaning: "chill out" and "relax".

4 | "EXCUSE ME, HAS THE LIVER GOT A NAME?"

DR ELIZABETH LEWIS

Psychiatrist, early activist for mental health rights and Nutritional Medicine Practitioner.

Bendigo, Australia

I really think I would be thrown out of medicine if I was training today. The way in which people were disembodied and treated as a disease, and not as a person in a context just made me really angry. I believe that we have a responsibility, to ourselves and to every individual in the world, whether we are in the caring professions or not, to treat each other as we would like to be treated.

My philosophy of care is treating people as humans. Pretty simple. But I am totally uncompromising about it, which isn't always so simple.

My philosophy of care is treating people as humans. Pretty simple. But I am totally uncompromising about it, which isn't always so simple.

It started long before I graduated. It started with my rage at teaching hospitals where I met the concept of "the liver in bed nine." I would say: "Excuse me, has the liver got a name?" My ethos has always been to treat everyone as if they are a member of my own family. How to do that is a bit of a minefield but I have an integrity that is sacred and I can't deviate from that. It does make life difficult sometimes.

It took me a long time to do my psychiatry exams because I didn't want to do it at the expense of anyone I was treating at the time. So that meant avoiding a lot of the requirements, for example all the various placements, because that sort of rotational system provided discontinuity to the patients. When people talk to you about their stories, their lives – that is an extraordinary gift. It's almost a sacred agreement and you can't trash it by saying: "Yep, thanks, that was an interesting story … I'll be working at X for the next couple of months, so I'll hand you onto Joe Blogs and you can perhaps deal with this, this and this."

Think about psychosis. If people are going to tell you really weird, scary and dreadful things that are happening to them, it's as intimate as if you are talking about their sex life. You can't just bandy that around like it's something to mock them with – which is what often happens in an institutional setting. You've got to treat their delusion with some sort of reverence. You can't say: "How's the woman who lives in your chest today?" I think that there is a real responsibility to finish whatever you start.

The other part of my ethos is that I don't believe that there should be two tiers of health care. I've always believed that the disenfranchised, and the world's now underclass, deserve as good a care as people who can afford the best health care. I won't offer any kind of treatment that I can't offer across the board. That's part of the uncompromising bit in me.

I never intended to go into medicine. My father had always said: "Do a science matric[1], and then you can do whatever you like." He said he would support me to do anything, which, as it turns out he couldn't, because he went and died. But it was the thought that mattered, and he certainly believed that women could do anything that men could. He was very good about that. I decided I was going to be an archaeologist, then a vet, then an architect, and then what I was really interested in was art. All I ever wanted to do was go to art school but that didn't really

---

1   Matriculation – school finishing certificate.

work with the science matric. I decided medicine was a soft science and that it would enable me to continue to be me – it would allow me to apply both left and right brain. Every year I applied for art school, every year I got in, and every year I rang back and said: "Oh, I think I'll keep going with medicine. I've got this far, it's got to get better."

I was forced to go to a private girls' school from a state school in my final year and I think that experience and the contrast made me even more aware and furious about the inequities between those who have money and those who don't. My career choice was in a way revenge on my father because if there was one profession he despised, it was doctors. He had had very bad experiences of doctors because he and a number of members of my family had a mental illness. I probably also went into psychiatry because of this family experience, to do something for people with psychiatric illness.

I was always aware of the really good aspects of psychiatric illness. I had a really good relationship with my father, and my uncle, who was my father's best friend. My father had gone crazy in the war and had a diagnosis of schizophrenia. My uncle also, it emerged, when he was in his eighties, admitted to us that he'd been diagnosed with bi-polar. They were extraordinarily intelligent, intense, deep thinkers, and throughout my childhood we had the most wonderful conversations. I could never understand why the rest of the world were not like them. I had always had this sense that there was nothing wrong with people being a bit mad. I also had this wonderful aunt who had actually topped the state in matric. She had gone off to the war in the Middle East and had come back abjectly crazy. She lived in a little house and had saved every *Age Newspaper* for fifty years, so her house would get smaller and smaller with all the stacks. She would walk to our house across the local park, shielding herself from sand, to come to see my mother. My mother would feed and wash her, and take her home and make sure she was OK. So, it was just part of our upbringing. And she was wonderful. She was this highly intelligent, wildly eccentric, fascinating creature.

Everyone would come to see my mum, she was a natural healer – she even used to collect every stray dog from within five kilometres of wherever we lived at the time. She was for the most part non-judgmental. It was that loving kindness that attracted people like a magnet. We always had people converging in our kitchen – there were always freshly baked cakes and biscuits because she would have been trapped yet again in the kitchen all day by someone, yet again telling her their life story. Or she was off, down the road, cleaning the house of the alcoholic lady with the violent husband; or picking her up and looking after her after an attack, washing her and dressing her, and cleaning up. She did that throughout her lifetime. She was one of those extraordinarily nurturing people. She had grown up in the country, and had suffered a lot of hardship. Her father had obviously also suffered from depression. She had gone out and worked at everything she could do, to keep us going when my father was ill, because in those days there were no sickness benefits. She was just kind. And practical. So, my mother, as a carer and a healer, was probably also the catalyst for my pathway to medicine.

I was always angry – angry about a lot of things. I was angry about the inequality of people's existence. In the early years, it was a very haphazard thing. I just became an activist whenever something provoked me. I guess, if I had a cause, I was OK. It gave me a focus to say: "This has to change." I nearly did obstetrics because I really objected to the way unmarried women were treated – the fact that women would have their babies and then have to hand them over, in absolute silence. There was this total denial that this woman had gone through all of pregnancy, then labour. Then the baby was taken away, often without the mother being told what sex the baby was. And then she would be put in a ward with twenty or thirty women and their babies; amongst them women who had had still-births. These were the things that seemed so obviously wrong to me, and so easy to fix. I'd go to meetings with the Single Mothers' Union, which eventually managed to get the single mother's benefit. If I had a focus, I could cope with a system that had so much wrong with it. If I could at least dignify anyone that I came into contact with, then I could survive.

I was also furious about the treatment of people with mental illnesses. My mother had held the whole house together, all alone, giving so much to others, but people had turned away from her because of my father's illness. And then, when my father died, all the people who had turned away while he was alive, came to the funeral. That is what is so sad about mental illness. There is an inner sanctum of people who are immensely important in one's life, and then a vast number of fair-weather friends.

I did an extra year as part of my Bachelor of Medical Science, to conduct a survey on the sexual morays of Australian women (touching on use of contraception, domestic violence etcetera). While I was still studying, I saw what happened to my peers who had graduated. They walked around after registrars, and they carried pathology forms, and X-rays slips. It didn't seem like very real medicine to me. During my final year a friend rang me and suggested I come to Broken Hill.[2] I decided I would have a bit more autonomy and good exposure and better experience than in the major teaching hospitals. I knew it would be a hands-on job.

So, I landed on this purple airfield – it was the most beautiful country – and I knew I was in the right place. I told them my interests – that I wanted to run a family planning clinic, and that I was interested in psychiatry. They said: "Go for it." I wanted to sort out in my own mind whether my interest in psychiatry was just my futile attempt to change the world, or at least change the ethos with which people with mental illnesses are treated. I had plenty of exposure to mental illness in Broken Hill and I think that's what cemented my interest. My colleagues would say: "I'll trade you an appendix for two neurotics." Or: "There's a road trauma coming in which I'm really into. Can you handle this psychosis so I can do it?" I was given every encouragement by the senior staff to do things the way I would have them done. They were wonderful, compassionate human beings.

---

2   Outback New South Wales, Australia.

It was the 1960s and I rocked up in front of the head of Mental Health Services in a tie-dyed skirt and sandals, looking like the original hippie, and asked for a job. They offered me a job at one of the large Psychiatric Hospitals. I was there for a couple of years during which time I became very involved with a number of people who collectively formed what was then known as 'Mental Health Action.' It started with about six of us and ended up with 600 plus members. For a while it was a very active organisation, which achieved quite a bit – a number of seminars, lots of media exposure, and eventually deinstitutionalisation. It was really the second wave of mental health reform (the first being Largactil, the first anti-psychotic drug, in 1950). We had something like 1400 beds and three trained psychiatrists. I had been there for about six weeks when they all went on holidays, and for a week I was it, with one person I could call on.

There was one female consultant there who had been raised in an orphanage, was raising three children of her own, and was amazing. She had trained under Professor Max Hamilton, who was one of the kindest, most well-respected teachers of psychiatry in the UK. I managed to largely work with her. She set up the first Open Admission Ward[3] in Victoria, and was also part of the Mental Health Action group. We set up a therapeutic community in the Open Admission Ward. We had some great nurses – bearing in mind that they didn't have much training in those days and were seen as peripheral to care. It was the beginnings of a culture of teamwork, part of that enabling – *you are with the patient more, you know and see more* – attitude, and integration of all the perspectives of the different professionals.

There were a lot of aspects of institutionalised care that were good. We ran a group programme which had art therapy, music therapy, and groups for young psychotic patients. Groups were in, in those days. We threw lots of babies out with the bathwater with deinstitutionalisation. Overall, I think the patients are probably better off with the system as

---

3   Unlocked, non-compulsory.

it is now, but there is still a huge gap in services available to support these people to live in the community.

Unfortunately my colleague was moved to another area because she made a TV appearance and made a statement on the appalling nature of affairs for our patients. She had taken a reporter through and showed these long, impersonal wards with little lockers at the end of the beds – she was demoted as a result of that. And that was the end of the Open Admission Ward. I did continue to try to run the groups although they gave me a huge proportion of the hospital to look after, which was intended to sabotage the whole process of groupwork. I managed to just extend my hours of work by about four hours a day, and managed to maintain the whole lot for a short time. I remember being given these three psycho-geriatric wards and wondering: *What do I do with this?* It was very much putting out spot fires: someone had bronchitis this week, or someone else got a bit crazier.

I figured that the best thing I could do was look at the notes and find out who had visited, try to get hold of them and try to encourage them to visit more. Sometimes you had to go back a long, long way in the notes to find that anyone had visited. I thought: *I can't change the ethos of any of this but I need to do something, so maybe if I can encourage visitors, I can start to help with breaking down the barriers.* The stigma of mental illness is wicked. There are people who just don't have visitors at all. They have no-one in their lives. All you can ever do is just extend kindness in those situations.

Then I moved onto another institution and worked with some great doctors. There are lots of things one can't change – I guess I took a stand on not doing things I didn't believe in. The practice of electric shocks and behaviour modification in an attempt to change homosexuals into heterosexuals was almost abandoned by this stage but I was, at one hospital I worked at, expected to be involved in shaming and humiliation in the name of behaviour modification. I had an awful consultant later in my training who did the most awful, disrespectful things with his patients. It was ghastly. I can't tell you exactly because it may be libellous.

I would always find an excuse to not be present at the time, and I would tell anyone who came in voluntarily for this particular programme that they should leave. At one stage, I said: "I will come, but if I come I will come with a *Truth* reporter." *Truth* was the gutter newspaper of the time. I was exempted and eventually the programme fizzled.

The other thing I did there was to help bring in informed consent. I decided ECT (Electro Convulsive Therapy) wasn't quite right. They were doing double-blind studies into it at the time and I thought: *This isn't fair, these people don't know what they're in for.* So I'd ask them: "Has anyone told you anything about ECT?" "Do you really want to do ECT?" And then I'd say: "I think you should go and have a glass of water." Then: oops, they couldn't do ECT because they'd had water. No ECT this morning, everybody's had a glass of water. I managed to get two out of the five other registrars to do the same and that, I think, was the beginning of informed consent for ECT.

My advantage when working in that kind of setting was that I was young – I could live on coffee and I could be there until 8 pm. In those days we had hospital gardens, so in fact the patients were at least fed well. But there were a couple of psych nurses who ran hostels (very bad hostels which we learned never to send our patients to), and they would come in at night and remove all of this good food, and cart it all off in the back of their trucks. And a lot of them would drink on the wards. There were a whole lot of really dodgy things going on. I was always trying to expose those things but the level of corruption was considerable. I managed to nail one awful psych nurse one night who had banged patients' heads against brick walls, and on this particular night, had gotten terribly drunk. I called in the Official Visitors, but somehow the powers that be heard that this is what was happening and they came in, filled this guy up with black coffee and carted away all the evidence so that when the Official Visitors arrived none of it was apparent.

I was involved in Mental Health Action, and writing the State Employed Psychiatrists Newsletter. We managed through Mental Health

Action to get interpreters for the first time, and we got patient phones. They were little things but they were immense. J ward in Ararat was closed down with media attention to the juvenile patients who were held there. It was the seventies – they were heady times. It was a time when we all fervently believed we could change things. We had fingers in all sorts of different pies – aboriginal health affairs, green-bans, environmental issues – things were changing. We had that sense that we could change the world.

The best way to effect any change at all is to come up with an idea in front of people in positions of power who, six months later, will come up with that idea and claim it as their own.

I'd often say: "I'm not going to discharge this person unless you can convince me that there will be appropriate follow up." Also with admissions, I'd say: "I'm not going to admit this person unless you give me carte blanche to treat them as I see fit." You can do a lot of really good work furtively in institutions.

The best way to effect any change at all is to come up with an idea in front of people in positions of power who, six months later, will come up with that idea and claim it as their own.

I'd not have breakfast then fill myself up with coffee and by early evening I'd be half psychotic myself, and I'd go and chat to all the people with psychosis and have this wonderful journey really honouring what was going on in their head. We'd talk about the symbolism of what was going on. Bottom line, they still needed an anti-psychotic, but they felt better that someone was acknowledging the awesomeness of what was going on for them. I used to love acute work, that whole thing of six cops coming in, the person strapped down on a stretcher, and I'd say: "Undo those and get out." Not showing fear was important – we used to always interview new patients on our own. It's the human thing, and it's touching.

I remember a wonderful guy who came in once who was probably from the Balkans – with very little English. He came into the ward having blown half his face off in a suicide attempt, and having had botched reconstructive surgery. In those days, the cleaners were mostly migrants – if I ever needed to know anything about the patients I would ask the cleaners. A couple of them were really supportive. Anyway, this patient had to have ECT and he was terrified. He'd had ECT prior to the suicide attempt. We decided amongst us that instead of ECT, we would give him anti-depressants and that we would hand feed him. So, I'd often come in early and feed him and talk to him (or try to). Two weeks later, he was fine and he was off. One of the most wonderful things happened: probably twenty years later, I was in the area where he lived, and I saw him with his dog. I recognised his face, and I was so awe-struck that he was still alive. You just think: *Oh, wow, that was good.*

At one stage, the nurses got really distressed with a young guy who was psychotic. Finally, they prevailed upon us to give him some ECT. It had been so long since I had given anyone ECT but I thought I had better do it because I had worked so hard on cohesiveness with the nurses. Anyway, I forgot to turn on the machine. I gave him the anaesthetic, did all the right things but just didn't turn on the electricity. The next day they all said: "See how much better he is? See, we were right." He wasn't all that much better but he wasn't lying on the floor. So, I did it again deliberately without power this time, and they again said: "See, he's even better; we were right." I had to admit to them then what I had done.

Even with ECT – the treatment and its effectiveness is in the eye of the beholder. That is the whole thing with treatment – its effectiveness is all in the salesmanship. If people believe that what they are taking is going to make them better, it very often will. I have had good results over my career because I give people as much say as possible over their treatment and the placebo effect works.

If somebody really believes in Primal Scream, it will work for them. If it becomes inevitable that someone is going to have ECT, I will encourage their belief in its effectiveness, to make sure that it has the best possible chance to succeed. There is no doubt there are times when it is useful, but I think in history it has been horrifically overused. There are still people who can remember patients being given unmodified ECT as a form of punishment.

When I did finally rock up to do the psych exams, the panel was made up nearly all of people who I had offended gruesomely in my twenties. They were actually wonderful. I was forgiven.

I love psychiatry because people with mental illness are extraordinarily honest, like children. Once that relationship is there, they tell me when they've been non-compliant and I go: "OK, you seem to be doing quite well anyway." People will tell you things. Things you don't want to hear half the time. Whenever you ask people the question: "Have you been sexually abused?" for example, you open up Pandora's box. Then you've got to deal with it.

My personal journey in psychiatry was from institutional care to Family Therapy at the Bouverie Clinic where I also became involved at the NOW centre in Coburg – a Whitlam years[4] experiment in having all services under the one roof. These experiences expanded my knowledge base in family and systems theories.

Next was motherhood with all its joys, trials and tribulations teaching me patience, humility and unconditional love.

A tree change move to Bendigo in 1980 followed, within a system more humanely created by Dr John Bomford, where my work was predominantly community and rehabilitation. I moved into the private sector in 1993 to ensure continuity of care for numerous long-term patients utilising a bulk-billing system for all. I explored Jung for a time with my mother, toward the end of her life, embracing the notion of living well and dying well.

---

4   Gough Whitlam was Australian Prime Minister from 1972–1975. His Government implemented a large number of new programmes and policy changes, including the termination of military conscription, institution of universal health care and free university education, and the implementation of legal aid programmes. From Wikipedia: https://en.wikipedia.org/wiki/Gough_Whitlam. Retrieved 26/09/2017.

The systemic notion that you can cobble together an effective treatment for people in six sessions is ridiculous. Life is a journey. People heal when they are ready to heal.

I'm hoping that in the field of nutritional medicine, which I have now found myself in, there is a future in which larger change is available. My interest in nutritional medicine began in the 1980s, but I knew I had to do my psychiatry qualifications first, to become more mainstream, to be more respected. Once nutritional medicine is widely accepted, we really need to establish Green Medicine: preventative medicine – eating well and living well.

The systemic notion that you can cobble together an effective treatment for people in six sessions is ridiculous. Life is a journey. People heal when they are ready to heal. Being a healing partner means being with them until that time comes when they are ready. When they say: "I'm ready for this," then they fly.

Well, it was a futile mission to change the world, but it's been a good journey. I guess you make as much difference as you can, hammer away at the edges. The little changes have been important along the way. It is the little changes, on an individual level that keep you kicking.

None of this would have been possible without the support of my husband, my children, friends and a garden. Gardens are places to either lose or find oneself according to need.

TODAY I DO NOT WANT TO BE A DOCTOR [1]

Today I do not want to be a doctor.

No one is getting any better.

Those who were well are sick again
And those who were sick are sicker.

The dying think that they will live.
And the healthy think they are dying.

Someone has taken too many pills.
Someone has not taken enough.

A woman is losing her husband.
A husband is losing his wife.

The lame want to walk.
The blind want to drive.

The deaf are making too much noise.
The depressed are not making enough.

The asthmatics are smoking.
The alcoholics are drinking.
The diabetics are eating chocolate.

The mad are beginning to make sense.

Everyone's cholesterol is high.

Disease will not listen to me

Even when I shake my fist.

---

1   Glenn Colquhoun, from *Playing God,* Steele Roberts, Aotearoa, 2002, p.74

5 | THE POETRY OF MEDICINE

DR GLENN COLQUHOUN

General Practitioner and award-winning poet. In 2010 Glenn was awarded a Fulbright scholarship to research medical storytelling programmes.

Kapiti Coast, New Zealand

I'm much more attuned to the way medicine feels, than to the way it thinks. The arts tell you where and what science to use, rather than the other way around. The art of the doctor is the art of story. Figuring out where a patient is in the narrative of their illness helps you to predict where to go in the consultation and then you can layer the science over the top of that. I have come to realise that the bedrock of all conversation is the art of story. Listening to someone's story gives you a feel for the shape of it – it is almost a tangible shape – almost like palpating an abdomen but it is existential, spiritual, possibly even a physical shape that

I don't discredit the science of medicine because if I've had a pain for two days in my right iliac fossa, I don't want someone who is kind to me, I want a bloody good surgeon.

we don't know how to describe yet. You can feel the ridges and the sorrows; the aches; the things they carry with them; their fears, quite often. Almost everybody is carrying something when they talk to a doctor – even if it's just nervousness about talking to a professional. And you can sense that, allay it, and get to the core of what is going on for them. And that connection then guides everything else.

I don't discredit the science of medicine because if I've had a pain for two days in my right iliac fossa, I don't want someone who is kind to me, I want a bloody good surgeon. If I break my leg, or if my daughter falls off the jungle gym, these are times when you want a body mechanic. But in General Practice, ninety-nine times out of a one hundred that is not what is going on – what is going on is a whole lot of other stuff, and spirituality is much more part of your medicine. I can't stop you having diabetes. I can't un-renal fail your renal failure. I can choose to use some medications, which might squeeze an extra per cent out of you, but even then, I might get that wrong and make things worse.

Twenty years ago I wouldn't have understood my practice through story. I would have thought: *No no, it's about blocking the uptake of serotonin in this neural pathway.* I still don't negate that, but people seem to survive irrespective of our pills – whether they've got good combinations or bad combinations – they just rock on in some ways. Medicine seems to me to have a lot more community and care in it than I was taught.

The stories that I'll meet in any given day – it's like reading a Dickens novel every day that I go to work.

For whatever reason, I've just seen a number of older people who are beginning to struggle with their thinking. Dementia really puts the cat amongst the pigeons in a family as you can imagine. The medicine takes a quarter of an hour – you do an examination, you do a set of bloods, you possibly request a CT[1], do a rehab referral, and you might talk about the use of some medication to help. But the negotiations with family go on

---

1   'CT' refers to a 'Computed Tomography' scan, and involves computer-processed combinations of many X-ray measurements taken from different angles to produce cross-sectional (tomographic) images (virtual 'slices') of specific areas of a scanned object, allowing the user to see inside the object without cutting. From Wikipedia: https://en.wikipedia.org/wiki/CT_scan. Retrieved 26/09/2017.

for hours, and these are about story, and about where people come from, as to how they cope. I find that fascinating.

The stories that I'll meet in any given day – it's like reading a Dickens novel every day that I go to work. So sometimes it pays to know more about Mr Micawber than it does to know about SSRIs[2], because it's Mr Micawber who you've got in front of you, not just an SSRI.

Patients don't make sense. They can be contrary, argumentative, ignorant – just as we can. They are balls of knowledge and ignorance and unless you decode that, you never get near them. And their experiences of us are often awful. You come to realise that when you start talking to them. We've sold out the profession a long time ago in some ways. We've stopped being involved in our communities – we've taken the money and run – and now we're moaning: "It's no fun anymore."

We need to unload and repackage the model. The waiting room really does drive a lot. I feel dirty almost sometimes, going to do a home visit. Like somehow I'm letting my colleagues down because it's in not an efficient use of my time. I might go and see an elderly Samoan man, for example, who has just been diagnosed with motor-neuron disease and I'm thinking: *Should I be doing this?* I think that's sad.

You see so much when you see people on their terms. And it's deeply humbling, and enriching – you're surrounded by their photos, their power, their television, their music, their cup of tea, and you give them *mana*[3] because *they're* looking after *you.* They bake you a biscuit, or make you a cake – and make you take the lot when you leave – and you let them do something for you. But it's extraordinarily inefficient if you're counting the beans. Possibly not if you count them in ten years' time, but if you count them at the end of this year; yeah. And it's good for the doctor. It will make you stay in medicine a little bit longer.

---

2   Selective Seratonin Reuptake Inhibitor.
3   Polynesian word for power.

It's a continual deficit model – you're here on my terms because something's wrong with you, and I'll fix it.

Taking a full social and family history, which can be hugely revealing, is very inefficient and just not economic at all in the short term. In the long term it has efficiencies but in the short term it means you get through a quarter of the patients. But, General Practice without that, you'd want to stab yourself in the eye, wouldn't you?

It's a continual deficit model – you're here on my terms because something's wrong with you, and I'll fix it. We've grafted this economic model onto community and care, and it doesn't work. You almost have to do what you're not taught at med school, just to get through a day. It becomes almost a siege mentality because we've lost the joy of medicine, because we've stopped seeing, because we haven't got time to see.

It becomes about the waiting room and keeping it ticking. It's like a teacher in a classroom thinking: *I used to love poems and now I'm teaching this poem again for the twentieth year in a row to these kids who don't care, and all of a sudden, I don't care either anymore.*

Medicine used to be a poor number-two wife to writing for me. My writing though has helped and influenced me in my medicine, and now the two are much closer. Poetry is an attitude of placing yourself in relationship to an object. Thinking about it is only one avenue. For example: a teapot. You can feel the teapot – you can feel the whiteness, the shape of it, the fecundity of it, the cave, the warmth of it. We can still have a deep response to it, even as an inanimate object. It is everyday, mundane, ordinary; and yet there is this sense that it can draw a response from you, like a child can, or an animal, or a beautiful landscape. When I write, it becomes like this process of imprinting myself around the teapot, pulling that impression off and pressing it into the paper. Then you play around with the paper. The process of poetry excites me because it is another way of knowing.

The more I started to see the possibilities of this way of seeing for my medicine, and when I started to just shut up and listen, poetry started to happen with my patients. I still need to be thinking about what my differential diagnosis is, and my management plan, but instead of ruthlessly concentrating on those things, I can listen deeply. You have consultations where you think: *What on earth is this person coming to me with? What do they want, and what can I do about it? No, I can't find you a job, I can't save your marriage, I can't tell you shouldn't have done that twenty years ago. I can't un-hurt you.*

If I stop thinking, I can have solutions to these things and get myself out of the way – if I stop worrying about the outcome of the consultation – people become narratives and poems. Some poems are just perfect in and of themselves, and medicine just becomes a way of editing the poem: changing a line here and there; untangling a bit here or there; choosing a different word sometimes; getting the right cadence. Sometimes all I need to do is show them their own story. I just say, for example: "Have you ever thought that this may be behind some of the things you are feeling, or the pain that you have been getting that has been investigated by everyone in medicine without finding a reason for it?" All of a sudden I find that medicine becomes extraordinarily exciting to me, as exciting as writing a poem. Sometimes that kind of connection – really feeling the person – only happens once or twice a day, or for a few seconds in a consultation, but it makes my day worthwhile. You do have to keep the waiting room flowing – being behind and people getting annoyed only encroaches on the possibilities for connection. Of course we also need to consider the objective. And to realise when we need to that: *Oh, this isn't a psychological process; it's a bowel cancer.*

I grew up in South Auckland, which is a melting pot of cultures in New Zealand – especially Maori and other Polynesian cultures. Those communities have been colonised by white, old-fashioned Western thought in a number of ways. They have inherited an almost missionary, receiver model of medicine that is quite old-fashioned. It is almost the medicine of our grandfathers that they still expect to have happen. In a sense you are looking at a sort of stratified layer of rock through time and culture about how medicine should be. This can rekindle in us how medicine was when we practiced in community; when Doctor Smith rode on horseback to your house and delivered your babies, took out your appendix and pronounced you dead.

We've created silos of medicine these days. Maori may show up to a hospital and we tell them off and say: "You've got to go to primary care first, then here, then this then that." They go: "Huh? But I'm sick, you're the doctor." In a sense, working in these communities simplified medicine for me, and there is a part of me that thinks that medicine should be that simple. We have made it very complicated. This community also taught me the strengths of community, and about spirituality in medicine. It is very rare that I meet a Polynesian atheist – it is about as common as a Polynesian vegetarian. It is just not in the culture. There is an innate and deep sense of spirituality. I see people all the time who have had messages from beyond, who have ancestors who they talk to, who bring messages to me. It is just not out of context to have a spiritual life. So those influences, as well as the fact that I grew up in a church which was also very tribal, made me very oriented to community and spirituality.

You have to recognise that you're not an objective bystander, that you actually carry a whole lot of baggage yourself. It's like you're a molecule of the medicine you dish out ...

My own ghosts are with me wherever I am in a consultation: a failed marriage; having a daughter who I adore; my dad who died over thirty years ago after slowly having the juice sucked out of him through Parkinson's disease. He was a classic, quintessential Homer Simpson type character – half blessed, half cursed, capable of mad, crazy male behaviour, and with a deep love for his family. He helps me with a certain kind of vernacular. And my daughter is always with me in the room, telling me how to be with this child or that child. And my ex-wife: all that personal pain, personal sense of failure that comes from loving and falling out of love and dealing with the debris; whenever a patient is dealing with heart-break – she's always there.

You have to recognise that you're not an objective bystander, that you actually carry a whole lot of baggage yourself. It's like you're a molecule of the medicine you dish out – engaging with a particular receptor in the patient's psychology. You connect with some people and not with others. Sometimes you have to wriggle and wriggle to find a way to connect in with their receptor site.

Our medicine becomes who we're connected to, what we care about, what we carry and haven't dealt with, and our sense of spirituality in the greater context. Those aspects of ourselves necessarily become much more a part of the conversation, although they remain unspoken. These parts of ourselves and our relationships can be a good part of the consultation. But we're slapped over the fingers all the time as doctors for bringing our subjectivity to the consultation. As if we don't? I mean, really? As if a faux objectivity isn't the concealed ghost of our Western culture anyway. We just need to acknowledge and learn the power of our own well-examined subjectivity, and its dangers.

You train, and there's lots of science and a lot of learning to do, then you graduate and you're terrified you're going to kill somebody or make the wrong decision. You are very focused on the assimilation of knowledge, and very aware of the technicalities of the consultation, and anxious that you're doing the right job. It takes a few years to get over that – not that you take things lightly, but after a while you relax with it and all of a sudden you start to listen and the medicine is taken for granted to a degree. Or maybe you realise that there's stuff that you only see once or twice a year and you'll have to look in the book. But when you relax a bit, you see the person and all of a sudden story becomes a lot more important.

I bowled into medicine because I love an academic challenge. I had studied theology for two years and done an Arts Degree, but I didn't really know where to go with them. By the time I finished studying medicine though, I no longer felt the missionary zeal – I had come to recognise what dangers it contains and I was full of doubt. My final years of med school and my first couple of years of being a house surgeon, I was horrified that I wasn't prepared to make the sorts of decisions I was being asked to make. I was scared and I thought I was going to kill everybody. I wrote a book of poetry called *Playing God*[4] really because I thought: *I can't just do six years of study and then leave – it would feel like too big a personal failure.* So, I decided that if I wrote this book of poems, I'd be able to leave and say: "This is what I gave back – this was my contribution to medicine." It was a response. I didn't care if no one read it, although it ended up getting into lots of nooks and crannies.[5] But by the time I got to the end of it, I had gotten over that hump of fear and doubt. It is a steep learning curve, but you do learn quite quickly. Plus, I was discovering the very beginning of that process of: *Wow, I really love these patients, what else is going to get me into the stories?*

For me, the turning point came during a third-year lecture on the anatomy of the cardiac arteries with a heart surgeon. With five minutes to go, he put up an overhead projection (that's how it was then) of a poem and I just stopped in my tracks. I can't even remember the poem now, but it made me question everything I was doing. I started to write again, and didn't stop. Sometimes it can be as simple as that.

I think to some extent you can teach the art of listening and relationship to medical students and young doctors. You can't guarantee that if you teach something it will be taken up, but that is true of anything. I think you can put young doctors in situations and ask them to just look differently. Ask them to watch what is happening, learn to be in relationship, allow themselves to be pressed upon. We don't just share things that pass between us by talking, or by reading each other's

---

4   Published by Steele Roberts, Aotearoa, 2002.
5   And won the Ockham New Zealand Book Awards for Poetry (Montana NZ Awards), 2003.

writing. People have this shape – two arms, two legs – but around them is an underwater continental shelf of ways they have been brought up, their joys, and pains.

I would say to students and young doctors: "Stop doing medicine for a minute – let's just learn about art, or poetry, or photography." I don't know anything that demonstrates it in a more concrete way. You've got to look at a thing, and look at it again, and look at the light, and frame it differently, and walk around it a few times. If you learn to do that with one or two things, then you can apply little bits of that seeing at times to a consultation. I think you can teach the artistic attitude.

I know the arts are not everyone's cup of tea. It may terrify some. But you can still encourage it. Writing is not about writing as much as it is about looking. Give them an opportunity to catch that frisson of really looking at something. And to see it look back at you for just a momentary wink from the world. Once that happens, you are never the same again. You know that feeling after a good movie and you walk out of the theatre and the blues are bluer and the reds are redder; and you're not quite right for about an hour, until you've read the business news again, and got yourself back into the 'real world'? It's giving them experiences of what art does – its ability to make us look twice.

We've become so defensive and careful about any kind of humanity or subjectivity in the consultation but we need to give doctors permission to see consultation as story, and elevate story to a type of science that has a predictive power. We just need to rebalance that connection.

I'd love to say to young doctors when it comes to studying the arts: "Pull down your pants and skate on the ice!" That's a line I first heard in the TV comedy 'M*A*S*H'.[6] It basically means: find your own way home. My knowing won't be your knowing. Be silly, if that

6   'M*A*S*H' is a 1972–1983 American television series developed by Larry Gelbart.

works for you. When you think you've looked at something, look at it again. Do that thing we did as kids and made our eyes go a little bit out of focus, and watch the shapes change. Do that. A lot. Demonstrate physically the process of altering focus, and it will seep into your work. Change your viewfinder, find ways to put yourself in different attitudes and perspectives.

How do you make somebody see something? It's like going to a gallery and being moved to tears by a piece of art, and some people going: "Oh, yawn, what's on TV?" Most doctors will know exactly what I mean if they've practiced for more than three or four years.

This sort of stuff is hard to teach at med school because really, let's face it, medical students – and I was one of them – they just want to know what's in the exam.

Look, I have to say, this sort of stuff is hard to teach at med school because really, let's face it, medical students – and I was one of them – they just want to know what's in the exam.

The attitude of the young doctors can be: "I am state of the art. I am the top two per cent of the education system. I need to know the knowing before I can think about the touchy-feely stuff." Your communication style might be worth five per cent of your assessment. That tells me what I need to focus on.

That's the way we think. It's a currency. Most of them *are* ripe for it, most of them are quite open hearted; they're idealistic, they care. But it sort of dies for a few years while they focus on all the science which needs to be learned. People tried to teach me this but I needed to know the root of the twelve cranial nerves man, and every pathway, and every muscle they lay back on. And I knew it, too! I got A+ in it! How many times have I used my knowledge of the cranial nerves in my career? Hardly ever, and I can't even remember most of them now. I'm not decrying the knowing by any means, I'm just trying to bring some balance back. I think we can plant the seed at least, and then, after some watering, it can grow. It's giving it permission, I think.

So, I'd have two medical schools: the traditional med school, and then another one after two or three years of practice. They tried to teach me consultation skills, but I didn't have consultations under my belt so people talking to me about consultations didn't make sense – I didn't understand that they have a life of their own. I'd love to have taken a year and then gone back to med school, because then I would have had more of a chance to know what I really wanted and needed to know.

In the second med school, I'd say to young doctors: "Trust your feelings. Talk to people. Have a mentor. Have someone you can ask fearless questions of, with whom you can pick up the phone and be vulnerable. Develop a relationship with someone who doesn't make you feel stupid, or that you're an imposition. At some point also accept the power that comes with your position and use it with some wisdom. Hang out with people with Alzheimer's. Go spend the day with Aunty Kate chopping firewood. Just look at all of life. What is it that makes us us?"

Failing has been the best thing that ever happened to me. What would I have done if I still thought I knew everything?

I think that is why older doctors get this stuff; we older burned out, failed, wrecked old bastards. In some ways, it's like we're better lovers and better parents and better doctors when we've failed. You know what, there's a hell of a lot we don't know. We haven't got it all figured out. There are many frontiers left.

Failing has been the best thing that ever happened to me. What would I have done if I still thought I knew everything? It is important to let people know that there is another state of mind, there is a developmental stage in the human being beyond adulthood. It's about recognising ourselves in context and connection to the rest of the world and asking questions such as "What does it all mean?" I couldn't feel at twenty the joy I feel now, because it's not laced with the defeats.

Just getting doctors to tell their stories is really powerful. There are dozens and dozens and dozens of beautiful doctors out there with huge hearts that have dealt with these things, have dealt with their own limits. Just getting them to tell their stories I think is powerful enough. You don't really have to do more than that. Just allow those stories to be told and get out of their way.

There is a long, clear tradition of doctors writing and telling stories. The objectivity revolution sort of stopped us from being wizards. There's good stuff about being wizards and witches. Also, there was a lot of bullshit so I can understand why the movement was to stamp it out, but I think in some ways we've thrown some of the baby out with the bathwater.

What I have noticed with my poems; as soon as you start telling the stories of your patients, instead of talking about randomised controlled trials, doctors come and start telling you their stories also, because they've got thousands of them. Putting it into words gives other doctors permission to say: "Oh yeah". And actually, most doctors do have the right stories of medicine, they just need to hear them from others to know that they're not alone. Medicine doesn't encourage us to be too soft and mushy. It's a toughen-up sort of profession. But the art of medicine is the art of story.

NB: At the time of this interview Glenn was working in a Maori health service which is reflected in the examples he gives. He is now working in a youth health service.

TODAY I WANT TO BE A DOCTOR [7]

Today I am happy to be a doctor
Everyone seems to be getting better.

Those who were sick are not so sick
And those who were well are thriving.

The healthy are grateful to be alive.
And the dying are at peace with their dying.

No one has taken too many pills.
No one has taken too few.

A woman is returning to her husband.
A husband is returning to his wife.

The lame accept chairs.
The blind ask for dogs.

The deaf are listening to music.

The depressed are tapping their feet.

The asthmatics have stopped smoking.
The alcoholics have stopped drinking.
The diabetics are eating apples.

The mad are beginning to make sense.

Nobody's cholesterol is high.

Disease has gone weak at the knees
I expect him to make an appointment.

7   Glenn Colquhoun, from *Playing God*, Steele Roberts, Aotearoa, 2002, p.75

6 | MEANING AND MEDICINE

DR BRIAN BROOM

*Immunologist, Psychotherapist and Author. Dr Broom is
Consultant Physician in Clinical Immunology (Auckland
City Hospital) and Adjunct Professor in the Department
of Psychotherapy and founder of the Post-Graduate
MindBody Healthcare Diploma and Masters program at
Auckland University of Technology.*

New Zealand

*"A symptom is a warning in the body that you
shouldn't go on living your life in the way you
have been living it."*

George Groddeck[1]

The most important thing that doctors can do for their patients is listen
to them. Listen to them at the beginning and listen to them at the end,
and find out who they are. If you fail to listen to the person beyond
listening for diagnosis and treatment, without listening to him as a
human being, you will miss a lot.

Diagnosis from one perspective can be seen as a pattern of
dysfunction recognised by a group of people who look at patients in a

---

1   G Groddeck, *The meaning of Iilness*, Hogarth Press / Institute of Psychoanalysis, London,
1977.

distinctively narrow kind of way, and who all agree on what treatment should be applied, according to that way of looking. In an important sense, the person you are treating has been reduced to a diagnosis, reduced down to a limited way of looking. At its very worst, diagnosis is centred in the clinician's mode of thinking, and is somewhat separate from the patient as a whole. I feel very strongly about this. I do not mean that we should not diagnose, because medical treatments have a very important place in healthcare. But, consider this: prognosis is a future predicted on the basis of a form of pattern recognition agreed upon by a group of people who see patterns in the same way, and agree upon certain courses of treatment. In cancer treatment, for instance, for all its potency, oncology is a certain way of viewing cancer, and designs treatment (and prognosis) accordingly. Thus diagnosis can become a kind of medical narcissism which places the doctor and her perspectives at the centre of the healing situation, instead of the patient.

> *Diagnosis can become a kind of medical narcissism which places the doctor and her perspectives at the centre of the healing situation, instead of the patient.*

I am not an alternative practitioner, but I am against any sort of practice that is not fully whole person-centred. I am principally known for my interest in working with meaning or story and medicine. I am interested in the relationships between life experience, and the meaningful things have happened to the patient, and the development of illness. Knowing these relationships between meaning and illness, we can often intervene to restore health.

But it is also about the healing relationship between the clinician and the patient. To really understand the potency of relationship, to work with, and give new meaning to that, is where much of healing lies. If you can deeply appreciate that your patient is somehow sacred, and deep, and emotionally and spiritually full of resourcefulness, energy and potential, then he or she will quickly sense this, and then you have a healing relationship. But this is language which a lot of doctors do not comprehend and would not use. It is counter-current within the dominant biomedical discourse.

The trouble is, you can't train for this stuff – it is almost as if you have to un-train. I have a high view of the value of caring – caring that is healing, not fundamentally professionalised or commodified. There are clinicians around who have really got what it takes to do this without any training, and others who aspire to it but who are quite impoverished in themselves, quite wounded probably, and have much to learn in becoming more effective 'healers'. There are as many who are called to the profession because of their own woundedness, as there are those called to altruism. Medicine does give power, and part of the attraction for some is ego. But if you work alongside these wounded clinicians for a while, you can nourish and nudge them, so that they become more human. Within the biomedical framework this is subversive. It is not about training, it is not about 'schoolishness'; it is about being human, and sharing humanity.

I think the health system is broken, and spiralling out of control economically. We are pouring more and more money and technology into illnesses, even though often this does not seem to be changing things in proportion to the investment.

Patients love it, so I have got to think we are right on target, but how do we get the power brokers to listen? I think the health system is broken, and spiralling out of control economically. We are pouring more and more money and technology into illnesses, even though often this does not seem to be changing things in proportion to the investment. Because of my frustrations with the blindness and unwillingness of the professions to adopt a whole person approach, there is a part of me that would welcome a crisis in healthcare. But another part of me fears the turmoil and suffering that would ensue.

I did a lot of science training but I never really saw myself as a committed scientist. I was more naturally inclined to philosophy and the arts. I like the quote from philosopher George Simmel: "The scientist sees because he knows, the artist knows because he sees."[2] This is very relevant to person-centred medicine as opposed to diagnosis-centred medicine.

I had a very religious and fundamentalist background, and experienced quite a lot of tension and uncertainty as I went through university. As I saw it then, there was a fracture between science and religion. I had a very enquiring mind and tried to hold the two together. And I could not simplistically and reductively give myself completely over to either one of them, excluding the other.

For me, doing medicine was a vocational thing. My religious background seeded the idea that life has a purpose and meaning, and that there was a meaningful pathway ahead. And from the age of ten it seemed that medicine was what I was destined to do. Certainly I remember that moment as a small boy when I chose to do medicine.

Eventually I went to medical school. That first day is crystal clear. I was there because it was a destiny, it seemed. I met other people who were there because they saw medicine as a way to get status and money. That was all very foreign to me – I was really quite naïve. Then after graduation came the task of choosing a specialty. Psychiatry intrigued me but I was also challenged and threatened by it. The psychiatrists I met, and the treatment models used, did not impress me. I teetered between internal medicine or psychiatry and the former won. I chose immunology because of mentor influence and because it was a new speciality. I was sent overseas to train, funded by the New Zealand Medical Research Council. I was committed to it but I felt it was somehow outside of me. In the meantime I was constantly developing a strong interest in synthesis and integration, and making sense. The old question remained: How do you draw science and religion together, for example, without having to toss one out?

---

2   Origin and accuracy of the this quote unclear.

I ended up setting up the Clinical Immunology Department at Christchurch Hospital and the Medical School, and was well on my way to becoming a bona fide medical researcher. But the dissatisfaction escalated. I was thirty-eight years of age. I was doing well, and I had a big research grant. But I looked ahead and thought something like this: *I cannot do this pure "science-y" stuff for the next thirty years, something would die in me.*

About that time, discussing this with a senior colleague and friend, I felt challenged to act, and to the dismay of medical colleagues, I resigned my position. I wanted to develop myself on the 'other side', to include psychological and spiritual perspectives in my work. But how to do that, with a family to support, and in the face of having the security of a flowering career? And actually I did enjoy much of what I was doing in internal medicine. I didn't want to give it all away.

I went into psychiatry for about four years. It was more difficult than I anticipated. In retrospect it was reckless, emotionally! By the end of the first year I was depressed and nearly returned to my immunology, but just in time I realised that was not what I wanted either. I think the depression was about uncertainty and the loss of an established internal medicine and immunology identity, within a social space in which I was well respected. I gradually found my feet.

An odd thing happened in my fourth year in psychiatry training. I was asked by the head of Psychological Medicine if I would like to become professor of psychiatry, on finishing my training. I sat there for what seemed like a long time (maybe only thirty seconds) and then said 'No.' There was a momentary tussle between feeling complimented and seduced by the prospect of certainty, and the question once again of what it was I really wanted, and what was at the heart of my shift into psychiatry. A voice within me said, *no – I didn't go into psychiatry to repeat something like my immunology biomedical career.*

I saw that psychiatry, whilst providing a very interesting training and experience, was hell-bent on furthering a strongly medical view of human suffering. I wanted to shift away from that. Entering psychiatry was a directional and transitional matter for me. I wanted to connect the emotional and spiritual side of human beings with my internal medicine.

At this time, I was involved with a very large and socially-oriented church. Eventually I told them I was interested in developing an integrative health centre at the Church, which would treat people from medical, psychological and spiritual perspectives. And, in 1987, this happened.

In this new Centre I reignited my immunology role and welded it together with my developing interest in psychotherapy. I found myself sitting with patients who had been referred with traditional immunological diagnoses, but because I now had the two hats on – the hats of both doctor and psychotherapist – I started seeing things I had not noticed before. I observed that patients were getting ill at certain times, which seemed important. But the most shocking, and powerful thing that I started to see was symbolic illness – or what I then called somatic metaphor. What I mean by this is illnesses that have a physical presentation that mirror beautifully what the patient is saying about their lives.

I had one patient, for example, of about seventy, with a severe facial rash. She had had it for five years, and it was so severe that the physicians had got to the point of a biopsy of her liver, thinking it may have been related to a carcinoid tumour. I happened to ask her when it had begun, using what I now call the smorgasboard question: "What were the most interesting, memorable, significant, difficult, problematic, hard, frustrating things that happened to you about the time you got ill?" Quick as a flash, she said: "Oh, it was when my husband got depressed." He had been seriously depressed, to the point of requiring ECT treatment. I asked her how this had affected her and she said: "I keep a brave face on it." She said it twice. I said: "You've got this rash on your face and you're keeping a brave face on it." She was taken aback and a bit sceptical. I asked her to come back to talk more. Five days later we talked about how it had been for her, supporting and managing this vulnerable and rather sick man all of her married life. After that, the rash disappeared.

My books are full of those sorts of stories.[3] Some of these illnesses are mild, some severe and some potentially fatal. They are all 'real' diseases, not just the accepted psychosomatic disorders. And, while not every illness is symbolic or metaphorical, by any means, those that are manifest a phenomenology that really challenges everything we thought we knew in mainstream medicine.

I know, as an immunologist, that there is the field of psycho-neuro-immunology, but I could find nothing there that tells us how meaning comes to be expressed highly specifically in the body, in the form of a symbolic disorder. These were 'real diseases' with observable signs and measurable changes. I had stumbled across a phenomenology that made it necessary for me to try to understand this synthesis between mind and body. What really interested me were the meaning-full diseases, because they raised hard questions which helped progress my thinking in terms of integration and understanding where people are at, and how they make and express meaning. I became convinced that it is nonsense to think that there is a discontinuity between meanings and the body.[4]

I started to accumulate somatic metaphors and stories around conditions that exacerbated at times of stress. What then became challenging was how to manage this growing arena of subjectivity and physicality as an active, consulting clinician. How do you talk to patients about this stuff? How do you communicate with people so that they do not feel stigmatised? How do you invite them into a process? And how do you write letters to the referring general practitioners? And so the first ten years was mostly about developing that. I was becoming more known and more accepted, and eventually I could not handle all the patients.

The next challenge came when I realised that psychotherapists behave as dualistically as doctors. I would send a patient with physical

---

3   B C Broom (1997) *Somatic illness and the patient's other story. A practical integrative approach to disease for doctors and psychotherapists.* Free Association Books, New York / London.
4   Broom, B. C., R. J. Booth, et al. (2012). *"Symbolic illness and 'mindbody' co-emergence. A challenge for psychoneuroimmunology."* Explore 8 (No 1, January / February): 16-25.

symptoms off to a very good psychotherapist. A patient might say to them: "I've got terrible tummy pain," and the psychotherapist might say: "Have you spoken to your GP about that?" This means essentially that the body did not belong in the therapy room. I was seeing the dualism playing out on both sides. So I started to develop supervision groups with psychotherapists who wanted to develop their knowledge around the body as well. That was also what led me to write my first book, which is pitched at psychotherapists and doctors.

My networks and supports grew and then a couple of us decided we were a bit isolated in Christchurch, so we decided to start a biennial national MindBody conference. The first conference was well attended – we got about 250 people, about fifty of them GPs and sixty to seventy psychotherapists and counsellors, with a smattering of other disciplines. It was a mixed bag of people who were looking for a place to belong, not satisfied with biomedical orthodoxy.

Some people attracted to what we do are into alternative and complementary medicine, but many are otherwise very orthodox. I have never seen myself as an alternative health practitioner. I am much more interested in a truly integrative work, which embraces both physicality and subjectivity. Most of our network are interested in 'mindbody' in the broadest sense. It's much more difficult, but more helpful I think, to see the patient, the person, as the integrative arena, not my methodology, or my discipline.

To be truly integrative is to be able see what is best for the particular patient in the particular moment in time, without fixation on one particular 'right way' of viewing things. At risk of appearing harshly judgemental, any strict adherence to a methodology is a form of narcissism, centred on the practitioner – because this is what I like doing, this is what I will believe in, and will offer you. Whereas, I feel really strongly about seeking to really know the patient and then explore the options which will work for them.

I went on to develop a multi-disciplinary post-graduate Diploma and Masters program in MindBody Healthcare for clinicians at the Auckland University of Technology, which has been a very positive thing.

I am also a consultant at the Immunology Department at Auckland Hospital. So, the wheel turns! I hadn't been a hospital consultant since 1981. They have welcomed me, and the whole department has moved gradually towards whole person care.

I think working alongside people and showing them the power of what you do is far better than preaching. In general the younger doctors like it. Initially I felt had to carve out the whole person approach in the department with caution. Gradually clinicians are becoming much more comfortable and natural with the integration of physical disease with emotions, meanings, life experience and stress.

So, what is 'mindbody' medicine or whole person healthcare? Everyone has a story, and if you listen very carefully to the little things that people are saying, doors open and you can learn an enormous amount about them and the factors that predisposed them to the illness, and factors that precipitated the illness, and maintain the illness.

This is in contrast to what we are taught in medical school which is to seek out more and more and more physical and diagnostic information. Stories are always implied in the few phrases and sentences that people use, right from the beginning of an interview. I listen very intently to the phraseology that people use, and if one is accurate in one's listening, and empathic, then the story opens up. From there it becomes routine to educate and help people understand the relationship between what they are presenting with physically, and what is happening in their lives.

The process in which resolution occurs is as varied as anything else in life. I could tell lots of stories about the way the 'story' approach enhances healing of illness and disease – some that resolved quickly, some that took a long time. If you did a survey of our immunology department, staff would say that many of our chronic patients are getting better quicker, and without the use of heavy medication. The most common question I ask patients is: "What was happening around about the time the symptoms started, and what happened at the time you got an exacerbation?"

I had a woman with severe vasculitic hives of the shins. It took three months to get rid of the persistent hives but over the course of the next three years the hives kept recurring after sexual intercourse. And the puzzle was, why? It took a long time for it to come out that she and her sister were survivors of ten pregnancies, the other eight of which had been aborted. Her mother had been quite promiscuous, and the daughter had played a role in protecting the father from her mother's indiscretions, and had always felt guilty about that. It was not until we started to deal with that that the issue resolved, but it took a long time to get to that point of connection and awareness.

If you listen very carefully to what people say, the important things float to the surface, out of both the conscious and unconscious terrains.

I have become very interested in the nature of the healing relationship between the clinician and the patient. Why do people get better with me? I am certainly interested, and I listen very carefully and accurately, so people know that they are known, safely and empathically. But it is not just a momentary empathy, it is also that they know I am there with them, and that I will go the distance with them in some way or other.

The problem with subjectivity, emotionality and meaning is that most clinicians don't have the right model in their heads so they can't make the connection between the disease and the subjectivity.

The other problem is that though they may be aware of the connection, they don't know what to do with it. Most doctors are trained to try to fix things. They have a very high view of their diagnosing and fixing expertise – of what they know and what they can do. That is what they see as their potency: that is their potency. It is hard to train a doctor to actually be with a person, to love them, and to be generously open to them, and to see these elements as part of the treatment, and indeed making their treatments more potent, especially where the usual instrumental things do not work.

One of the reasons we set up the university program instead of just providing a series of workshops is that after a workshop you go home, and things change for the first day or so, and then it all gets too hard because the structural and economical orientation of practice is such that it all feels too big, and you just cannot hold the new perspective together with your usual way of being, and then you feel a failure.

Perhaps I am a masochist. Throughout all my experimentation I survived the uncertainties of all this change, but it is not realistic to expect lots of people to do that. The students who come into the part-time university course arrive all bright-eyed and bushy-tailed, and within the first two or three months they struggle because they are trying to implement the new learning in their work lives, and they get rattled. But by the second year they're getting confident and building skills, and they are able to handle themselves differently, their patients differently, their colleagues differently, their disciplinary bodies differently, and so it is quite a big change. It can happen, but it cannot happen just by information. It has got to be nurtured and developed and lived. These days whole person treatments are mediated via relationships between whole person-oriented clinicians and psychotherapists.

I am lucky that I have generally been well respected by my profession, although I know some do not understand. I am probably a bit timid when it comes to politics. That might change. People cannot dismiss me as 'alternative,' and many see me as adding value.

Unfortunately medical training is a systematic process of indoctrinating you with a limited view of personhood, and teaching you to function in a relationship between two people which is highly reductionistic, and limited.

I did have one very public difference of opinion after a presentation I did to my Australasian immunology peers. I was confronted by an immunologist who did not believe that people are anything more than a 'biochemical bag'. Some people do get really nervous. I was recently on a national panel for a rural education forum in Sydney. It was difficult, because while people liked what I was saying, they were also scurrying to put themselves in the right – a kind of self-protective thing. That is what we do as humans.

I'll be audacious now and say to young doctors, and doctors in training, that a lot of what you are learning about disease and patients, without an emphasis on therapeutic relationships, is wrong. Or at least the assumptions underlying it are wrong. And, unfortunately medical training is a systematic process of indoctrinating you with a limited view of personhood, and teaching you to function in a relationship between two people which is highly reductionistic, and limited.

I am sorry but it is not good news. If you want to develop yourself as a doctor, start working now on your ability to relate to people.

I would tell young and training doctors that if they want to practice really good medicine, then they need to get their own personal issues sorted. Whatever constraints you have in your personal relating to others, these will affect your doctorliness. This is difficult for me to put out there because medical students will say this is too hard. We are social beings, and it is very difficult to say to medical student: "You need to think differently to your teachers." We want to belong. *Who the hell is this doctor who says this way we 'know' is wrong?*

I think change will occur on many fronts. In our work we are just part of the whole. I think it is necessary for some research to occur so that these ideas are not only clinically and philosophically plausible, but they can also meet evidence-based medicine front on. But the problem is that biomedicine has a very narrow view of evidence. It is hard to know how long the randomised controlled trial evidence-based medicine craze will last, because while there is such an undercurrent of anger at the depersonalisation implied by it, it still has a powerful hold supported by pharmaceutical and technology interests. Everyone who has vested interest in the healthcare system tends to sing from the same hymnbook, but underneath many are dissatisfied in some way or another. It takes a lot of courage to give voice to this. It needs really intelligent, articulate and politically savvy persons to speak out.

It is hard to be a gentle whole person-centred healthcare sort and a raging prophet at the same time.

I think my role in New Zealand has been to stimulate some of the beginnings of this change. It is urgent to get a significant group of young doctors through the whole person healthcare training – it is all very well to encourage the allied health professions but the people who hold the power and the ones who are the least inclined, are the doctors. If I had twenty million dollars, I would like to set up an exemplary outpatient clinic with a strong research element in which rigorous whole person-centred medicine is practiced. I have no doubt it would attract clinicians and would attract patients, and I have no doubt at all that the research would show a dramatic improvement in outcomes.

I've always been an explorer. I'm not really happy unless I'm crossing boundaries. I need to be pushing ahead, not standing still. My spiritual symbol is a river. I've always had a strong sense that I am travelling down a river. Sometimes I get stuck on a sandbank and I do not want to move on. Then I push out and find myself going against or across the current, and then I find myself in white water and I hate it, I nearly tip out, then I find myself on a broad expanse and I am really travelling and I am waiting to see what is around the next corner – it always feels like there is another corner. It is not just a metaphor – it is a far deeper sense of purpose, future, horizon. I can see there are challenges to that metaphor as one gets older. I think my concept of spirit and God has become less specific and less known – there's not a wrap of theology around it. In fact, theology feels too analytical to me.

I do feel, in the end, if one must be a reductionist, then there is a reductionism in health care that I could embrace and that is: the art of healing at its core, is a loving transaction of some sort. I mean this in the broadest sense. And the task of a healer is to have loving intention, to create a space where a person can feel that intention, can feel safe with it, and flourish inside it. None of this is incompatible with the inclusion of biomedical treatments.

"He may be called wild because of his passionate nature which wants to help where others have resigned or are hiding their impotence behind the mock techniques and exact diagnostics."[5]

---

5   Schact, Introduction, G Groddeck. *The meaning of illness.* London: Hogarth Press / Institute of Psychoanalysis, pp 7–8, 1977.

7 | A WITNESS AND AN ALLY

DR KATIE MOORE

Paediatric Oncologist, Monash Children's Hospital.

Melbourne, Australia

We really don't have a good understanding of both the number of people who are struggling, and the severity or complexity of the struggle in the medical profession. The stigma around mental illness in medicine is still very, very prevalent. So as a profession with a high incidence of mental illness and suicides, we still don't handle it very well. I don't see easy answers in addressing this, but I think that as a group, doctors have a lot of vulnerabilities to burnout, or anxiety or depression. This is both intrinsic to the individuals, but it is also exacerbated within medical culture, and also reinforced by wider societal views and norms.

It is partly the fact that it is a somewhat self-selecting population of academically successful, often quite competitive people who end up in medicine in the first place. So you have this pool of predisposed individuals, and medical school really exaggerates that competitiveness and perfectionism. It is a recipe for disaster.

In some ways the degree of perfectionism and anxiety start off a bit like an evolutionary protective measure. For instance, if you break your leg, it needs to hurt so that you do not step on it for a short period of time – that is adaptive. But then, if you go on like that for months and months, and the pain is still there and you are still not walking on it – that is maladaptive. If you use that metaphor for medicine, it is necessary for doctors to have incredibly high standards, and to avoid mistakes – because the consequences of those mistakes can be catastrophic for the person that you are treating. So the high standards start as an adaptive behaviour. But then it can become maladaptive, because rather than looking at systemic ways to prevent mistakes and harm, it becomes individualised, and individual doctors feel that they can never make a mistake. Clearly that is impossible, because we all make mistakes. So I think you can understand where that world view has come from about doctors striving to be completely infallible. It usually comes from good intentions of wanting to protect patients, of wanting to give good care, of understanding the severity of the consequences if you are a bit slapdash, or you have not slept well the previous night. People do have good reasons to be perfectionist and not to want to fail, but it is an impossible standard.

It is clear that the institutions, organisations, colleges, hospitals and medical schools have responsibility for this issue as well. It should not be left on each individual's shoulders. In terms of quality and safety, there are mechanisms those institutions can put into place to prevent mistakes. But I do believe that organisations are still sadly very quick to apportion blame if there is a problem, and most doctors know that – so everyone's always terrified that there is going to be a complaint, an investigation, or litigation. And I think society's expectations on doctors more broadly are a mixed blessing too. Doctors are held in very high standing in the community. That level of respect and trust can be conflated with personal worth; so the prospect of failure means you are falling from a high place. Most doctors probably don't go into the profession for the prestige, but they quite like it, and identify with it when it happens. But once you have achieved that standing in the community, and you have worked incredibly hard, you've made sacrifices, and all your loved ones have made sacrifices, the idea of failing is huge. It is just huge. I think doctors find that concept really frightening and threatening. I don't in any way want to conflate burnout, or anxiety or depression with 'failure'. But I think that some doctors may still feel that way, and those very attitudes contribute to the development of mental health problems – and then a vicious cycle can develop.

I also have a bit of a beef with the way that doctors are selected in the first place. Even going back into the way our school system operates in defining success – it just makes me despair. In the Victorian system you're ranked against your peers – there's no absolute mark or bar that you have to achieve – you only have to be better than the next person. As a philosophical concept, I think that is really problematic. So you get all these high achieving people rocking up to study medicine, who have proven that they are good at doing exams. But built into that academic success is the concept that students are always in competition with each other, comparing themselves against each other, not collaborating with each other.

I get lots of resumes of medical students and junior doctors with their reports and their academic scores. They are all top of the class; they won a prize at medical school; they got scholarships; got invited to speak at conferences. They've got all the academic ducks in line, and then they kind of have to prove their bona fides around being a "really rounded person." So, you can't just play the piano for joy, you have to get Grade 8 with distinction, and demonstrate it with a bit of paper. If you play soccer, you have to be the captain of some State ranking team. I can just see it on these pieces of paper the kind of pressures that these young, embryonic doctors are already under to prove themselves as exceptional, before they even get into their careers. I think it is remarkable that half the doctors are actually sane, because I think there is this unattainable standard. Then you get 200 of these people in medical school on the same course, all still trying to outrank each other in specialness and perfection.

I don't see how that can be a pathway for human qualities to come through. I don't think it is necessary that you topped the state in science, and played in a youth orchestra, and in a State sports team. You have to have a level of competence of course; you have to have an ability, and the system has to have some way of selecting candidates. But what I don't see in that selection process is an appreciation of the importance to our profession of kindness, tolerance, teamwork or respectfulness. Usually the students will use some of those words in their little biography on the front of their resume, and pay lip service to these qualities. But it's clear that there's this crazy, ever vanishing target that people are trying to achieve in order to become doctors. There's a real lack of diversity amongst the medical students coming through, and I think that doesn't serve the populations – who are being treated – very well. I really think something needs to be done about a pathway to medicine which better privileges compassion, honesty, humility and empathy.

I think it is time to be having a very clear conversation as a profession about what human qualities we want to embolden and encourage in our doctors.

And once people graduate from medical school, in paediatrics at least, they get their intern jobs, then they'll probably get a junior resident job because there are more jobs available at the early stages of their careers. But not everybody then gets accepted into the training programme for paediatrics. So, at the very outset, when you should be forming yourself as a new doctor, you're always looking over your shoulder at your colleagues. All the fun is drained out of it because you are always trying to get one step ahead, to get the next job. I do quite a lot of educational work for our unit, and I observe high levels of career stress at early stages. Again, some people seem quite robust and it's kind of like water off a duck's back to some of them, but a large minority, I would say, find it really difficult. I don't know what the answers are, but I think it is time to be having a very clear conversation as a profession about what human qualities we want to embolden and encourage in our doctors.

I would just love to remind junior doctors to try to find some joy in their work. Enjoy the process as well as the end result, and don't be too focused on the outcome in terms of 'career'. Really look for and find the value in those human interactions between you and your patient, rather than in the big academic achievements. It really doesn't matter whether you get a publication in some prestigious journal. It matters that you are compassionate, present and willing to listen to people, and willing to learn from them.

I really believe that there could be more humanities subjects incorporated into medical training and ongoing medical professional development. I think there's a lot to be gained from music, art and literature. Harvard University, for example, has a Humanities in Medicine Department. I appreciate that everybody's time is finite and that nobody can do it all, but I do think there needs to be some balancing influences and cross-disciplinary fertilisation in our training. Books and poetry, for example, can express human experience and give you an incredibly empathetic window into people's lives, in a way you simply cannot get from molecular biology.

An example of the linear thinking within our profession is the really artificial split in how the human body and human mind are treated. For example, there is still a big divide between psychiatry and everything else. People pay lip service to seeing the 'whole person,' being holistic; whatever the buzz word is. But in practice, in terms of service provision and how health services are actually funded and set up, the two don't really meet. I was at a Medical Bioethics conference this week and in one session there were some mental health professionals from various fields in the audience who were asking questions to the medical panel. There were some really good questions but the panel just could not understand them because they were literally speaking a different language – the words they were using and the theoretical framework they were coming from – it was just completely different. There is a lot of work still to be done in understanding how the mental and the physical are reciprocal; you can't split them. That kind of thinking is still considered to be quite alternative and yet it is actually quite scientific.

I am doing a Masters in Family Therapy and I am the only doctor in my course, so I feel completely like a fish out of water. Everyone else is either a psychologist or social worker, or works in family violence, or in homelessness. They have really good grounding in the conceptual frameworks, which I don't; and of course they don't have any understanding of my work context. But in the medical world, it is quite confusing for my colleagues when I say I'm doing a family therapy degree. Firstly, people say: "What's that?" Then I explain that it is like being a psychologist, except that it is about treating the whole family, not just an individual person. Then they go: "Why would you do that? Wouldn't you just refer them to the social worker, or a psychologist?" I see it as a really important framework for informing my work, and for becoming aware of some better ways to support families whose child is really sick and has a serious illness. Childhood cancer is not discriminatory. It affects anybody in the population, any family. We get families who come to us who have many vulnerabilities, and other families who come to us with great pre-existing function. Sometimes the psychosocial factors that we are dealing are nothing to do with the cancer diagnosis, but often the cancer diagnosis will compound any cracks that are already there. We are quite good at supporting paediatric oncology patients from a psychological perspective these days, but there's so much work we could be doing better with the wider family. Oncologists generally conceptualise 'family' in terms of what the family unit can do for the patient, but we don't really have a framework for understanding what to do if we see the parents' marriage falling apart because of the stress of the child's illness, for instance. And siblings are often completely invisible because everybody is so focused on the sick child. The siblings get sent off to granny or grandpa, or to go and stay with friends, and they have all sorts of other difficulties to deal with. It really makes perfect sense to me to be seeing the child and their illness in the context of their environment and support systems. It affects the entire healing trajectory for the child.

The specialties have become so separated from each other, and the communication can get lost between them. Our default response, which

I hear all the time, is: "Don't you have a GP?" General practitioners must get swamped mediating between all the different teams, but someone has to help the patient try to make sense of all these competing claims. The poor patients are often lost in the middle, and that whole burden of co-ordinating care gets dumped on the GP to sort out, because nobody else thinks it's their responsibility.

I have unfortunately had plenty of experience on the other side of medicine too, as a patient and as a parent of a very sick child. And I think about it all the time – about how other families navigate the system with none of the knowledge, or contacts or resources that I had. Even though it was a devastatingly difficult time for me, I still did have the grit and the knowledge to say: "Stuff that, I'm not following that piece of advice," when I needed to.

I had a very complicated pregnancy with my fourth baby. She was not growing and nobody could work out what was going on. When she was born she seemed okay at first. She was on the small side but we thought she just needed to fatten up a little bit and grow, and it would all work out fine. But then she struggled to feed, and she became sicker and sicker. She was my fourth baby and I had breastfed all of them, so I knew there was something not right. I felt strongly that there was something more going on than just the fact that she was very little. I kept asking them to come and have a look at her, and to see that she wasn't feeding. She did gain weight in the hospital because she was being fed through a tube at night, but then they discharged us home and she immediately became really unwell. It emerged that she had a problem with her heart; she was in heart failure. When babies are in heart failure, they use excessive amounts of energy just to pump the heart. It is really hard for them to get enough calories in, to actually gain weight and grow. We were in a double bind because she could not put on enough weight to be safely operated on, but she couldn't put on weight until they resolved the problem, which required an operation. It just went on and on. Eventually she was able to have the surgery and they were able to help her.

That experience affected me both as an individual, and professionally, in really profound ways. I now really, really get the impact that it has on the family when you have a sick child. You are already so busy as a family of small children anyway, but then when you have a really sick child, it just tips the balance. As health professionals, we just do not appreciate that enough. You kind of understand that it is anxiety provoking, and distressing, and that there's grief and trauma for parents and for the children. But we don't really appreciate enough just the day to day grinding logistics of having a sick child, and how it affects the other siblings, how the family is often split between different locations, and how someone has to stop working because there's just too much to do. At one point we took our daughter home on nasogastric feeds. We were happy to do that because we thought we knew what it would entail, but I had no idea how gruelling that was. All those times I had been telling other families to take their baby home, how great it would be to reunite the family, and that the baby would gain weight – I had no idea what I was asking of the families. And I think of that as a low impact 'intervention'! Then I think of all the other things we ask of families in caring for their children at home. We just have no idea.

I have had my own experiences as a patient also. I had just re-established my practice after our third child and was still a relatively junior consultant, but I was trying to build some traction and build up my career a little bit. I was finding it an incredibly stressful period of time. It wasn't like being a junior doctor where there's this kind of hierarchy and if you don't know the answer, you pass the buck to the next one up the line, and if they don't know the answer, they pass it on to the person at the top. Suddenly, I was pretty much the one at the top, and people were asking me tricky questions. All the easy stuff was being done by someone else, and I was left with really hard decisions about what to do if a child relapses and there is no protocol for that particular scenario; or how to deal with it when parents and staff have opposing beliefs about how to treat the child. I was really struggling with that sense of enormous responsibility, with an appreciation of how desperate the situations were for some of the families I was dealing with. And I was simultaneously juggling three very young pre-school children at home. I had no downtime. Everyone I've spoken to who is a doctor and has children has said once you have your own it changes how you feel about things. I found that period of time really, really hard and I got very anxious a lot of the time.

Then I had this very difficult pregnancy with my fourth child and before she even was born I was finding day-to-day work really demanding and stressful. I had one particularly difficult case at that time which involved family violence, child protection and number of other complex, scary issues. I was quite unwell physically as my pregnancy was not going well. I was physically enormous – I was huge, waddling around, and I was also on crutches because I had really bad pelvic instability from the pregnancy, so I was in a lot of pain and could barely walk. It was a perfect storm. When I finally did go on maternity leave, I was consumed by my own medical issues and then my daughter was born and all hell broke loose. But in the midst of all that, even though I was not officially working, this particular case was so distressing for everybody back at the hospital that different people would be phoning me up, and keeping me up to date on what was happening there. And I was at home with all these other difficulties, and I didn't feel like I could stop this awful external information dripping onto me. So I ended up with significant, really bad anxiety. I think the catalyst for that anxiety was work, and then it was compounded by the pregnancy and my daughter's illness. I certainly can't hold up my work as the only culprit in that situation, but it was very stressful and difficult, and I hadn't really properly dealt with the traumas at work.

Some time later, I became significantly depressed – properly depressed – needing to be hospitalised. That one particular case at work had massive, long-term downstream effects. It took nearly four years for me to feel ready to return to work. It came to the point where

I felt that if I didn't go back to it, I was never going to be able to because I would have deskilled and lost so much knowledge.

On the flipside of the work difficulties, the director of our unit was incredibly supportive of me. I tried to resign a couple of times and he said: "No." He just ignored me basically; he just kept telling me to take another year of maternity leave. Eventually I came back sheepishly and said: "Maybe I'd like to come back," and he said, "Great, great." He really made it possible for me to do that in a sensible way; he didn't just dump me straight back in. He organised my workload so that it was appropriate, so that I could try just re-build my knowledge base and my skill, and build everything up slowly again. In some ways medicine was a really huge factor in my burnout, or mental illness, or whatever you want to call it – but it also has played a huge part in my recovery.

Going through something like that is completely individual. It just happened that I had a good relationship with my boss. I did tell him about my pretty serious depression but, while I have not completely hidden it, I have not felt the need to share my story more widely with others. It hasn't really cropped up, although sometimes people ask why I took so much time off, and I usually pin it on the fact that I had a sick baby.

I remember the psychiatrist who was looking after me commenting – without apportioning judgement – he said: "Katie, you are so ashamed of your depression." I kind of thought: *Well, it's hard not to be.* Partly that is a feature of the illness itself – that is what depression does. But also, I think that doctors who have mental illness are not exaggerating the possible reaction to revealing. People have strong instincts that are valid about how they might be treated if they reveal their difficulties. In a way, I was protected because I was on maternity leave, so I had an 'excuse'.

Just last week I saw in the paper that 40 per cent of Australian women have had a formal diagnosis of anxiety or depression.[1] I don't

1   The Jean Hailes, 'Women's health survey 2017', surveyed 10,000 Australian women – see https://jeanhailes.org.au/news/revealing-australian-womens-health-worries-and-concerns. Retrieved 29/09/2017.

know how they measured it, but if you take that at face value, and then if you think that doctors are overrepresented in that population – because there are definitely statistics to show there are higher rates of anxiety, depression and suicide among medical practitioners than in the general community. That means even if you are being incredibly conservative, there must be a high proportion of female doctors in Australia who have a formal diagnosis of mental illness. But where are they all? You don't hear about them – they must be 'in hiding'.

I reflect a lot on the balance between the public good about revealing my story, versus the personal cost, the exposure. There are really important ethical considerations in all of this. In one period of maternity leave I decided I was going to do a Masters of Bioethics, which I did. I'm not sure about some of the essays I wrote when I was absolutely sleep-deprived and exhausted! Anyway, it became a real fascination for me; how you have this theoretical framework to think about what you *should* do, as distinct from simply what you can do in medical terms.

I also bring my bioethics training to the table when I'm discussing things with families. It expanded the way I think about families, about treating children, and how to best make some of the really, really difficult decisions we are often faced with. I find it valuable on an individual level, but on a systems level, there are also things I would like to do. If I had boundless energy and time, and I was not busy making packed lunches and all the rest, I would like to invigorate medical ethics more formally into our Children's hospital. I believe there is a really big role for ethics and I think there is probably demand for it as well.

There are a few different things happening in this space internationally, like Schwartz Rounds. You probably already know about medical grand rounds where somebody stands up and presents a paper, or a case, and then everybody discusses the symptoms, diagnosis and the latest treatment. Mr Schwartz was an American man who was a lawyer with interest in health. He had cancer and died quite young, in his forties. But before he died he set up a foundation, in his own name, to promote compassion in healthcare. Their particular thing is called the Schwartz Round – there's quite a formula to it: basically it is taking that grand round model, but discussing all the human aspects of a case.[2]

I have heard a number of American colleagues say that if they were looking to work at a hospital, they wouldn't even consider it, and they wouldn't recommend the hospital to patients, if it did not have Schwartz Rounds. It is seen as a fundamental reflection on the culture of the particular hospital. It is not seen as fringe, or hippy dippy – it has become incorporated as fairly standard practice in hospitals in the US – I think that's a really good model.

I've also heard about a programme in the United States which was set up by two social workers from an adult oncology Unit. They had done a lot of writing therapy with patients, and then they set up a writing group that combined doctors and patients. They said they had to really, really fight for it because people had all kinds of concerns about boundaries, professional ethics, and just not wanting to pour out your soul in front of the people you are treating. But by all accounts it has been a powerful two-way healing process for the people involved. These are really interesting ideas, and I would love to look at doing something similar here.

At the Bioethics conference I was recently at, one of the presenters came out with: "Relationships are a means to an end, but they are also an end in their own right." So in other words, having great relationships with patients might help achieve health goals such as stopping smoking or taking diabetes medication. But, just as importantly, those relationships between doctors and patients are health promoting in and of themselves – warmth, empathy, compassion and human connectedness have intrinsic

---

2   "Schwartz Rounds are a place where people who don't usually talk about the heart of the work are willing to share their vulnerability, to question themselves. The programme provides an opportunity for dialogue that doesn't happen anywhere else in the hospital." From http://www. theschwartzcenter.org/supporting-caregivers/schwartz-center-rounds/. Retrieved 21/09/2017.

worth in their own right. I truly believe that bearing witness to people's suffering is vital to doctors' work. By that I mean seeing the patient without judgement as a human being in all their wholeness and particularity. And letting that person *know* they are seen and understood. I have a personal motto to be 'a witness and an ally' – a concept I first read in my family therapy studies, but that I think is absolutely essential to the rest of medicine as well. In my own experience as a patient with depression, I was incredibly fortunate to be cared for by professionals who treated me in this way, and their example continues to inspire me now that I have gone back to my own work.

Really, at the end of the day, what good does medicine achieve unless it ends up with meaningful relationships, and the ability for people to participate in those relationships? I mean it widely as well. I wish for better relationships among and between doctors, in a way that is honest and accepting of human frailties and imperfection, and supportive of each other. I feel that if there were real, honest, compassionate relationships within medicine, it would take away a lot of the competitiveness, secretiveness, burnout and mental illness. And it would be better for patients too.

I hope that we continue to find wonderful scientific discoveries that can alleviate suffering. But I hope that in the pursuit of all that science, we don't lose sight of our humanity and other people's humanity, and that we can find a way to demonstrate our humanity as individuals alongside our professional responsibilities.

Usually when people ask what I do for work I just say I'm a doctor. Then they ask what kind of doctor and I say I'm a paediatrician. Then they ask where I work, so eventually it comes out that I am a paediatric oncologist. People are often horrified – they recoil and say: "Oh God, how can you do it?" But I actually really love this area of medicine, it is generally very hopeful. Oncology means you can see the whole person and you get to know the children and their families, generally for long periods of time. You get to truly understand the family and their context. It's all about the relationships.

8 | "THE BEST OF MY KNOWLEDGE AND ABILITY"[1]

DR TRALEE SUGRUE

General Practitioner and Homeopath.

Wellington, New Zealand

I'm fascinated by the human body. I've always been really into healing. I used to make hospitals for my dolls. My mother had an old Red Cross manual, which I learned off by heart as a child. I remember on one occasion analysing our meals at home and telling my mother that we didn't have enough vitamin C in our diet. She was not impressed! I've always been into what foods can be healing and that sort of thing. As a child, I always had the feeling that I wanted to be a doctor.

I found my way to homeopathy when I was studying medicine. They wanted us to broaden ourselves a bit so they had an option which determined that for a certain number of hours of the week, you could study whatever you wanted – it could be music, philosophy, anything. A bunch of us decided we wanted to use that time to learn about alternative health. I'd never heard of homeopathy but one of the group knew a homeopath and invited her along to talk to us. I was entranced.

---

1   "I will exercise my profession to the best of my knowledge and ability" is a phrase out of the Hippocratic Oath, an ethical code to which all graduating medical students in many countries around the world must swear allegiance. Named after Hippocrates a 5th Century Greek doctor, who is considered the 'Father of Medicine.'

I just sat through that lecture, hung on every word and thought: *This is me. This is what I want to do.* I went straight to the health food shop, found a funny, dusty, Indian smelling little book on homeopathy, took it home and read it and was even more convinced. My next opportunity came when I saw a poster advertising a talk by a homeopathic pharmacist through the Sceptics' Society. I went along and again I hung off every word. The first woman I had heard speak was not medically trained and the little Indian book had a few dodgy parts from a Western medical perspective, but here was this conventional, Western-trained pharmacist who was giving the scientific perspective and from that moment I was a committed homeopath. It was at that point in my training when I was starting to feel overwhelmed by all the things that can go wrong with the human body. To have this solution presented to me at that time was like a miracle.

I worked for a while in a hospital in an area of poor people who don't access health care very readily. So they would turn up at hospital with issues which should have been seen to weeks earlier. If there was something going on for them that Western medicine couldn't work with, I'd say: "This is what's going on for you, I can give you Panadol. I'm also a homeopath, you could try this instead if you like." Most of them would say yes. I had my little homeopathic first-aid kit with me and I would dispense the remedies, and I'd write on the little packet what the name of it was. People were then turning up at pharmacies saying: "This was so great, I need more of it." Word got out amongst the hospital hierarchy and they wrote me a letter telling me that I could not dispense homeopathic remedies. I wrote back to them quoting their own website about best practice and care, and citing the oath I had taken to become a doctor: *"That I will exercise my profession to the best of my knowledge and ability."* I told them that I couldn't not offer a remedy which I knew could help. I felt I had no choice – this is what I had to do.

So, I lost my job. I was helping some people, but that wasn't allowed. I was doing the conventional bit as well. Their fear was: "We don't know anything about this and therefore we might be liable if something goes wrong." I had felt so hamstrung at the hospital. There was such great need and it felt like all I was doing was one tiny drop in the ocean. It was distressing that they wanted to put barriers up to care that people could be getting. And relatively speaking, homeopathy can be so cheap too.

If someone is suffering, I want to have everything at my disposal to help them get better.

These treatments are actually proven by randomised controlled trials, but the medical establishment won't even look at them. I know one of the researchers on natural health supplements who was a very narrow-minded doctor, willing to only consider things within his own constricted framework. He published articles and made recommendations but it seems he wouldn't even look at the evidence for homeopathy.

I bought an ordinary conventional General Practice, and I started to see people as an ordinary GP and when there wasn't another option, I'd prescribe homeopathics. When it helps, they come back for more. And they do, because it works. Homeopathy basically helps your body do more of what it can do, to get better. That's what I've been doing now for thirteen years and I love it. I love mainstream medicine too. Homeopathy can be fantastic but it can't do everything. I like to do things properly. If someone is suffering, I want to have everything at my disposal to help them get better.

I got investigated by the medical board a few years ago. It was a visiting anaesthetist who reported me in relation to an extremely complex, high needs patient who I was actually treating with conventional medications. It went on and on for about fifteen months. In the end, the Medical Council sent in their assessment team who said everything looked wonderful. We are a small practice and we need to be small because I see people for quite a long time. But we do dot all the 'i's and cross all the 't's and in the end, everything was deemed to be looking good and we got all the ticks. Basically, we couldn't have had a better result – in many ways it was a great affirmation of the way we are doing things.

You are always at risk of attack from your colleagues if you are doing something that conventional medicine doesn't understand, or doesn't want to understand. That's the problem most of the time: they just don't want to understand. It would be so easy for them to because those of us integrating multiple healing tools are willing to talk about these things.

I think the block is because medicine is so demanding. You are just full on trying to cope with every day. I suspect the thought of trying to expand your mind to take on something you don't know anything about just seems too much. But we've all got sub-specialties and special interests in our work. We don't need to criticise those who have got interests we don't share or understand.

I've just been back in a hospital as a family member of a patient. Hospitals can be so hierarchical and bureaucratic. My grandmother, who had just had a stroke, was getting cramps on the stroke side of her body. She was in obvious discomfort when I arrived on the Friday. They had her charted for magnesium but it's a really big pill and she couldn't swallow it. So I said: "OK, let's crush it'. And the pharmacist said, 'No, I'm the hospital pharmacist and I can't do that." I said that I couldn't see any reason why we couldn't crush it but he was adamant that we mustn't. So I went off to a pharmacy the next day, which was a Saturday, and bought a jar of magnesium powder. I took it in and the nurse said, "Oh, fantastic, good stuff, the doctor will be able to chart it on Monday." I said: "Can't you just call someone?" And she said: "No, no, it will have to wait until Monday."

When I worked at the hospital I found it very impersonal. The patients would go back out into the world and I would never see them again. At least in my own practice now, there is still a lot of need but people can keep coming back to me so that we can work together towards wellness. I help along the way as much as I can. It is wonderful to be able to help people. It is also so personally rewarding. It is just a fantastic job to be able to learn so much about people – I'm seeking to understand people and every nuance as deeply and fully as I can, and wow, what an amazingly rich world that is to be able to experience people's lives in that kind of depth.

My philosophy is pretty simple. I care about people. We've got a Maori proverb on our wall: *"What is most important? I tell you, it is the people, the people, three times I say, it's the people."*

9 | PUTTING THE PATIENT AT THE CENTRE

DR CATHERINE CROCK AM[1]

*Physician, Royal Children's Hospital, Melbourne;
Founder and Executive Director of the Australian
Institute for Patient and Family Centred Care; Founder
and Chair of The Hush Foundation, and producer of the
Hush series of therapeutic CD's for families and patients.
Churchill Fellow, Order of Australia and mother of five.*

Melbourne, Australia

I had been off work for several years having my own children. The hospital approached me and asked if I would consider coming back and co-ordinating the procedural tests, bone marrow tests and lumbar punctures on children with cancer. On my first morning back on the job I thought: *What is going on here?* We were holding these kids down, performing punctures without anaesthetic, week after week. These children had to go through this not just once – some of them thirty or more times over three years – and they're screaming in the waiting room because they know what's about to happen when they come in.

I've always been really shy and never spoken up, never made a fuss or anything, but this was a turning point for me. I just felt something had to be done and that it was urgent.

---

1   Member of the Order of Australia, a high honour bestowed upon Australians by the country's sovereign for actions or deeds that benefit the nation.

Initially I went about making changes quietly. I was spending many hours talking to the children and their families, chatting to the hospital CEO, to the head of the cancer unit, and to other staff, and researching different methods of pain relief for these children. The anaesthetists had an enormous amount of knowledge but they had been disconnected from what was going on in the treatment rooms because they weren't there; they deal with pain in theatre. They were quite surprised to hear what was happening.

"We've done it this way for 20 years and no one's ever complained."

With help from the families and staff, we started trialling an alternative approach. It all happened rather quickly and I hadn't even had time to run it past the people who were sending the patients to have these procedures done. I spoke to the head of oncology who was really supportive, but I found out later that he didn't pass the information on to the rest of his team and some of them became really stressed and upset about it. One of the oncologists said to me: "We've done it this way for 20 years and no one's ever complained."

I had sat with these families and asked them what they wanted and needed, what it was like for them, and I had gotten all this really rich information. It was fascinating to find that they rarely told any of their experiences to their treating oncologists. The families were so grateful for the care, and so aware that their child's life was in the balance. They would see their doctor three times a week for three years and not mention the amount of distress these procedures were causing them. They didn't feel able to share that this bit was really awful, and for many of them it was the worst part of the whole cancer journey.

We formed a group called 'Together We Achieve,' which involved several families. They told me reams and reams about what the hospital experience was like for them, and what their thoughts were for improvements. They would tell me, for example, that sometimes they would have to wait for six hours – for a blood test, then for a doctor, then for an x-ray. They'd tell me that they were afraid to get up off the plastic chair, even to go to the toilet, in case they would miss their slot. They were given a time to come in, but it bore no resemblance to when they'd actually be seen. They all had to come in at 7.00 am for morning theatre, and some of them weren't even seen until 12.30 pm. The poor kids, who had fasted from the night before, were climbing the walls, and everyone was getting upset in the waiting room. The parents suggested staggered admission times but theatre said: "No, theatre doesn't run in that way." I went back to theatre and asked: "Why not?" The minute you suspend all previous conceptions about how things must be done and ask why not, you can often find creative and simple solutions.

I worked with the day surgery team and asked them to just try staggered admissions for six weeks. That was over fifteen years ago, and we haven't looked back. It is one of the most efficient lists in the hospital, and no one is left waiting for very long at all. Surgeons often say that they need the patient there ready, as soon as they are ready to go, but with four patients in a block, if someone's late we can just shift the list around and it still flows. And when parents feel their time is being respected, they come on time. It's all about working together and valuing everybody's expertise, including the patients' and their families.

One father suggested that families be given a pager, like the doctors and nurses had, so that they could take their children to the park while waiting. It's like flipping the respect thing on its head – the doctors' and nurses' time is not the only valuable one in the equation – everyone's time is valuable. The father helped me to get a donation of pagers – we got 150 of them, which are all around the hospital now. The nursing staff weren't very good about telling people they were available at first, they just threw them in the drawer and didn't give them out. So one of the parents made a bronze plaque. We didn't even go to the signage committee – that would have taken a year and a half – we just glued this thing up on the wall, letting parents know that they could ask for a pager.

People started to realise that you don't have to automatically think: No. You can actually go: "There's a good idea. How do we make that happen?"

Another suggestion which came from the families was to bring the pathology trolley to the children in oncology. These kids have really low blood counts and shouldn't be around people with infections, yet we would send them to get bloods done on the ground floor where they would have to sit for an hour and a half in a room full of people coughing and vomiting and with diarrhoea and all that. There was resistance to that suggestion – staff thought they'd need more trolleys, more staff, and that there wasn't an appropriate room to do it in.

I went and talked to the lady who allocates the rooms and asked if there were any rooms on the sixth floor on this particular day. She said: "Yeah, room 19's been vacant for a long time." I asked pathology if they would try it for six weeks because I thought we could see how it goes from a staffing perspective, given that was the same number of patients and blood tests, just in a different spot. It went like an absolute bird. Fantastic. So easy.

People started to realise that you don't have to automatically think: No. You can actually go: "There's a good idea. How do we make that happen?"

The families came up with so many brilliant suggestions. They wanted a whiteboard in the waiting area so the parents and staff could communicate with each other. So we put up a whiteboard. They told us that the waiting area was just terrible. At this stage (before the staggered admissions system) we were bringing twelve families in at 7.00 am for morning theatre, and it would get pretty noisy and chaotic. The parents told us that the TV in the corner was driving them nuts, and asked if maybe we could play relaxing music instead. At that stage the hospital had a small amount of music therapy, which the parents had seen, so they helped me raise money to employ a music therapist for our unit. We held huge fundraising concerts for a few years: we sold pins at the Caulfield Racecourse until our feet were totally worn out. We eventually built up the music therapy unit to such an extent that the hospital had to realise that it was core business, and they started to fund it. The music made a huge difference – you'd just see the look on the parents' faces when the kids were engaged. It had everybody joining in, even staff who were coming through to do consents or whatever – they got a bit of a bounce in their step.

The parents then talked about how confronting walking into the actual operating theatre was. Staff get used to it because we're in there all the time, but of course the children and their parents find the overhead lights, and all the machinery quite scary. So they said: "What about some music in here?" I got some commercial CDs at first, and I used to just play them, but they weren't really right. Some would

> *The creative person goes: "Oh my goodness – this is really where you work every day? That's very challenging." It makes the staff go: "Oh, let's have a look around here – yeah actually, this isn't normal."*

be OK but sometimes you'd think: *These aren't really appropriate in here.* So I brought musicians in and asked them to think about designing music for that environment. That was how I started to develop the Hush CDs.[2]

The big step for Hush came when we'd done three CDs and Paul Grabowsky, a jazz composer, came to me. He'd had experience in the hospital system himself and said he'd like to give back in some way. Composing the music especially for the hospital theatre environment was a really new way to do things. We've continued to do it that way,

2   Dr Crock and her team of leading musicians and music therapists have created a Hush CD every year since 2000, which have since won prestigious music awards, the support of talented and high-profile musicians and composers and are widely acclaimed and used in hospitals, clinics and privately throughout Australia. The Hush Foundation has since been established to expand this work to 'Transforming the culture of healthcare through the Arts' and their work now includes three plays, videos and a book. https://www.hush.org.au/. Retrieved 12/10/2017.

and it's really grown. Every time a composer or musician came in, it really refreshed the staff because they notice the environment again.

The creative person goes: "Oh my goodness – this is really where you work every day? That's very challenging." It makes the staff go: "Oh, let's have a look around here – yeah actually, this isn't normal."

The sound recordist said to me the other day: "Listen to the ambient noise in this room." Working in it every day, we are unaware of it. The buzzes and the pumps and the pings and the trolley being wheeled; stuff being dropped onto it – we need to work out where the music's going to sit in all of that. You wouldn't want it to be overwhelming, you don't want to turn it into a cacophony, but you also don't want it to get lost.

It has a really big impact on the musicians too. They tell me it is one of the most challenging and rewarding things they've ever done. You have to be really careful with the type of music. You can't afford to be winding people up – you want a sense of optimism and hope. To begin with, we thought we wanted lullaby music, but we've moved on now to music that makes you feel like everything's going to be OK. Music can either take you to that place, or to a more melancholy, wound up place. Often the parents are only just holding it together – there's an awful lot happening and they are only just OK – you don't need to push them. It's OK to cry but you don't want to be pushed there when you have no choice over it, in front of a room of people. So we try very hard to get the music right.

Each album takes about a year and a half in planning and execution. We set up our own foundation and we have incredible volunteers. We've got massive support from the community. Because the musicians and composers we are using are Australia's most amazing, the ABC Radio loves playing it; they love the cause, and they broadcast our launches live. It's fun, and it's wonderful having that creative side to what I'm doing – it keeps me going when some of the other stuff is tough. Yesterday I sat in the sound booth chilling out, chatting, giving occasional advice on the vibe. The music is now in waiting rooms, wards, treatment rooms as well as the operating theatres, and we donate albums to twelve children's hospitals around Australia. It has been music on hold at the hospital when people ring in. Hush music has spread to aged care, palliative care, mental health units, childcare and schools around the world.

Over the years of working closely alongside patients and families, we've made lots of changes to make the system better for patients. This is where the whole idea of the Australian Institute for Patient and Family Centred Care came from. It can be so simple when you get all the voices around one table, look at things from a slightly different angle, and come at it with a 'can do' attitude.

The Institute has been a very organic thing. I started talking about it back in 2007 when I'd been to the International Conference on Patient-Centred Care in America. That was incredibly inspiring. They've had an institute running there for twenty-five years and I came home with the idea that we needed to get the momentum happening here and do something similar in Australia. I knew there would be people around Australia who were thinking like this, but we hadn't had a chance to connect before. We started around my kitchen table with a group of about twenty and we met monthly for about eighteen months. Eventually we decided that in order to do more than just connecting via random emails, we needed to be some sort of entity. That was in 2009. The first people on the Board were those who were reliably round the table in the early days. They came from different walks of life – we've got health professionals from different areas, patients and family members, actors, comedians, writers, story-tellers, musicians, composers – all sorts of creative brains. I was really keen to make sure that it is quite a different organisation to some of the others that are around in health care. We merged with The Hush Foundation in 2016 and currently have 400 Associates across Australia, New Zealand, Canada, United States and Japan.

That all led to my applying for a Churchill Fellowship to go and study patient and family-centred care around the world. After I got the Fellowship, I remember being totally overwhelmed by the idea of being away from my family for eight weeks. I got on the plane in tears, but when I landed in Boston my first appointment was with Lucien Leape, who is like the grandfather of patient safety, and I hit the ground running. We spent the day mulling over what to do about looking after the people who are working in healthcare, and about the impact of workplace culture on patient safety. The second appointment was with Don Berwick who was head of Medicare / Medicaid in the USA – he was just about to get that appointment, so I was so lucky to get to see him. We talked about how patient-centred care is actually quite easy.

The Churchill opened a lot of doors and evolved as I met more people. I met Saul Weingart at the Dana Faber Cancer Centre in Boston who had been looking at the involvement of family members in detecting medical errors. Bev Johnson from the American Institute for Family-Centered Care said that she asks front-line staff: "If I gave you a magic wand, what would you do to improve the experience of the patient?" There are some really positive things hospitals are doing in patient-centred care.

There is an organisation in America called Planetree, which oversees and advocates for patient-centred care in healing environments. There were really beautiful hospitals with valet parking for patients, healing gardens, music, and signs saying: "Hush, people are healing here." In Ireland, I met Margaret Murphy who had lost her son through a whole series of medical errors when he was nineteen. She's now become the head of the Patients for Patient Safety Network for the World Health Organisation. One of the things Margaret talks about is how, six weeks after her son died, she went back into the hospital. She said the lifts opened and the young registrar who had been on duty the weekend Kevin had died was in the lifts. He just looked at her, stricken, and said: "Oh my God, I didn't think he'd die." And he ran out of the lift. Her response to this was: "The system might have forsaken us but it had forsaken him too – how's he meant to be able to sit with families, when he hasn't had support to deal with his part in this?"

At my hospital, the reactions from other staff have varied greatly. Some senior staff were quite opposed to the changes, and on multiple occasions my job was at risk. I was warned that my level of patient contact and involvement was inappropriate and unprofessional. I was told that patient-centred care isn't part of my job. And particularly in the early years, some of my colleagues felt really threatened by my perspective, and the way I was working with families. Because the families were feeling empowered and respected in our area, they started expecting the same respect elsewhere in their hospital journeys. They would recognise when other aspects of their care were unreasonable and complain. One group of families had suggested a number of sensible changes to hospital protocols, but not all staff appreciated their efforts, with one senior hospital executive describing them as 'renegades.' I was told I was setting patients up to expect 'Gold Class Service'.

On the other hand, many senior staff were fantastic. Some years back, an oncologist from one of the world leading hospitals in Canada came to our programme and described it as unbelievable, saying he was 'blown away' by what our team had achieved. This would not have been possible without the unwavering support from our hospital CEO at the time. He completely understood what we were trying to achieve. For years, he would meet with me for an hour or more, often weekly, discussing and authorising all the planned changes we were making. And many other staff really got the message and the need for change. They saw the benefits for our families and patients. It's definitely been draining at times, and the changes we have achieved have come at a personal cost. But at the same time, working with families is so rewarding every single day.

"The biggest challenge for patient safety around the world is how staff treat each other."

I worry less these days about the danger of speaking up because when I did my Churchill Fellowship, I found that around the world they are worried about disrespectful behaviour amongst colleagues impacting on the safety of patients. I realised that when a doctor has negative interactions going on in their professional life (and these are common experiences in health systems around the world), they are not as safe at the bedside with their patients. I think I knew this underneath, but on the very first morning of my Churchill trip, Lucian Leape said to me: "The biggest challenge for patient safety around the world is how staff treat each other." I thought: *Wow, that's summing it up.*

They're having all sorts of big round table discussions about this culture problem and what can be done about it. The Commission that registers all the hospitals in the US has sent an alert around, saying that poor behaviour amongst colleagues is a patient safety risk because it fragments teams and leads to people not feeling safe to speak up about problems.

Occasionally while I am talking with families, nursing staff may stand there, looking frustrated and thinking: *We're waiting for you, can you just get a move on?* But it's important to spend quality time. These children have a long-term relationship with the hospital. When I spend time with a child and their family, I'm building trust with the family – it's an investment for the next time and the next time and the next time. Each time it will be quicker because the child will be less traumatised.

We had a lady just recently whose nine-year-old son had a diagnosis of leukaemia. One of the anaesthetists was having a bit of a whinge to me about her; about how she always brings her toddler who crawls all over her while they're trying to get the mum and the nine-year-old to theatre, and how annoying it was that she brings the toddler with her. Straight away I'm thinking: *You wouldn't bring your toddler if you didn't have to.* So I went and sat with her before we took her into theatre, and acknowledged how tough things were for her at the moment, especially having to bring the little one in as well. She said: "Tell me about it – my partner is in a real state and lost his job, then he ran off and I haven't seen him since." So, it's not just about her being an annoying person, it's that she's having a hugely distressing time and didn't have any other option. She's sitting there, the nine-year-old is sitting at the table with a naso-gastric tube coming out of his nose, looking pale and terrible and sick, and the three-year-old is climbing on her like a climbing frame, grabbing her face trying to get her to look at him. It's really obvious what's happening to this lady – she's really focussed on the nine-year-old but she's being literally pulled in all directions. She told me a bit more about what was happening with her partner. What happens in these situations can be that the dads go off to 'bring in the bacon' and often remove themselves, trying to hold it all together. I suggested she encourage him to come in and get a little bit involved, that it might make the journey a little bit easier for both of them. We got the social worker involved. We did our procedure and I didn't see her again for a week. A week later I saw them from a distance and there's mum and dad and the two kids sitting up there. I went up and introduced myself to the dad, saying: "I'm so pleased to see you here – this is a pretty difficult journey you two are doing – if you can do it a bit together, it is going to make it a little bit easier." The next week, he came into day surgery and mum stayed home. It's very simple. Families aren't asking for a lot. They're asking to be listened to and treated with respect.

I think some clinicians need permission that this stuff is actually OK to do. And to not be afraid of connecting with their patients. Don't judge families; genuinely connect with them and understand their perspective. Leadership really needs to understand and support it too. At one of the hospitals I visited on my Churchill trip, staff have permission that if they see that it's a patient's birthday which has gone unnoticed, or there's some special occasion for a patient, they can go to the gift shop and buy something and put in on the tab. Do you know how much it cost? Seven thousand dollars for the whole year. And it's priceless in terms of staff morale, in staff feeling that they are trusted by their organisation, and that they can actually do something to make a difference for these patients.

I love teaching this attitude to the next generation of health professionals. I put a lot of emotional energy into talking about this stuff with them. The students think they've come to watch how someone does a lumbar puncture, and they get an ear bashing about what's actually going on amongst the team in the room, and how patient-centred care starts. I walk the students through the whole thing – right through to recovery at the end to meet the recovery nurses. That's really satisfying. They go back inspired to take it back into their practise, and then hopefully it will spread a bit further.

Patients need to see themselves as part of the team, and sometimes you need to specifically invite them to be part of the team. It is a really difficult situation because they're so vulnerable, but they really need to step up to the mark and just make it clear that they want to be involved, they want to have all the information, and they want to be treated with respect. The more they're involved, the safer it is. We can't do without their perspective. We do without the patient perspective at our peril.

Every single time I've done a talk since my Churchill experience, people have gone away saying: "This is not rocket science. I could do this in my hospital." And the stuff about bullying and disrespectful behaviour between staff – every time, people come up and say: "This is happening in my organisation – thank you for saying it publicly – maybe we can start doing something about it."

Sometimes within the hospital machine, it's like we're speaking a totally different language – I'm speaking about respect and kindness and trust, and they're speaking about accountability, bottom lines, and KPI's. It's a very strange conversation.

Every week I meet a new family, and learn something new. It is such an honour to share these journeys with people, to get to know them a little bit. It is a privilege to be able to help when people are in a situation like that. I really love my job when I can see someone feeling reassured, or a little bit safer. I don't want to just be a doctor doing a procedure. I can do that very effectively but it's not about that. Treating people with respect, kindness and trust. They're my three things. If you do that you can't go far wrong.

Sometimes within the hospital machine, it's like we're speaking a totally different language – I'm speaking about respect and kindness and trust, and they're speaking about accountability, bottom lines, and KPI's[3]. It's a very strange conversation. It seems so ridiculous to me that patient-centred care is the work of crusaders. It's sort of embarrassing.

It has been refreshing and energising for me to be able to spend time with people from the creative arts and have them help us improve the healthcare environment. They look at our issues through quite different lenses and reflect them back to us. Renowned playwright Alan Hopgood AM has been an inspiration to me. I collected hundreds of stories from patients, family members and healthcare staff, and Alan has carefully crafted several plays for Hush. The plays cover issues of patient-centred care, staff culture and behaviour, communication and patient safety. The plays are very simply staged. We perform them in hospitals in the lecture theatre, seminar room or wards for all staff and patients. Following each play, we hold a discussion forum – we hear staff open up about distressing culture problems amongst colleagues, about patients who don't feel heard or cared about and also about wonderful stories of respect and great care. We have done hundreds of play performances over several years and the impact is incredible because of the conversations that get started, and continue long after we have left. Often the leaders in the room are staggered by the things they hear from their staff. It seems like a safe space for people to speak.

After hearing many, many stories of bullying amongst staff and the negative effects both on staff and patients, I realised we have a crisis that no one really has the answer to. I was fortunate to meet futurist Peter Ellyard, who suggested a more positive mindset. Rather than language around stamping out bullying, think about a preferred future: of a kind health system. Out of this conversation came the idea of a Gathering of Kindness. Getting health professionals and patients together to talk about kindness to everyone involved has been very exciting. We held a small event in 2016 with some very bright people brainstorming this together. People talked about joy and meaning in

---

3   Key Performance Indicators.

their work when everyone is treated with kindness. The concept is continuing to gain ground and now is spreading to lots of different hospitals and health settings.

My dream for healthcare is that it could prioritise and meet the needs of patients, their families and staff – on all levels – physically and emotionally. And that it will transform into a much more respectful and kind system, and a much more even playing field which values all different levels of experience and expertise. It's a big dream and I'm a persistent optimist – I just don't know how long it's going to take.

10 | TO BE VULNERABLE IS TO BE STRONG

DR MARK DAVIS

Psychiatrist, Balint Group Facilitator, Meditation Practitioner and promoter of clinician wellbeing.

Wellington, New Zealand

I have enormous affection for my profession. A happy, healthy, integrated, self-aware doctor is so important, because we are so intimately involved in the lives of others. Opening ourselves up to self-awareness is crucial. It is really the bottom line for anything. There is a lovely quote from Lao Tsu: "He who knows others is wise, he who knows himself is enlightened." That is so true. We take ourselves into every role – whether it be husband, father, professional or whatever. Who we are, and our connection to, and knowing of ourselves is fundamental, and influences everything, including our work. That is the bottom line for me.

I've always followed my calling. I was interested in awareness, and meditation twenty-five years ago. Back then it was considered a bit new-agey. I'm not at all new-age, but I'm really open to things that are about being a *full human being.* All that always made sense to me. I've always kept up the psychotherapy aspect of psychiatry. I kept doing really solid work, and added the meditational and awareness aspects in because I found it useful for patients. It meant a lot to me personally, and I felt it could be integrated in for the benefit of my patients. These days I get asked to give seminars at GP conferences on self-care and meditation. I enjoy this increasing interest in meditation that now exists at mainstream medical conferences.

I've done a lot of teaching in doctors' health, on meditation for doctors, and run retreats for doctors. I typically start a retreat with a questionnaire on self-care. It's a way of getting people to go inside and ask questions of themselves and their lives. I often invite spouses to the retreats as well, and impress on the doctors the importance of bringing their spouse. My mum was a GP's wife and I saw the impact on her of the medical work, and how involved she was, as we as medical kids were too. Especially as a rural GP – his work was his and our world.

I'm naturally an extrovert, but the reflective, contemplative part of me has grown over the years, especially as a result of my self-reflective and meditational activities. I have struggled emotionally at times over the years. I discovered and acknowledged a few years ago just how anxious I often was, underneath my coping. That's been a journey into the reality of who I am, which has been humbling. I think it punctured some of the self-protective, over-compensatory ego aspects I had going on. I used to think I had to be 'tough on the outside'. I've always tended to be a loving and emotional person but I could be brittle at times, a bit oversensitive and competitive with a slightly prickly edge. As I've explored that with personal work and self-inquiry and meditation, I've gradually gone more inwards and faced and experienced what is really there. I discovered the paradox of "to be vulnerable is to be strong" – that was where to find my strength.

In my clinical and medico-legal assessment work (which is the bulk of my current practice) I do long, often three-hour, consultations initially. I've put a line in the ground and said I'm not going to rush people through in an hour. I value the work and the people too much to think I can know so much about someone in no more than an hour. The detail of the questioning and the understanding of peoples' whole life from birth is quite therapeutic and healing in and of itself for clients / patients. I really enjoy being at a deep level with people and helping them open up. I try to be just there with them.

I find my work incredibly satisfying. I love meeting people from all walks of life. I try to create a physical and emotional space that is a place of acceptance and wisdom and healing.

None of this awareness or insight was something I was conscious of about thirty years ago. I stumbled across it accidentally – when I was looking around for more teaching opportunities, and I did a workshop on couple therapy. At the end of the workshop the teachers taught us a *grounding* technique. I'd never heard of this before but it was a change point in my life. These people were also running meditation workshops, but I had no interest at all in going off and learning about 'Sanskrit mantras' and things like that. I didn't realise then that *grounding* was the most profound meditation there was, in that it is entirely about being aware / mindful of the reality of the present moment. But as I gradually opened up to the ongoing exposure to the meditation that these teachers were introducing (and did so over 25 years that I was connected to them), I expanded at a deep level, and that became part of the new and profound journey of my life thereafter. It's been a very interesting journey – and life-changing for me.

I've been going to Silent meditation retreats now over the past twelve years. It is basically a week of actual silence (no talking) where the focus is to enter into and be at-one with the present moment. It has been a fantastic experience, and also very challenging. Through this process, I became increasingly aware of "awareness" itself; and, existentially these were profound moments. The exploring of that has been amazing for me. It is just pure experience there is no book, no teacher. Just me.

My technique for grounding, which I share with patients also, is that in the midst of every feeling, whether it be euphoria or despair, I ask myself: *What is the experience in my body?* And so I notice that, then notice my feet on the floor, then notice the sounds, notice my breathing. Something shifts when you become the noticer rather than the doer. Instead of being lost in my emotions, I am present to them. It's not the tsunami wave running the show: I'm in the tsunami, harnessing it, engaged in the ride. That is what all the great books on mysticism say too. I feel really reassured by that. I have discovered from my reading and discussions that I am not alone with these insights.

There's only me living this life – I can't live anyone else's. So I want to know how to really live it fully, really be in it. I feel very blessed to have learned how to be more in touch with it.

I've done yoga, meditation and exercise every day for the last thirty years, and I do ongoing supervision and personal therapy work. I'm doing more now than I ever have, actually. Enthusiasm is connection to the life force I think.

I hope that my openness to this wisdom, which I find so personally enriching, is also of benefit to my patients. I think there is nothing better than being deeply heard by someone who is staying in their own process, whilst they are being open to you. If I can provide that as a listener, I don't think it gets better than that.

Sometimes I just speak for myself – "this is my experience" – just let people hear that, and that might be enough; that might be all they need to or are able to hear. I also ask people when they consult me: "What do you want to get out of being here?" "How can I help you?" I don't want to be forcing things upon them that they didn't ask for. Every consultation is different and things can change with the same person from week to week, or even in fifteen minutes. I often say: "Am I on track?" "Is this what you want from your time with me?" That's the mutuality, the sharing part, and I think it's a way of respecting the relationship. I think it is a very valuable thing to bring to consultations with patients, from a doctor's point of view. I feel like I've got a lighter touch these days, I feel more balanced internally so I think I do better work now. I'm not so pushy.

The Balint work[1] is a wonderful microcosm of the doctor–patient dynamic. I love helping the doctors drop into being with the group, with the cases, with the patient being presented, with the presenter. Ideally a Balint group is a state of *"group being-ness"*. Balint work is often extraordinary – it can be a very natural flow and creative process. I think the Balint process works because of the leadership which guides the group. There is one (sometimes two) person designated who cares

---

1   A Balint group is a group of clinicians who meet regularly and present cases to each other to discuss. The aim is a group process of exploration and for the medical participants to transform uncertainty and difficulty in the doctor–patient relationship into a greater understanding and meaning that nurtures a more therapeutic alliance between clinician and patient. From Wikipedia: https://en.wikipedia.org/wiki/Balint_Society. Retrieved 18/8/2017.

for the group, who will hold it so it can do its work, who is not part of it. I think that structure and the leader's role is very important to what can happen in the group. It enables the work to occur.

A typical Balint group will involve a doctor presenting an interaction they had with a patient, and their feelings about it (for just five to seven minutes), then the other doctors explore and speculate on all the layers of that interaction. It's a setting in which you can explore those layers and have permission and space to think 'outside the square.' You can be very creative and open and say 'left-field' things, and also be real (but respectful) about your feelings. As a group develops intimacy, it can go deeper, and doctors can be more honest about feelings they have that might not otherwise be OK to talk about. There's no advice, no diagnostic formulation. It is just: *Here it is;* and everyone is just with it (the material and the discussion).

Communication skills in medical training and medicine generally should be given higher priority, and learning about oneself as an instrument to promoting deeper empathy. An excellent medical training would, in my opinion, start at the core, at the centre of the person: self-awareness first, then learning about the layers of self as you relate to the various roles in medicine. For example, the various layers of stress on the job, and all the other skills required to be a doctor. Then on top of all of that, you would start learning how to apply the various technical skills related to the job. It is about applying a template of vision around developing oneself as a self-aware and humane human being.

Doctors are human beings first, and doctors later. Just like anyone else whose work has such an impact on others – such as social workers, teachers, parents – it's developing our personhood that we need to put our time into.

Doctors are human beings first, and doctors later. Just like anyone else whose work has such an impact on others – such as social workers, teachers, parents – it's developing our personhood that we need to put our time into. We just seem to be missing our connection to our core. We get so outwardly focused on things to do, and people to engage with that we forget to 'go in' – to retain inward awareness while connecting outwards. I just think our growth as a doctor would benefit from learning those skills.

There is a culture in medicine of doctors not caring sufficiently for themselves. I think that probably starts at medical school. Some elders in the profession and medical teachers are pretty emotionally tough and shut down and they model and advocate a rather masculine, and less integrated approach. I think inherently there is a tension in how to balance the 'masculine' and 'feminine' aspects of ourselves in practice, just as there is tension in how to be both 'left brained' and 'right brained.' You believe that you might have to shut down your heart a bit to cope with some of the emotional pain of being a young, and at times stressed, doctor. I think that was also part of my early developmental stage in the profession too. A couple of my friends were really into meditation in their early 20s but I had no call or draw to it back then. Yet my own journey took off at a later age – it is a question of timing and readiness.

> *There is a really damaging culture in medicine of doctors needing to know everything. They are often perfectionists and pleasers.*

There is a really damaging culture in medicine of doctors needing to know everything. They are often perfectionists and pleasers. It is a real bind: because the patients really want, of course, high-order thinking and knowledge, but they also want sensitivity and someone really caring about them. And they expect them to also care enough to take all the time that is needed to do all of the thinking and the research, to inform themselves about how best to act on your behalf. The stakes are high, especially in medicine. When the stakes are high, we've got to make sure that our own personal systems are working well. Part of that is achieved by relaxing and 'letting go' because with this comes humility and equanimity – and saying: "Ok, I'm doing my best."

This book, I am sure will provoke self-insight and self-examination. When the pupil is ready, the teacher will appear.

11 | LIFESTYLE AND PREVENTION: THE FUTURE

ASSOCIATE PROFESSOR VICKI KOTSIRILOS AM[1]

Holistic General Practitioner, founding President of the Australasian Integrative Medicine Association (AIMA), former & founding Chair, Royal Australian College of General Practitioners, Integrative Medicine working group, Lecturer, Advisor and Writer.*

Melbourne, Australia

My interest in being a doctor started at a very young age. I was always daydreaming in primary school, and off in la-la land, and then when I got my period in year seven, it was like an awakening. Literally overnight my awareness was raised and I made my mind up to be a doctor at the age of twelve.

I grew up in St Albans in a very poor working-class background. I was the oldest of four, my migrant parents were mostly working and I pretty much raised the other three children, particularly my youngest brother. To want to go to university and be a doctor was unthinkable for a girl of my background at the time. A couple of teachers picked up my interest and abilities and I was guided and kept on track by those teachers. I am very grateful to them to this day.

---

1   MBBS, FRACGP, FACNEM, FASLM

When I got into medicine it was mind-blowing for my family – no-one in my family had ever been to university and none of my siblings were showing any interest in going down that path. University was like a whole new world – I moved out of home, went to parties and had lots of fun; although I always felt like a loner and didn't really fit in amongst all the private school kids. I just didn't have the same mindset. I seemed to attach myself to the lecturers, and again, was lucky enough to have a few who were great mentors and were very kind to me along the way.

When I graduated and was doing my internship, I remember saying to a patient in casualty: "Natural medicine doesn't work – throw them [the vitamins] in the bin." I was very passionate about mainstream medicine and gave it one hundred per cent. I was very orthodox and just said and did what I had been told and taught. By the end of that year of internship, due to the stress of hospital work, I was smoking, overweight, feeling depressed and had a relationship breakdown. Furthermore, I had an abnormal pap smear, an early sign of cancer in situ. It was a huge shock and a real turning point in my life. I had been doing long shifts, sometimes more than 24 hours straight, I was getting very little sleep, was stressed, sun-deprived and my relationship had, not surprisingly, not survived. I remember thinking: *I've made it. Here I am, a doctor – all that work, all that kudos – and I'm not happy.*

After the operation, I decided to take a year off and go to Greece to visit relatives. I was lucky to meet a guy at a conference in Greece and he gave me his backpack, his money belt and a book called '*Let's go Europe*' and told me to go and travel, and to not waste a minute. So off I went, staying at youth hostels, catching trains by myself from one country to another. For a young Greek girl at that time and of my background, that was a very big deal. I travelled for seven months, stopped smoking, lost weight, got a tan, looked great and gained confidence.

When I got back to Australia I was rearing to go. I was straight back into it, night shifts and all, and was loving it. I had great colleagues but after a time I could again feel my health deteriorating due to the stress of working in a hospital. Luckily this time I had a reference point and I knew where I was headed. I had a good friend who introduced me to meditation classes. I went along and it was absolutely what I needed. It was a beautiful nurturing environment and I just cried and cried, feeling all this grief from the past pouring out, and the discovery of my true self for the first time. I took everything in, learning about the power of our thoughts, philosophy of life, attitudes and perception, about turning negatives to positive, about Reiki[2], and I bought lots of books and devoured and soaked up everything I could find about this new world of thinking. I became more spiritual through the practices and connecting closely with nature through daily bushwalks.

Meditation practice also helped me cope through the night shifts whilst working in hospitals. Because my whole attitude had changed, my energy had changed. I loved my work and devoted all my energy to it. I was also doing lots of healing courses on the side, such as hypnotherapy and acupuncture. I always trialled evidence-based complementary approaches for my personal health needs. I kept some and abandoned others.

After a couple of years of working very hard, I realised that I didn't have a boyfriend. I used to walk my dogs along a creek behind my house and meditate by the creek. On one occasion, I looked up at the sky and said: "God, I'm now ready for my life partner." I went to work the next day and one of my patients at the hospital, who knew I loved liquorice, gave me a whole bag of it. I popped it in the top pocket of my white coat, chewed it all day, and didn't realise until that night when I got home that my teeth were all stained and black. I couldn't brush it off. The next morning, I went to the dentist worrying that my teeth were decayed! He said: "no problem," and cleaned it all off. I thought he was pretty cute and we got talking about work and travel. I got home and thought: *Geez I like him, what shall I do God?* A voice replied: "Ask him for coffee." So I did. Within three months he proposed, and

---

2   Reiki is a hands-on energy healing process that aims to promote relaxation and healing, and reduce stress.

we are now married with two children. Two days after asking for 'my life partner,' I found him!

After five years of working in the hospital, I ventured into General Practice. I was seeing one patient every six to ten minutes in the practice where I worked, which didn't suit me at all. Through my own personal healing journey, it became very clear to me that I wanted to start a holistic practice of my own. I was about twenty-eight at the time, and I went into practice with my husband so I could spend more time with patients to provide a more holistic and lifestyle approach to healthcare. I started from scratch – no patients. My best friend was my first patient! I soon became very busy and was enjoying my work, providing more consultation time for patients, reinforcing lifestyle advice and using the extra skills I had learnt along the way, for example nutritional medicine, acupuncture, counselling and hypnosis.

Later, some time in the early 1990s, I remember reading the *Australian Doctor* magazine at one stage and seeing a front-page article implying that doctors using alternative medicine would be investigated by Medicare. I thought: *Hang on, this could be me!*

I had never thought of myself as 'alternative'; my College supervisor had even come to work with me to help me complete my College training. I always used evidence-based techniques but I was certainly incorporating elements of healing which I had not been exposed to or taught in medical school. I called up several colleges including the Australian College of Nutritional and Environmental Medicine (ACNEM) and told them about the article and asked if they minded if I invited everyone who had done their training course to an emergency meeting.

That was how the Australasian Integrative Medical Association (AIMA) formed; to act as a peer group of like-minded holistic doctors, and I became the founder and founding President. Our aim for AIMA was to bring collegiality, support and a sense of connection and belonging for holistic doctors, but also to help set standards by being guided by the scientific evidence in the area of integrative medicine. We were not abandoning what we had been taught, we were widening our scope of practice to provide patients more holistic lifestyle advice and, like tools of a trade, include evidence-based integrative therapies, and if needed pharmaceutical and surgical approaches. It was developing an art in medicine that was relevant and patient-centred. We could understand the concerns related to alternative medicine, and our role was to help the profession sort out the good from the bad, guided by the scientific evidence.

I was blessed to be supported and mentored by a really good group of influential people around me, especially some of the leading academics from Monash University at the time – including Dr's Craig Hassed, Steven Sommer and Richard Hetzel, who inspired and guided me. We wrote to the Australian Medical Association (AMA), and the Royal College of General Practitioners (RACGP) asking to meet with their leaders to put our case. At all times we were very clear that we didn't want a fight, that we wanted to belong to, be of service to, and work in harmony with the profession. We were interested in being guided by the evidence, integrating holistic therapies that had evidence into our practice, with a focus on mind–body medicine and lifestyle advice. We wanted what was best for our patients, without doing harm. We used positive and respectful dialogue at all times. This approach seemed to strike a chord. Within two years we became a special interest group of the AMA, and five years later with the RACGP. Professor Kerryn Phelps, former president of the AMA, formed a Federal committee during her presidency and developed a position statement on complementary medicines. This was a ground-breaking moment. Having established a credible and trusted voice on evidence-based integrative medicine within the medical profession, I was later invited to work for a number of bodies such as the National Prescribing Service for research into complementary use by the medical profession, the Australian Health Practitioner Regulation Agency (AHPRA) as an auditor and assessor, the Therapeutic Goods Administration (TGA) to help regulate complementary medicines in Australia and assess safety issues, and the Health Insurance Commission, now called the Professional Services Review (PSR), as a panel member which investigates doctors who are accused of improper practice. My presence on all these Federal Government committees, the work I

I think integrative medicine will be the future of medicine. Pharmaceutical medicine alone is not the answer. Lifestyle and preventative health will be our focus.

was doing in helping to understand and set standards in the poorly defined area of complementary medicine, and my continued service to the RACGP to help educate doctors of Australia to maintain high clinical standards was breaking down doors, building bridges and beginning the dialogue with these respected institutions. I continue to this day to serve for the RACGP, AHPRA, and the PSR, who I highly respect and value, and am truly grateful for the opportunities and the continuation of respectful dialogue in the area of integrative medicine, as it is an area often poorly understood.

I think integrative medicine will be the future of medicine. Pharmaceutical medicine alone is not the answer. Lifestyle and preventative health will be our focus. You can see it already happening. For example, a random survey of Australian GPs by the National Prescribing Service found that about thirty per cent of GPs are actually using complementary medicine and describe themselves as practising integrative medicine (to varying degrees), and that the majority of GPs (up to ninety per cent) prescribe some kind of complementary medicine such as fish oil, vitamin D or glucosamine.[3] It was a very important benchmark study and was the first government-funded study of its kind. The study also highlighted the lack of knowledge Australian doctors have in relation to the dangers of complementary medicine, and helped open the door to a number of position statements and the curriculum statement on integrative medicine that I assisted with, within the College of General Practitioners, as they recognised the widespread use of complementary medicines by our community, and the importance of GPs being well informed of the evidence, benefits, risks and side-effects

---

3   Brown J, Morgan T, Adams J, Grunseit A, Toms M, Roufogalis B, Kotsirilos V, Pirotta M. *Complementary medicines information use and needs of Health Professionals, General Practitioners and Pharmacists.* National Prescribing Service, December 2008.

to advise our patients appropriately. I respect and value the RACGP as my peer group and feel blessed to belong to a family of GPs!

We are so privileged to be doctors. I aim to be a good role model not only for my medical peers, colleagues and medical students by practicing medicine from a holistic, lifestyle-focused approach, but also for my patients in being a good role model for good health. I practice what I preach – a healthy lifestyle, and I meditate and do yoga daily. I also wanted to set high clinical standards in General Practice and work from a place of excellence and evidence, whilst being patient-centred and holistic. In 2007, my practice won the Practice Excellence Award by our accrediting body AGPAL (Australian General Practice Accreditation Limited)!

It is important to remember we are doctors first. Just spending time with our patients is invaluable to develop a good doctor–patient relationship and have time to motivate them to improve their lifestyle. I try to work from the heart, listen, provide eye contact and be present during the consultation. That alone is the door to opening up the healing process. I believe my own personal spiritual and healing journey has made me a more compassionate, caring, trusted, understanding, heart-centred person and doctor.

Being heart centred is a great placebo. I understand the pain our patients feel. I see an avenue of hope for all. We may not necessarily cure everyone, whether we use complementary or mainstream medicine, but helping patients to adopt positive lifestyle changes such as changing to a healthy diet, improve sleep, reduce stress, daily exercise, resolve conflicts, connect with nature, can improve quality of health and life in all patients no matter what disease they suffer – including cancer. It is our job to help motivate and make them feel better and improve their quality of life.

I nurture and sustain myself by giving myself a ninety-minute lunch break, and I meditate and do yoga at least three to four days per week, in nature if possible. I get to bed early at 9 pm, avoid computer use in the evening and eat well with the family. I don't forget to laugh and enjoy life. I escape to nature as much as I can and I cherish time with family and with my kids. In my spare time I run a farm, bush walk, have a veggie garden and am involved in my Bayside community when in the city to care for our local environment. I think being connected to my local community and having mindful interactions with people sustains me also.

Knowing how much my lifestyle benefits my own health, it is easy to give lifestyle advice to patients because it comes from my truth. I try to be a good role model to my patients. I give lifestyle advice in every consultation – we talk about diet, stressors, exercise, the right amount of sunshine for production of Vitamin D, what changes they could make in their lives for prevention and good health, improve quality of life and hopefully a speedy recovery.

I love being a doctor. I'm always rejuvenated and inspired by my patients. I trial new innovative therapies that are evidence based, and not harmful, to help them. The science is constantly changing and I love keeping up with the evidence. I enjoy sharing this evidence through lecturing, medical writing and I have for years written a regular monthly evidence-based column titled 'Integrative Perspectives' in *Medical Observer* magazine that goes out to nearly every Australian GP.

I love lecturing as I have had great guidance and mentoring through my career, and now it is my turn to share the knowledge. And I love my patients, I love spending time with them and creating a trusting and loyal bond with them. I feel grateful and privileged. I have continued working as a respected, caring GP with a focus on lifestyle and prevention, combining evidence-based nutritional medicine, acupuncture, counselling and hypnosis into my practice. I am inspired by my patients and passionate, as I witness first hand as they improve in their wellbeing with simple lifestyle changes and holistic therapies.

Due to my extensive voluntary community services, continued Government work, and helping to improve standards in healthcare, especially in an area poorly understood and challenging, in June 2016 I was honoured to be awarded a Member (AM) in the General Division of the Order of Australia for: *'Significant service to integrative medicine, to health practitioner standards and regulations, to medical education, and to the environment.'* In January 2017, I was further honoured and awarded an Australia Day Environmental Award by Bayside City Council, for *"Recognising outstanding and long-term leadership, action, and advocacy for coastal and natural heritage protection in the City of Bayside, and generating community awareness of the value of our Bayside environment."*

Whilst there have certainly been challenging moments in my career, when you come from a background like mine and a childhood with many dark moments, I am so grateful for my extraordinary achievements. My mentors guided me well, and taught me that whenever there is a negative comment or situation, this is an opportunity for respectful dialogue and understanding, and in a really respectful, collaborative way – to educate and build bridges. This is not head stuff; it is heart stuff. It comes from a deep place of respect and passion, and people feel your authenticity and mostly respond positively.

* Dr Kotsirilos is co-author of *A guide to evidence-based integrative and complementary medicine*, Kotsirilos, V, Sali, A, Vitetta, L, Elsevier Health, 2011; and is Adjunct Associate Professor at: La Trobe University, (Department of Rehabilitation, Nutrition & Sport Medicine, Faculty of Health Sciences); University of Western Sydney (National Institute of Complementary Medicine (NICM)); and Monash University, (Department of Epidemiology and Preventive Medicine, School of Public health).

12 | HEALER, HEAL THYSELF

DR MEABURN STANILAND

General Practitioner with an interest in transformational men's work, rites of passage for his sons and teenage boys, meditation and Balint psychotherapeutic group work.

Wellington, New Zealand

I sometimes wonder if I can continue in medicine. What is coming up for me at the moment is a bit of a feeling of being overwhelmed in terms of the world around me. There is some kind of madness, a lack of connection between real, live stuff in the world – like nature, and human interaction – and the complete lack of reality (for example in the financial world, which seems so removed from what is happening on the ground). I'm seeing that reflected in my practice with all the programmes about screening and cardiovascular risk assessments, and immunising anything that moves. This kind of population-based medicine has depersonalised our practice. We are paid a bit more if we meet certain targets, run certain tests. It is really affecting my enjoyment of my work. It is the complete antithesis of where I feel the real healing lies – at the soul level.

I'm not really working out of a scientific place, even though I've passed ninety-four exams as part of my journey to being a doctor. When I'm practicing though, I feel I am relying more on my intuition than on the science. Right from the beginning, even before I studied medicine, I had this absolute desire to be with people in a particular way in my work. I always remember an uncle who had fought in spitfires and hurricanes in the Second World War, which had affected him deeply

and he had a bit of a breakdown. I
remember two or three meetings with
him where something I couldn't put my
finger on happened. I just had a really
lovely feeling from being with this man.
I have always really felt strongly and

*Just keeping people alive
is not the main reason
I'm a doctor.*

passionately that I wanted to have quite intense connections with people
in my work. Just keeping people alive is not the main reason I'm a
doctor.

I have always worked intuitively but I have felt guilty about that
until now. Now I feel like it is time to own and honour that part of me.
It used to feel like a giant failure, for example, when a patient died. Now,
instead of thinking: *God, I've failed, I don't want any more to do with this*
– I feel: *Gosh, that's a really important part of what I do.*

It is really about the importance of community and connections. I
strive to learn more about the family, relationships, community and
connections of my patients. And they are my community too, and those
connections feed me. That is a really big part of it for me. I enjoy
walking with people who are in difficulty, and sharing their joy as well,
not just their difficulties.

As a young man, I think I thought I was going to go out and change
the world. It was just me against the world, trying to make my space
in it. Ten years ago, I started to do a lot of personal work. I began to
get a clearer picture of myself; that I didn't have to do it alone. I was
doing counselling and groups and I was alarmed after a while how it
impacted on my work. It was like: *Oh, yeah, I feel more present here, and
less worried by what comes up for other people.* I remember at one stage
when I was younger I could be quite anxious about what was coming
with the next patient: What would I be faced with? Would I know how
to deal with it? It could be just ageing, but I do think doing some
personal work had a lot to do with moving beyond this. It gave me a
lightness and an ease in my work. I feel more able to help more people.

"Healer, heal thyself." I think that is what I find myself yearning for, for my patients. I have a lot of men coming to me with depression. I'd certainly locked up a whole lot of stuff. I think every man could benefit from some kind of exercise in opening themselves up to their vulnerabilities. It's not for everyone of course – I'm a certain personality, with my own life story. I am deeply connected to animals and to nature – that is one of my healing grounds.

If I could give advice to young doctors, I would say look around for a mentor. Even if someone doesn't turn up, just the intention to look, to choose not to walk alone, is a path in itself. Keep looking – when the time is right, the right person will turn up. Whatever job you're in, I would say try and adapt it to what your soul is asking of you. Be open to changing direction a bit to stay in line with your soul. Don't work too hard. Be less focused on the security generated through making money, and be more focused on living, and living a bit more simply.

Trust your patients – they have got a lot of intrinsic knowledge about themselves. Don't think that your basics are going to be relevant for everyone. Trust what other people have formulated for themselves and help them be healthy within that. Sometimes in my life, little things that people have said have made a big difference – in that environment, be free with positive stuff because you can make a big difference.

I feel a bit self-conscious saying all this. Am I good enough to tell my story? Is my story worth it? Or rich enough, or good enough for other people to look at? My life is just that, I guess, like anyone else's: a story. We can only do what we can do in the world. I used to think being in medicine was about me helping other people, but I think it is just as much about me helping myself as I help others.

13 | HEARTS IN HEALTHCARE

DR ROBIN YOUNGSON

*Anaesthetist, Co-founder of Hearts in Healthcare[1],
author of* Time to care: How to love your patients
and your job[2], *and* From HERO to HEALER –
Awakening the inner activist.[3]

Raglan, New Zealand

In my experience healthcare and hospitals are pretty unhealthy and sick places to work in. I was an anaesthetist and a clinical leader working in a highly technical hospital environment when I had an opportunity to be part of a steering group involved in a huge overhaul of the hospital to a 200-bed emergency hospital. I had the opportunity to design, build, equip and staff this new hospital and do something about changing the culture to make it a more people friendly, caring, and compassionate setting which was to serve a very multicultural, underprivileged community. I became very passionate about re-humanising the system, creating a place that worked for the patients and families, as well as for the people who worked there.

In the midst of this process I was invited to share my story and my passion at the Australasian Integrative Medical Association Conference.

---

1   An international online movement with the aim of rehumanising healthcare: http://heartsinhealthcare.com/.
2   Rebelheart Publishers, Raglan, New Zealand, 2012.
3   Rebelheart Publishers, Raglan, New Zealand, 2016 – available as a gift at: https://herotohealer.org/. See also Ted Talk: https://www.youtube.com/watch?v=jTYSzLtbYTU. Retrieved 12/10/2017.

I had never even heard of them and I got a little worried because I didn't really know what integrative medicine was, and almost everyone in the audience were, to my mind then, these slightly weird people who were all involved in some sort of complementary medicine practice. I thought: *What do I really know about this?* But Joan Campbell, who was organising the conference said: "You've got real passion, that is what you know."

Many of them had fled from mainstream healthcare – they could not sustain themselves in that system, so they were trying out some kind of different practice in a setting that sees people, and not just diseases and technology.

I've presented at lots of different conferences, but always hiding behind PowerPoints and a lectern. I had a sense that this one would be much better if I talked from the heart and made myself vulnerable – seeing as I was talking about being vulnerable – about care, compassion and love. So, I asked for the lectern to be removed off the stage altogether. And then ten minutes before I went on stage I threw away my notes. I had forty-five minutes to speak, with no slides and no notes, and I just trusted that I would be able to string together something coherent and tell some meaningful stories. In a state of fright, I stood up there, gathered myself and began to speak. Something extraordinary happened – there was an unbelievably profound connection with the audience; many people cried at some of the stories that I shared. There was just something really remarkable happening.

Many of them had fled from mainstream healthcare – they could not sustain themselves in that system, so they were trying out some kind of different practice in a setting that sees people, and not just diseases and technology. I think it was extraordinary for them to hear a mainstream hospital based specialist, let alone an anaesthetist, talk about care and compassion and love and vulnerability. I think it blew people away. In a mainstream hospital setting it is absolutely taboo to talk about these things. It was the very first time that I had ever spoken out in public about them. It was a life changing moment for me.

If you look at all the people who work in the health services, I believe that the most vulnerable are the most senior, especially the specialists, and I think it is to do with the nature of our training. We really have a technologically driven and disease focussed practice. We objectify patients. It is a process of brutalisation and dehumanisation. We're kind of created to be gods who are supposed to fix and cure everyone, and we feel very vulnerable when we can't fix or cure. I mean, the worst thing for a hospital specialist is to have to say: "Well, I'm very sorry but there's nothing else I can do." That feels like a devastating failure of professional purpose. Equally, if you make a mistake, if you harm a patient through an error, that's an awful feeling, irreconcilable with your idea of yourself as an expert who is supposed to fix and cure.

In our training, we don't have the opportunity to learn or develop any of the skills, attitudes or practices to support people as human beings, to bring compassion and caring and mindfulness to our practice. We are left completely bereft of any source of self-esteem when things go wrong. Difficult patients are infuriating because you feel so incompetent – no matter what you try to do, they reject it, then you feel incompetent and that makes you feel bad. That is what I see when I see so many hospital specialists who can behave so arrogantly. The more I see arrogance, the more I look for the fear behind it. I think people are extremely vulnerable and it's absolutely not the done thing to discuss anything about personal feelings about vulnerability, about caring about your patients.

To give you an illustration, I worked at a major hospital in Auckland for over ten years as a specialist and in that whole time I only heard one specialist, once, talk about his vulnerability with his colleagues. I was anaesthetising an obstetric patient for him and the day before he had been doing a caesarean, which had gone horribly wrong and the patient had ended up having a life-threatening haemorrhage. They had operated for six hours, she had required a huge blood transfusion and everyone had thought she was going to bleed to death and die on the table. Somehow, they managed to get it under control and she survived. He said to me: "Robin, that was such a harrowing experience, I really didn't want to get up and come to work today because I couldn't face the possibility that someone might die on my table." That's the only specialist I've ever heard in ten years share this kind of story.

There is a very high ideal of clinical detachment, which leads to the objectification of patients.

When I stand up on stages, I talk about making mistakes and personal vulnerability, seeing the whole person, being humble and respectful, and about mindfulness. I got an invitation to present at the grand round[4] at one hospital to a multi-disciplinary team. I told some really personal stories and talked about some aspects of this. At the end, the chair asked if there were any questions or comments, and there was a deathly silence. Everyone filed out without saying a word, but afterwards people came up to me in secret, or sent me an email saying they had been really moved, or it had reminded them of something they had been through themselves.

There is a very high ideal of clinical detachment, which leads to the objectification of patients. For example, they talk about the appendix on ward four – often they don't even refer to the patient by name. There's a lot of evidence and a bit written about the brutalising, dehumanising aspect of hospital care, the hidden agenda at medical schools, and the way that we're treating patients and each other. Johanna Shapiro, for example, who has written a lot on this topic, wrote a wonderful paper called, 'Walking a mile in their patients' shoes: Empathy and othering in medical students' education'[5] It's about the socialisation of medical students in their training, during which the bullying and the abuse is just endemic.

---

4   A teaching tool and ritual of medical education and inpatient care, consisting of presenting the medical problems and treatment of a particular patient to an audience consisting of doctors, residents and medical students. From Wikipedia: https://en.wikipedia.org/wiki/Grand_rounds. Retrieved 17/9/17.

5   *Philosophy, Ethics, and Humanities in Medicine*, vol. 3, no. 10, 2008.

I was really good at clinical detachment in the early days of my career. When you've been through that kind of training and socialisation, your only source of self-esteem is expertise; being the hero doctor; being perfect at everything you do. So when you make an error or you can't help someone, that is such a devastating and profound threat to your source of self-esteem. If you don't have the interpersonal skills and the inner resources to show compassion and love to your patients, you have nothing left.

I can think of many patients who I just completely abandoned after something went wrong. They were harmed and I couldn't even talk to them, which probably harmed them further. I would hide from them. And I think that's common. So you'd have this series of wounds in your own heart, with no means of healing them. But when you come from a more humane perspective, you discover that there is a world of things you can do for your patients. You discover that you can do absolutely nothing except be present without anxiety, to just listen and bring your heart. That is actually very powerful.

I've got used to breaking rules all the time. Now, time and time again, I just get up and mention the unmentionable and try to reach people's hearts. It is usually received with a lot of emotion.

I really believe that the overwhelming majority of people who come into healthcare have a genuine desire to care and provide compassionate, whole person care. I think there are very few who in a mercenary kind of way come in to just earn a lot of money or feed their egos. But our humanism gets really suppressed in the training and socialisation and the kind of institutions that we have. I believe there's a deep desire for it that's really close to the surface. What I find is that when you stand up and start talking, it gives other people permission to start talking about it. What I've come to recognise is that there is a kind of tipping point in individuals. People are going along on a path of trying to seek something that is more profound, better and more fulfilling. They've started to discover the sheer pleasure of just simple acts of kindness, and often it will only take a very small influence to get them to a point where suddenly they're on the path to flourishing.

Long before I ever spoke, I had been concerned about the patient experience and I've always deeply empathised. I don't know why that is exactly, but I have noticed that I am much more affected by my patients than some of my colleagues are. Many years ago, I started up what was called the Clinical Leaders' Association. We got some funding from the ministry and we made a DVD of people telling their stories of what it is like to be a patient in different settings, which became a learning resource for health professionals. We would show these DVDs and get people to explore their own experiences of being a patient, or that of a loved one, and discussed ways to be more sensitive to the things we as health professionals do which cause distress to patients, and what we could do to be helpful and healing. I had done this work with senior clinical leaders and about three or four months later, one of them came rushing up to me with excitement and said: "I need to talk to you, I really need to tell you something that's happened. A month or two ago I got a referral to see a seventy-eight-year-old patient with seventy-two different diagnoses – heart failure, hypertension etcetera, etcetera. She had been on the ward for two weeks and hadn't made any progress. They asked me to go up onto the ward and do an assessment, and when I began that, I noticed that she was quite distressed. It called to mind some of the things you had been talking about in the workshop. I put down my clipboard and I said I can see you are really worried about something – are you able to tell me what it is? The patient explained that she was desperately anxious about a pet at home. She needed to phone someone, and every day she had asked to use the cordless phone, and every day she had been rebuffed and told that the phone was only for staff. She was told she had to use the patient phone, which was some way down the corridor. She was seventy-eight, half blind, couldn't walk very well and she just couldn't get to the phone. So I said: "I'd like to help you." I dashed off downstairs to the shop, bought a phone card, took her to the phone and we made a call to her niece. The patient cried because it was the first time in two weeks that anyone had listened to what was most important to her.

One had the sense that the course of her clinical treatment changed that day. Her heart failure and angina started getting better, things started progressing. This whole exchange took about ten minutes, then the consultant went back to doing her 'proper' job. This colleague told me that she had been feeling quite exhausted and burned out, wondering whether she could continue doing this work at all. When she went home and reflected on this experience, she realised

> *There's a downward spiral to depression and burnout and there's an upward spiral to really flourishing. The gap between them is really small and it only takes a little nudge in one direction to set the spiral off.*

she got more pleasure, fulfilment and satisfaction out of that single act of kindness than anything she had done for ages and ages. By the time she came to work the next day, she said she had decided that she would redesign her role and be a caring person first and an expert second, and that every day she would look for some opportunity for a small act of kindness. She said: "That was six weeks ago and it's like I have a new job and I'm a new person. I'm just full of energy." She was beaming; she was just totally transformed.

I've heard that kind of story a number of times and that's what makes me hopeful about the work we are doing. That there are so many health professionals who just need a little bit of help, a bit of encouragement to change their practices just a little bit, in such a way that connects them a little more with patients. They find that so fulfilling. The response they get from their patients is so different that it is powerfully self-reinforcing. There's a downward spiral to depression and burnout and there's an upward spiral to really flourishing. The gap between them is really small and it only takes a little nudge in one direction to set the spiral off.

What I really want to achieve with Hearts in Healthcare is to try to create a global community of health professionals. I want to connect the one per cent who really want to do this stuff and change the system. There are sixty million health professionals in the world, so one per cent is an enormous number that can have a profound influence. We want to give them some inspiration, some ideas, some toolkits and resources about how they can build their resilience and find practices more fulfilling, joyful and satisfying. Get them on this path of flourishing and become evangelists for others – so we can change the system from within.

It's not without its challenges. We formed a charitable Trust at our hospital a few years ago to support this work. We had high hopes of changing the culture – we knew how little it would take to get people to work into a different way. My hope and dream was that we could build that into the fabric of the organisation and create a kind of international centre of excellence in compassionate healthcare.

Then there were changes to management personnel, who were all into management restructure, as they tend to be, who just tore apart the whole inspirational leadership team at the hospital. Almost all of us lost our jobs – all the most inspirational people – all the ones who cared the most lost their jobs, and all of our leadership roles were just abolished. I was at a conference in Canada and I got an email that contained a proposal for a restructure and got to page sixteen to discover that my role was to be disestablished. That was how I was informed of it. That was very distressing. I continued to work as an anaesthetist at the same hospital for several years after that, feeling very at odds with the management, and in profound conflict. I tried to continue the work of the Trust and we started one initiative, which was a new version of grand rounds called compassionate rounds. They were multidisciplinary meetings for lots of different kinds of hospital staff and services, to come together and talk about the human aspects of caring and patient care. Those were very popular. We had some really profound dialogues but the institution wasn't willing to support them. They closed down the meeting room we were using and weren't prepared to give any funds towards them, nor provide any assistance, so eventually we just gave up and stopped running them.

We still kept trying to do something. We had this great idea that if health professionals are just so flat out that they just don't have time to care in their working day, maybe we could give them the opportunity to be in their workplace when they're not actually being paid,

It was just death by a thousand cuts really and I eventually decided to walk away from it altogether.

when they're volunteering their time, and that they could use that time to reconnect to the heart of their practice, with patients. They're not allowed to do clinical work, they're just there. We had a number of people who said they'd like to do this so we wrote a draft policy. I had the support of the HR[6] manager and one of the senior nurses, and we knew we'd have to wrap it carefully in policy to protect the hospital. We wrote it very carefully. We then took the proposal to the senior management team. They vetoed the whole thing. They said: "Everything we do is about compassion and care, and there are all sorts of liabilities with volunteers." Despite the fact that we had all our ducks in line and we had the support of senior people, it was just too threatening and difficult. None of this was an intentional undermining of caring and compassion by the management, but their perspective and priorities were such that that was the practical effect of much of what happened. It was just death by a thousand cuts really and I eventually decided to walk away from it altogether.

I formed a very simple company, Hearts in Healthcare, and have invested my own money into the cost of building the online community and platform. I offer it as a service to healthcare professionals and patient advocates all around the world. If I ask them to pay a modest annual subscription I think that will generate enough revenue to support quite a wide range of activities. I also decided that writing a book on how to be a happy nurse, doctor or therapist was perhaps the most important thing I could do, so I published *Time to care* in 2012. It shares all the stuff

---

6   Human Resources.

we have learned over the years about compassionate care with a lot of new knowledge about positive psychology and neuroscience, wraps it all up together and basically says: "Here is the really big evidence base for why this is so important, why it is going to be so good for you, why you can be so much more happy and contented, and why your patient care is going to be transformed. These are the really simple practices that can get you past your own personal tipping point to flourish in your role as a health professional, and how you can influence others."

I've been thinking for years and years and years about how we can put all of this knowledge and evidence together and have a concentrated focus on meeting patients' basic human needs. Some basic things which are really neglected are keeping patients warm, giving them any kind of nutritional food at all, and comfort and basic pain relief in an emergency department. There is a nice expression in the Maori language about a nest of comfort. That is what we should be doing in hospitals, creating a nest of caring where we keep people warm, feed them, and create comfort for them. Those are three things we heartily fail to do for hospital inpatients, even if we provide good clinical care.

My daughter was in a bad car accident when she was a teenager. She broke her neck – a C1 and C2 fracture – and spent three months in spinal traction in one of the biggest hospitals in New Zealand. It was a big flash modern hospital and the clinical care was excellent, but the neglect of her basic human needs was appalling. They would wheel in her meal trays, then take them away again an hour later. Here's a spine-injured patient who can't feed herself, and the staff were too busy to do it. She was just starving away in hospital. These are not exceptions; these are almost the rule.

There's extremely strong evidence that lack of nutrition for patients in hospitals dramatically increases infection rates, mortality rates, length of stay and the need for lengthy rehabilitation. Yet what happens in the management world is that budgets get screwed down into all these independent little boxes and there is a budget for food, which isn't seen as having anything to do with clinical outcomes. We spend about $1.50

per patient, per day on providing food. It's completely impossible to provide good quality, tasty, nutritious food for patients on that budget. You save a few thousand dollars on the budget here, but what you don't factor in is the downstream costs because you can't measure these things. Even though the evidence exists that these things would ultimately provide better patient care, they don't appear on anyone's bottom line budget. So making the economic argument is helpful, but it is not enough to convince managers who are stuck in this machine-like understanding of how an organisation runs.

The way that systems change is that you get individual pioneers who are very isolated, lone voices in the wilderness, having a very difficult time of it. But they dedicate their lives to their beliefs, they keep on going, and they form little communities of like-minded people around them. Then those communities start to link together and eventually you get a certain field of influence that leads to critical mass that eclipses the whole system. So instead of trying to persuade anyone to do anything, the key is to try and connect all the early adopters, who are alone and struggling in a hostile environment, and bring them together to form communities of practice. When they feel supported and validated, they can share inspiration and resources. It's an underground movement, a counter-cultural change. It has to be underground because we threaten the very grass roots on which orthodoxy stands.

My personal strategy is to completely give up trying to persuade anyone of anything, and to almost completely ignore authority figures, whether it's the profession or the institution or the managers. There is one chief executive of a Health Board in Rotorua who invited me down to meet her executive management team. We talked for an hour and a half about compassionate care, and she said: "Well, this is actually what were here for." She's one out of twenty hospital directors in New Zealand. She's got an inspirational director of nursing as well, who is a great supporter and just kind of gets it that health care is actually about caring for people.

There are a lot of encouraging signs. The government-appointed Healthcare Ombudsman in the United Kingdom published a report in 2012 called: 'Care and compassion?'[7], which had case studies of the appalling treatment of patients, and was basically pointing out that there was something seriously wrong here. It went to the British Parliament.

People are so burned out and so overwhelmed and so resentful. When you get them to the place where they feel it is a privilege instead of a burden, they start to flourish. It's really about choosing your own attitude.

I've been appointed an Honorary Senior Lecturer at the University of Auckland, with no academic qualifications but just on the basis of the work that I've been doing, which is nice. The medical school there is funding an e-programme on empathy that I'm helping to design. I get the opportunity to give a one-hour lecture to second year medical students. What is nice is that when they come through in the fourth year they say: "Oh wow, I remember your lecture." They have given me the award for the best lecture by an external speaker, and all I do is talk to them about being a human being and treating their patients as human beings, and about care and compassion and finding some practices that help strengthen that – whether it is mindfulness or simple acts of kindness. There are little green shoots in places.

People are so burned out and so overwhelmed and so resentful. When you get them to the place where they feel it is a privilege instead of a burden, they start to flourish. It's really about choosing your own attitude.

Over the years I have given over 200 speeches in a dozen countries. While we received many invitations to speak from organisations representing nursing, integrative care, palliative care, faith-based networks, whole-person care, professional wellbeing, and healthcare

---

7   http://www.ombudsman.org.uk/care-and-compassion/home. Retrieved 12/10/2017.

communication, much of mainstream medicine ignored our efforts. Up until fairly recently, I had never been invited to speak about compassion at a specialist medical conference, medical education conference or quality improvement institute. My own professional colleagues in anaesthesiology steadfastly ignored my efforts for seven years. That is changing now though.

Perhaps the most extraordinary invitation was from Humana, a huge healthcare insurance and provider company in the USA. They have 15 million enrolled patients and an annual turnover in excess of $40 billion. I spoke to an eager audience at the company headquarters and was live broadcast across their regional offices. It's apparent that Humana is working hard to shift the priorities of its business, to focus on health rather than just disease, and to create an exceptional experience of care for every one of their patients. If we can positively influence the financial powerhouses behind healthcare, then any change is possible.

At long last, the message of compassionate whole person care is getting through. The tide has turned.

At long last, the message of compassionate whole person care is getting through. The tide has turned.

14 | THE JOY OF BEING A GENERALIST

DR VERONICA MOULE

Rural General Practitioner Obstetrician, Homeopath and practitioner of anthroposophical medicine.

Castlemaine, Australia

I tend to attract people who wouldn't otherwise go and see a doctor. I like that group of people. I am that group of people. Many people who see me are wanting to challenge the illness paradigm and take responsibility for their health. Most of them want to have creative conversations about their illness, and around the esoterics of what their physical illness might mean. I think it's important to work in this way in a mainstream setting. Most people want a bridge. I don't think they want an exclusionary, one-size-fits-all model. Holistic means including Western medicine – you can't be whole if you exclude that. General Practice is holistic in a lot of ways even if you're practising in a mainstream way.

There seems to be this acceptance in the profession that you shouldn't invite yourself into an interaction with someone, that you should stay separate. But the joy is in the interaction, in being human. The times that feel really potent and creative and healing are the times of coming together between myself and a patient.

It's hard to know how much influence our early formative years have on opening our eyes to the breadth of opportunities in this career. There is beauty in that time of naïveté, gathering experiences, and trying to make sense of those experiences. When I look back on that time in my life, there are several examples of the flowing interconnection of people and stories that resonated or stretched me deeply and profoundly.

I have attended a birth where the woman was profoundly deaf, back in those early formative years. It was beautiful. She had soft gentle music playing, which was unusual at the time. There was no space for words, just presence and touch. I don't think there's much space for words in birthing anyway. It was very peaceful and beautiful and very potent for me to learn, so early in my career, the importance and capacity of presence and touch.

When I was working at a major regional hospital, in my intern year, my last rotation was with the surgical unit. We admitted a woman and man of Eastern European descent. They had been found together by the woman's husband. He was angry, jealous, and he bashed them both with a steel pipe. They spent a week in hospital recovering. I saw her again the following week at her outpatient review appointment. She was a gentle woman, and we had a brief and nice acknowledgement. She drove home from the hospital, then her husband shot her dead in the driveway. He then drove to a remote area and killed himself. It was shocking, watching the news in the hospital that night, and realising our patient had died.

My next rotation was in birthing, in the big hospital, 'conveyor-belt' antenatal clinic format. It's an interesting thing working in those clinics – with the piles of medical records stacked high, and constantly replenished as we take one from the top and work our way through. Often in this 'randomness' the same folders would land in the same doctor's hands. I picked up a file of a woman with the same surname as the woman I had cared for in the surgical unit. She was the wife of the deceased woman's son, a man who several months earlier had lost both his parents. I saw her several times antenatally (as per the randomness model of care).

When she went into labour, I was rostered on for the delivery suite. She introduced me to her husband as the doctor who had cared for his mother. Then she laboured, and knelt up on the bed, in a position of reverence I've rarely seen in birthing, and birthed her baby girl into my hands, whilst calling out the name of her mother-in-law, calling her spirit into the room. Sometimes I feel we are guides on an unknown path, participating in a family's story.

Once, I have been privileged to support a woman in birth, care for her family as it grew, and then care for her in death. Privileged to be offered this opportunity to hold someone in death and terminal care, through presence and breath, and to feel her depth of trust in me, founded from her birthing. And for her family to feel her trust, allowing them to sit deeply in their grief, not needing to fight or advocate, allowing them to instead navigate the sadness of their loss – loss of mother, of sister, of daughter, of soul-mate.

And there was loss for me; she was a wild, crazy, dynamic mother of four. She lived down the road, I saw her at the local pool, we laughed together. I was pregnant when she birthed her baby; she was my peer – we were alike in many ways – and she was my friend. In her last week, we spent a few hours together each day, and as I said goodbye to her, there was this moment where we shared a breath together – do you know that kind of experience? I've had it with my babies before – where there is this connection, almost this falling in love again and again and this breath which comes with it. We shared this breath together, which was very beautiful. It was a moment of absolute presence.

Years have passed since her death. I still care for her family, as she knew I would. There is a knowing between us that needs no explanation, a safe place for her children.

There is such beautiful opportunity in this work, to hold people, really hold them – their emotional wellbeing, as well as their physical. People reflect on the kindness of their carers; whether they felt listened to, if they felt they could trust their direction, if they are in the hands of wisdom or ego.

It's not complicated to look at a protocol and say: "This is what you should do." But to actually be present with someone, and have that sense of journeying so that they can find their own way of doing what they need to do, that's really special.

I think the connections and the intimacy are the most beautiful part of the job. That's what we're here for isn't it? To have these pure moments. It's not complicated to look at a protocol and say: "This is what you should do." But to actually be present with someone, and have that sense of journeying so that they can find their own way of doing what they need to do, that's really special.

And that's easy, in a way, to do with birthing, because it is such a profound unfolding, opening experience, but this also happens in a normal GP consultation.

Patients present with more than their illness; they present with the complex bundling of their life events and traumas, all mixed up in their individual personalities, layered with their dis–ease.

Sometimes people turn away from Western medicine because they feel unheard. Western doctors can also get frustrated, if we think the patient doesn't hear us. We don't need to feel wounded by patients making their own decisions, or get angry. We can own our frustrations, and either find another language or way to communicate, or deeply listen and accept the patient's wishes.

And patients can change their mind. The decisions that people make at one stage of a significant illness are not necessarily the same decisions that they will make with progression of disease. We are working in a convoluted human soup of insight, denial, delusion, wanting, letting go of philosophies, holding tight to philosophies, searching, reaching out ...

It's actually a really creative job. Sometimes you have creative moments and sometimes the answer's not clear but words come to you in a creative way. I think that's the joy of being a generalist. I look at specialists in hospital and I don't find the idea of that – and all its rigid structures – appealing at all. It's important for those who work in the hospital system, and for me when I work there with acute illness and women birthing, to try to make it creative, and bring a human connection.

Hospitals are funny places: they are full of people who work in hospitals! It is their home space, their idea of normal, their sense of community, their place of gossip.

Hospitals are funny places: they are full of people who work in hospitals! It is their home space, their idea of normal, their sense of community, their place of gossip.

I was a peculiar registrar – I used to sing going up and down the stairs in the hospital. I tend to challenge some of my colleagues without really meaning to. I'm quiet, and I think I'm more of an advocate for the patient than most. I believe patients really should have a right to decide what is best for them and that that right is greater than the hospital's right to tell them. That makes me a potentially difficult person in a hospital, but I feel that's one of the jobs I have to do – to give a bit of extra responsibility back to patients, for them to be allowed to say: "Well actually no, I'm not happy to do that," even if that's what the hospital wants. That doesn't have to be done in a confronting way. This is more apparent in birthing, as we have well women, challenging themselves with labour and birth, aiming for empowerment. That's a different group to sick and vulnerable patients looking for help in easing their pain and ailments. For some women, if they feel they are being told and not being made part of the decision-making team, they will put up a wall and it can become a difficult experience for both sides.

When I first moved to our town I had a bit of a difficult time being accepted by my colleagues. I was the first doctor to arrive in town having done the new specialist GP training, I didn't bring a GP husband with me, and I was a part-time, pregnant, female doctor who was into homeopathy. I was a bit unusual for a small country town. There's scope for judgement from the mainstream in that list! I also had very clear personal boundaries and my family came first, which caused a few problems with some of the other GPs in terms of the expectations of teamwork on the emergency rosters. They hadn't made allowances for pregnancy and breastfeeding prior to my arrival. The first couple of weeks here I had many patients giving me dire warnings because one of the earlier female GPs here had committed suicide. They were coming in with their diagnoses of what had happened to her, and were warning me to take care of myself.

A lot of my journey has been personal and I can't separate myself from my work. I have studied anthroposophical medicine, homeopathy and nutritional medicine, which I use on myself and my family, and incorporate into my practice. My midwifery knowledge comes partly from my own birthing experiences, but even before I had children, I am fortunate that I had the capacity to be present and allow the unfolding. I have been incredibly lucky with my own birthing experiences – they have been deeply personal, private, respectful unfoldings of myself and my children.

I look after myself by reading, playing music, writing, contemplating, exercising, and eating food which respects my body as my temple. I think I've just kept taking maternity leave to stop the burnout. That for me is always a really creative experience, taking time out to be really present with my babies – the opportunity when they are babies is profound and beautiful. I also do 5 Rhythms dance once a month which I find sustaining and healing. 5 Rhythms dance is a form of dance that opens me, and shows me my inner self.

There are great responsibilities in this work and in life. These responsibilities sit in my body, embodied. This is a good thing – at times of intensity or crisis, such as an obstetric emergency, there is a knowing that comes, that is beyond cognition, a knowing in my hands. Sometimes though this can be uncomfortable. We can't respond to all crises with breath and flow. We do feel fear, shock, responsibility calling us into action. These feelings can get stuck in my body. The dance helps me release the stuck feeling, and helps me integrate the experience. I'm becoming more aware that there are some experiences which I embody, when I feel this sense of responsibility deep in my core. It's two-sided – it is deeply enriching and it is a great honour and an amazing experience to feel something that deeply, but I need to be aware not to continue to hold those experiences physically. Creative physical release is powerful for me, and the dancing community bears witness to this, and supports it. They hold me, whilst I hold others.

What do we hold? How do we integrate? What do we hang on to, and what do we release? How do we let these experiences wash over and settle in our bodies, our minds, our cellular memory?

The human side of medicine, the presence, feeling the emotion, guiding, bearing witness, receiving; these are the special moments. Deep listening, guidance without judgement. Those moments in patient's lives, when everything changes – nothing will ever be the same again. Birth, death, major transitions. What an incredible honour to be present and available to people at these fundamental, formative moments.

My hope is that medicine will become more personal and less technological and focussed on protocol. You do need to immerse yourself in guidelines and recommendations, to be able to responsibly step beyond them. To have creative thoughts, you need to know the Western medicine well. You need to know it, to know where the breath is within it. That's kind of anthroposophical – immersing yourself deeply and finding the breath within. The breath is like being in the grey zone. Medicine can be quite black and white.

Anthroposophical medicine is a creative framework of looking at people in an holistic way. It brings together the physical, life-force, emotional and mental, and spiritual parts of us into a structural format. It looks at patterns that humans form, looks at how people fit within the patterns, and explores how you can create balance in the system in various ways. It recognises polarities and brings them together into a whole. It is based on the philosophy of Rudolf Steiner who was writing this back in the 1920s, but it feels very contemporary. Healthcare is filled with people telling their stories, and us trying to read or interpret the problem from the story. Anthroposophy brings this to another depth of whole.

It is the patients who will take the doctors on a journey. They will need to be gentle with their doctors in the process.

I've heard lots of stories about patients seeing alternative practitioners and not telling their doctors about it. I'm not sure what is to be gained from that. I think there is a slow awakening and doctors will awaken at their own speed, but it won't be a linear process, it will be a step-by-step process. It is the experiences with the patients which will bring the doctors through it.

It is the patients who will take the doctors on a journey. They will need to be gentle with their doctors in the process.

15 | OPEN HEARTED SURGEON

DR SHARAD PAUL

Skin Cancer Surgeon, General Practitioner, Lecturer, Student, Author (fiction and non-fiction) and social enterprise owner (bookshop and literacy charity).

Auckland, New Zealand

"Dreams belong in the clouds. If not, we'll not move mountains to reach them."[1]

Curiosity and creativity are things that have underpinned my practice, research and life. For nearly two decades, I have spent a day a week teaching creative writing to school children in economically disadvantaged areas. There is plenty of evidence that teaching creativity and curiosity help STEM (Science, Technology, Education and Maths) subject performance. Why does creativity help you understand how a cell works or figure out math solutions? Essentially, it helps with problem-solving. We learn science as a series of facts – for example, in medicine we emphasise facts and concepts as to what cells or hormones do. But to figure out answers to specific problems, we need a degree of creative thought – for example why does a cancer cell behave in a certain way? Creativity and curiosity are better at solving this, as they allow us to step outside the frame and look at the big picture. I've been credited with

---

1   S Paul, *The kite flyers*, Harper Collins, India, 2015, p. 172.

inventing two different surgical operations and in both cases, I was trying to solve a problem, not improve existing techniques.

Most children think science is a collection of facts, and it is easy to miss the reason for the importance of scientific thought. Even most of my colleagues in medicine have become siloed within specialties, and no longer scientists in the creative sense of the word. More emphasis is placed these days on Medicare billing than dreaming up answers to challenges we encounter in experiments or labs. This is because most knowledge regarding anatomy and physiology is learned in medical school, and later, accessing peer-reviewed journals and guidelines automatically deliver us new 'facts'.

Science should be about curiosity, observing and gathering information about everything in nature or life. That's why schools have science and math fairs – to help develop the curiosity to seek out solutions or understand why things happen. You don't need a double-blind study to show that making something fun increases skill levels.

Today it is difficult for many New Zealand school children (or children anywhere) to even dream of becoming a doctor, as our medical world has become increasingly elitist and expensive. It is partly to instil some self-belief, that I spend my time teaching less advantaged children. Last week I was at a school re-working Humpty Dumpty and reckon the kids wrote the best Humpty Dumpty rhyme ever! We had a good fun morning.

Medicine wasn't my first choice of career. Maybe it was pre-destined, maybe not. But that was the life I was surrounded with. Some people consider medicine a calling, others a business. Whatever it is, I was doomed. This vocation was possibly imprinted in my genes. My latest book, *The genetics of health*[2] is about genes, germs, geography and how our diets and actions affect our gene expressions. My parents, grandparents on my mother's side, uncles and aunts were all doctors – surgeons, physicians, dermatologists, ophthalmologists and psychiatrists.

---

2   S Paul, *The genetics of health*, Simon and Schuster, New York, 2017.

My grandmother studied medicine at a time when women completed the same course but only men were called doctors; women like my grandmother ended up euphemistically called "licensed medical practitioners" even if they did the same job. My grandmother died from hypertension because the relevant drugs hadn't been developed yet, and being a medical pioneer, she was brave enough to face death and explain it to her children.

I learned that the hope is the best medicine, love the most powerful drug and knowledge only does good when excellence becomes a habit.

My parents left lucrative medical careers in the United Kingdom to pursue medical mission work in India and they were a big influence on me. Being surrounded by hospitals and wards all my life meant there was less mystique to medicine, and a door that seemed mysterious to others seemed a natural part of my journey. My parents taught me through the way they lived life that medicine was not about treating illness, but about human beings.[3]

I learned that the hope is the best medicine, love the most powerful drug and knowledge only does good when excellence becomes a habit.

So, medicine ended up the path I chose. People say paths and roads are different – paths are things that come with a sense of familiarity, in a landscape that is already part of you, and that may be the explanation. Roads are built to order; they are more mainstream, more corporate. In that sense, I've really walked an unconventional path.

In our long meandering medical journeys, we may have put off having babies, buying houses or might have suspended other interests. Finally, we end up with two decisions: What we do with our knowledge, and how we overcome our innate fear of failure?

---

3   My latest book is dedicated to my parents, and my grandmother's story is also told in that book.

There are times when I feel lucky to be a doctor. Most of them relate to the simple things in medical life, not great diagnoses or scientific papers I have published, but stories about humanity and why small intersections of lives matter in medicine. I shall give you two examples:

I was invited to speak at the Dalkey Book Festival in Dublin in June 2017 alongside Bernie Sanders, Colm Toibin and other big names. My phone rang. It was a ninety-year-old patient who asked me: "Dr Paul, what starts with G and is on the forehead?" "You mean Glabella?" I said. "Thanks," she answered, "I was entering a crossword competition and thought you'd be the one to know." In these days of global-roaming phones she would not have known I was at the other side of the world in a different time zone, about to present to a large audience. But I was humbled that she felt she could ask me. All my patients have my mobile number – and considering that since 1996 I have examined over 150,000 patients at my practice, most doctors I speak to think I am foolhardy. But people do respect your privacy.

The other story that comes to mind is about a patient who had worked for several years as a doctor in India and recently retired to New Zealand to be with her daughter. Her melanoma had revealed itself with no warning. She had gone to see an eye specialist complaining of blurry vision in one eye. She had noted intermittent flashes. She had initially self-diagnosed herself as having a possible retinal detachment. By the time she had seen an ophthalmologist her symptoms had disappeared. She was wondering if she still needed to see him. The diagnosis was devastating: malignant melanoma of the choroid. They recommended removing her eye urgently. "I've got less than two years," she said to me. I tried to reassure her, saying melanomas are often unpredictable. "Don't try to be kind," she said. "Skin melanomas you usually deal with may be different. I know the mortality rate for this. I've come to terms with it." This lady, as both doctor and patient taught me more about choroidal melanoma than I had known until that point. She, unlike other patients was not under the false impression that removal of her eye would help. She knew all the statistics. "All it does is prevent a blind red eye," she said as a matter of fact, "removal of the eye can increase the risk of liver metastases." She had had her eye removed and had been treated with radiotherapy before she had begun researching this in earnest. Six months later her scan showed a liver full of melanoma spread. A year after she had first had her melanoma diagnosed she was dead. But not before she had taught me lessons about life, melanoma and living life with melanoma.

My conversations with this patient were really about the questions that we don't address at medical school: What goes on inside the mind of a person riddled with cancer? What can you tell someone who knows she is dying? How is a young doctor, who has barely lived life, going to ease the mind of someone old enough to be his mother – and God forbid, counsel her?

I listened to her. Sometimes in busy medical practices, we don't listen enough. But someone nearing death has that gravitas. You had to be psychologically prepared to hear her side of the story. She had lived her life as a doctor and would end it as a patient. All of us will be in this position one day.

As a doctor, I am blessed to partake in this daily narrative from my clients – patient histories, family stories and reminiscences. That is one reason I also trained in family medicine after initially training in plastic surgery. The rough narratives of patients, chopped up into carefully controlled time-slots of medical appointments. Good stories. Great stories. Sad stories. In the end, all patient notes and investigation results end up like good novels, do they not? Unpredictable to the very end. If we could all see the last page of the story of our life, would we bother with today? Ultimately, we end up as characters in these stories, and that is where our immortality lies.

I've always been oblivious or naïve to the politics of medicine. I tend to focus on a problem and get on with the job. I'm a doer. In 2003, I was awarded a Health Innovation Award by the New Zealand Government for establishing the first skin cancer service that integrated primary and secondary care, that is GPs and specialists. I was in a perfect position to do this as I was a hospital consultant as well as had GP training. This system reduced waiting lists dramatically and (as an unintended consequence) affected volumes at some influential and successful nearby private practices, and that created massive opposition to my methods that exist even today. I started the first GP training programmes via the University of Auckland department of surgery in 1996, and a decade later we also set up the first primary care skin cancer unit in Australia. I was one of the international advisers behind the founding of the skin cancer in primary care department of the University of Queensland. Both were created after massive opposition. Medicine is very siloed and specialised, and in areas that overlap like skin cancer (treated by GPs, plastic surgeons, dermatologists, general surgeons, Ear Nose and Throat (ENT) surgeons, ophthalmologists and more), there is very little cooperation and everyone thinks they are better than the other group. I'm not sure what that's about. It may be the way we train doctors or the over-competitive entry pathways.

Those were difficult times as I was merely focusing on patient-needs and wasn't prepared for such antagonism given that I didn't have anything personal to gain from it. It taught me first hand that there needs to be separation between public and private systems to avoid conflicts of interests. These continue to be poorly managed.

Ron Paterson, former Health and Disability Commissioner for New Zealand and an international expert on complaints, healthcare quality and the regulation of health professions surprisingly mentioned my work in a lecture on 'Care, compassion and charity: Do they have a place in modern Medicine?'[4] He said: "I have no doubt that many individual doctors quietly and routinely provide free care to patients who cannot afford to pay. That is certainly true in New Zealand. A few come to public notice. One, whom I know personally, is Dr Sharad Paul, a GP specialising in skin cancer surgery from a clinic in Blockhouse Bay in Auckland. Dr Paul provides around 7,000 free skin check consultations each year,

---

4   Ron Paterson, Inaugural Ball Memorial Lecture. https://www.nzma.org.nz/journal/read-the-journal/all-issues/2010-2019/2015/vol-128-no-1427-18-december-2015/6768. Retrieved 23/09/2017.

and has provided this service since 1996. He has been honoured with several public awards … But Dr Paul has also faced fierce resistance from some surgeons and dermatologists. Doctors who provide high quality, charitable services may be ostracised by colleagues who have different motivations in the practice of medicine."[5]

I've faced numerous other setbacks; too many to list, but this is a natural part of life when you have moved countries or been a change-maker. I've learned the art of negative capability and that has kept me productive. Keats, the poet who dropped out of surgical training to "save his soul" wrote about the concept of negative capability. Negative capability is essentially a creative state where we can acknowledge the world without reconciling it; Keats considered it a high-energy state that makes one innovative. It is the ability to say: "It is what it is," and accept both success and failure. If faced with a surgical complication, I try to deal with it and study why it happened, not take it personally as an injury to the ego. Disappointment does not have to damage your soul. I believe people spend too much time worrying about the success of others. I've often said your ability to climb a mountain is not directly proportional to the times you fall; likewise, your ability to climb the summit is not related to someone else's ability to do the same. I guess this reconciliation with life is my version of negative capability.

In a guild like medicine or law we are confined by rules, convention, expectations; our world is constructed for us and we merely live in it. Don't push the envelope, don't rock the boat. This is a low-energy state where negativity often sets in and creativity can be lacking.

I am a very positive person so don't want to dwell on the negative, or on being targeted or personal attacks, as I love my life and am content. However, what I've learnt is this – many people may not say this openly, but when you fight a good fight you do have many people supporting you, even if you feel isolated. So, to people in similar situations, I'd offer this quote by George R. R. Martin:

---

5   Ron Paterson, as above.

"My own heroes are the dreamers, those men and women who tried to make the world a better place than when they found it, whether in small ways or great ones. Some succeeded, some failed, most had mixed results ... but it is the effort that's heroic, as I see it. Win or lose, I admire those who fight the good fight."[6]

These days medicine has become ego-driven – you finish your fellowship or board exams and embark on a path of good money but little empathy.

I have taught almost 800 students a year in New Zealand, Australia and internationally since 1996, when I first began teaching skin cancer surgery at the University of Auckland. As an educator, you just try and impart any wisdom you have and try to unearth curiosity. The good thing about teaching is that you learn as you go and it sharpens your game. I love teaching and don't worry about whether students end up following my advice. That's *their* journey. The most important thing for a doctor is to love to teach and share knowledge (after all, 'doctor' derives from 'docere' in Latin which means 'to teach'). As my career progressed, all these things helped me find meaning.

And we need to continue to learn also. I believe all surgeons or doctors need a good coach or mentor throughout their careers.

These days medicine has become ego-driven – you finish your fellowship or board exams and embark on a path of good money but little empathy.

The current models we have are simply not sustainable or affordable – irrespective of whether we have a National Health Service (NHS) system like the United Kingdom or a private insurance-based system like the USA. In New Zealand we have a system that was initially modelled on the NHS but today does not

---

6   From interview between George R. R. Martin and Patrick, published on 'Pat's Fantasy List', Dec 2008, http://fantasyhotlist.blogspot.com.au/2008/12/interview-with-george-r-r-martin-and.html. Retrieved 23/09/2017.

offer comprehensive coverage. 'Waiting lists' in New Zealand were replaced by 'booking systems' for political expediency. This basically meant that many procedures that couldn't be done in six months could simply be rejected by the system. Suddenly hernias, veins, and non-melanoma skin cancers were no longer done in the public system, leaving many people with health needs that were not met. It played right into the hands of surgeons who could under-perform in one sector and over-perform in the other. We need to manage conflicts of interests better and in my view, you should either work in the public system or private system, not both.

The current system is unsustainable. It is like climate change. Eventually the changes simply have to happen, just as the earth has a geosphere and a biosphere that are linked. Without health, there is no real wealth, and yet the current economic models simply don't address the problem. Whether we like it or not, we've reached an era where the economies within and outside medicine are in constant flux. To be sustainable, we will have to break down old gates or replace gatekeepers. Things like Fellowships or Societies look good on our certificates but are only concepts to our patients – skills and sympathetic care are more important. If the iPad was a medical device, would we in medicine have never allowed Steve Jobs to create it? After all, he was a drop-out. A passion for medicine as a vocation is more important than the subjects chosen at school. The reality is that all physicians whether in primary or secondary care, or in academic life learn new skills every day and sometimes will make interesting mistakes.

The best healthcare reform will be when doctors understand that medicine needs to be viewed as a vocation and not a business – and we will all be better off for it. My dream is for a system where 'care' is really a part of healthcare.

No health system that works on a business model (of creating more supply and demand) can find enough money to fund a population's health.

The best healthcare reform will be when doctors understand that medicine needs to be viewed as a vocation and not a business – and we will all be better off for it. My dream is for a system where 'care' is really a part of healthcare.

The real reform needs to be from within the profession – an introspection. I've spoken of what I call 'beyond medicine' – by which I mean we must encourage our patients to live well and take responsibility, but importantly our own lives beyond medicine must set an example. That's what *The genetics of health* is about. Let's be good human beings too. Medicine isn't called the noble profession for nothing. This is what professionalism is all about.

I think changes will happen not because of medicine but in spite of it. Technology will make many diagnoses automatic and patients will access their health information as they do their bank balances.

I was recently asked to deliver a keynote at a national medical students' association conference. I was trying to go back to the days when I was a school student and later a medical student, like those attending the event. That made me feel really old, even ancient – I graduated from medical school thirty years ago, probably before most of them were born! I told them that the most important lesson I learnt from those years as a young doctor is this: what you have demonstrated about your proficiency or even about yourself until now will have little to do with what you will end up doing even ten years from now. You or I may feel we have bumbled along until now but we can turn it all around. There is always hope. There will be many people who will doubt your ability or say that your dreams are impossible. Remember this: they are not you.

In the study of educational methods, teachers are taught that rewarding achievement is far better than punishing mistakes. However, I can't think of a single stage in my surgical training where this was applied. In general, the view was: if you abused or shouted at the registrar in front of everyone in the operating room, his or her performance would improve next time around. Bizarrely, as explained by Daniel Kahneman,

Nobel Laureate in Economics[7], both views are right. Essentially, all performances are random – we all have good days and bad days. If we have a particularly good day, the next day seems less. This is really nothing but randomness, which is the only universal truth.

If luck doesn't exist, then is talent born or made? How do we actually create winners? Malcolm Gladwell and I were at a literary festival together. In his book, *Outliers: The story of success*[8], he essentially asks this question: is talent born or made? He attempts to quantify talent and success. If you wonder how Roger Federer or Rafa Nadal manage to pull off seemingly impossible shots, there is an answer: 10,000 hours of dedicated practice. If you do something twenty hours a week for ten years, you'd have completed 10,000 hours, and end up as good as anyone else in the field, provided you have a passion for it. Of course, if you didn't love what you were doing, you were hardly going to put in 10,000 hours of purposeful practice. What this means is that anyone can be the world's best at something if you put in the time. And medicine is no exception. Perhaps that's why our work is called practice.

When I studied law after medicine, I came to realise that just as law doesn't translate into justice, medicine isn't always about health. Medicine and Law are old guilds, full of rules, pompousness and restrictions. Neither automatically does good, as one may expect. Health requires the patient to take responsibility, ask questions and seek answers; medicine requires doctors to remember the *raison d'être* of the profession: to help or heal, not run a business. There is a passage in my latest book, *The genetics of health* that offers advice:

> "There's a fundamental difference between medicine and
> health. Modern Western medicine works on an illness
> model – you have a disorder that gets cured, either by
> taking a chemical or by undergoing a procedure. But

7   D Kahneman, *Thinking fast and slow*, Farrar, Straus and Giroux, New York, 2011.
8   Turtleback books, St Louis, 2011.

we know that, in some cases, even placebos can work if we believe we are taking the real thing, especially for symptom control . . .

We cannot place complete faith in the medical industry at the expense of our own individual health. We won't find good health in medicines, be they derived synthetically or naturally. Drugs are meant for curing certain conditions or alleviating symptoms, not as sustenance. Even in the wellness industry, there are people pushing unscientific products. So it is our responsibility to understand our wellness – and sometimes, we have to look back before we can move forward."[9]

Because of my background of having studied law as well as medicine, I am often asked what the best medico-legal advice is, and I say this: "If you treat your patients as you would treat yourself or your family, things will be OK." This is my underlying philosophy. This simple philosophy would make us take good care, lower costs and not recommend unnecessary procedures, and would by default define what should be the fundamental paradigm for procedural medicine, but increasingly it isn't.

So, I just keep working – doing things that I am passionate about. The awards or accomplishments were never my aim and were most unexpected. I found the Ko Awatea International Excellence Award for Leading Health Improvement on a Global Scale deeply humbling. It was awarded at the Asia Pacific Forum (APAC), and the citation said it was for practicing "patient-centred medicine and improving health on a global scale." As most of my work has been in lower socioeconomic communities, any 'leadership' on my part has been purely accidental.

I guess that if you keep up the good fight, eventually rewards will come, and this legitimacy has allowed me to be able to converse with

9   S Paul, *The genetics of health*, Beyond Words / Atria Books, New York, 2017, xii.

and (hopefully) inspire the next generation of doctors whose challenge it will be to fix a broken system.

As doctors, our enduring mission is to heal, or to improve lives afflicted with illness. This must not be an automatic choice, but something we need to consciously think about, irrespective of financial rewards. To me the most humbling thing about being a doctor is the trust patients have in our knowledge. People trust us with intimate details of their lives – things they may not reveal to a spouse. With that trust comes a responsibility. How can it make sense otherwise? For a seventy-year-old depressed lady with a life full of interesting stories to see a twenty-five-year-old junior doctor who has barely experienced life, or for a twenty-five-year-old to have a seventy-year-old surgeon to perform delicate surgery – all is underpinned by trust.

* Dr Paul is Adjunct Professor in the Faculty of Health and Faculty of Creative Technologies at the Auckland University of Technology; Senior Lecturer, Skin Cancer, at the University of Queensland; and Hon. Senior Lecturer, Faculty of Surgery, at Auckland University. Dr Paul is also an author and evolutionary biologist with a Masters in Medical Law and Ethics, and currently completing a PhD in cutaneous / dermatological surgery. In 2007, he invented the first new skin graft technique that reduces costs, pain and healing time for patients, and he has presented this new technique at international conferences. He was awarded New Zealand Medical Association's highest honour, The Chair's Award in 2012 and the same year was a finalist for the New Zealander of the Year Award. In 2015, he was awarded the Ko Awatea International Excellence Award for Leading Health Improvement on a Global Scale at the Asia Pacific Forum (APAC), the largest medical gathering in this region. Outside of medicine Dr Paul runs an award-winning café and bookstore called the Baci Lounge, in Newmarket, New Zealand. Proceeds are used to fund literacy programmes in low-decile Auckland schools, with the aim of helping children to "dream with

their eyes wide open." When he is home, he teaches creative writing to disadvantaged children (by visiting schools personally once a week, and funding school libraries). He has also served on the National Commission of UNESCO (United Nations Educational, Scientific and Cultural Organisation). Dr Paul has been described in the media as "one of the most inspiring, intelligent and compassionate men you are likely to meet" (Source: NZ Medical Association. 'Renaissance Man Wins NZMA's Highest Award' https://www.nzma.org.nz/news-and-events/media-releases/renaissance-man-wins-nzmas-highest-award) *TIME magazine,* in 2008, called him "Open Heart Surgeon (*TIME,* July 17, 2008)." Dr Paul's popular books include: Fiction: *Cool cut,* Picador, 2007; *To kill a snow dragonfly,* 4th Estate, 2012; *The kite flyers,* Harper Collins, UK, 2015; Non-Fiction: *The genetics of health,* Beyond Word / Simon and Schuster, Australia, 2017; *Skin, a biography,* 4th Estate, India, 2013; *Dermocracy,* Collins, India, 2015; Poetry: *De nature melanoma* Middle Island Press, USA, 2015.

16 | "I'LL LOOK AFTER YOUR CHILD"

DR PETER HOWE

Paediatric Anaesthetist, Royal Children's Hospital.
Melbourne, Australia

I did medicine because I was a smart kid in a private school and I really only considered medicine and law as career options. I didn't want to do law, so I found myself doing medicine. This is a common story for many of my medical friends, to be honest. My best friend's dad was a football club doctor, and I loved going into the rooms after the games. Maybe that was part of the reason too.

I did an intern year and I decided to do paediatrics. I wasn't completely sure why – perhaps it was because it seemed the hardest speciality to get into. I just had this sort of ultra-competitive spirit. So I ended up at the Royal Children's Hospital (RCH) in Melbourne as a paeds trainee. I was offered a job at the end and I could've kept going that way, but I had a terrible first year. All we did was stick needles into children. Children used to cry when they saw me coming! We did lumbar punctures and we also did muscle biopsies; punch biopsies with needles the size of your finger. You'd have to hold the child down and whack it into them. It was just awful. And then I did the cardiac surgery job where my job was to get 10 ml of serum (if you let the blood cells separate from the liquid, the liquid remaining is the serum). A lot of those kids had scrambled hearts, so for various reasons, some of those kids had more cells than serum. Sometimes you need a huge amount of blood for a small amount of serum. I remember standing there with a broken needle in the back of a child's hand, draining blood into a collecting tube – drip by drip by drip – and the father is going: "This is insane." So, I decided well before the end of the year that I was giving up paediatrics, and I kind of thought I was giving up medicine as well. I used to walk back home across the park going: "I hate my job, I hate my life."

I went off and did different things. I tried to make a living as a professional singer. Guess what my income was in twelve months as a professional singer? Zero. I got a second audition once, when Phantom of the Opera was moving to Sydney. It was to be in the chorus as the understudy for Raoul, the male lead – he looked a lot like me so I suspect I got the audition on height and weight rather than singing talent. I sang my song the best I'd ever sung it – and at the end they all said: "Thank-you!" with big, fake, cheesy 'Don't call us, we'll call you' smiles, and showed me the door. In some ways it was a very humiliating process, but it was also nice to be clear that if I'd got the part, I was ready to move on from medicine.

I gave singing my best crack but after being unemployed for a year, having a job as a doctor was looking better. So I went back to it and did various go-nowhere jobs for a few years, feeling like a mercenary without any sense of it being a calling. The guy who was the head of the Intensive Care Unit where I was working was an anaesthetist. I thought he had the best job. So I applied for anaesthetics and they gave me a probationary term at the old Preston Hospital. The boss there was a really good bloke and it was a really good department and I thought: *This will do.* So I did the training and the exams – from Darwin of all places. Fran and I had just married and were having an adventure up north. It was a great place to live, and again a department full of great people, but I couldn't really say that I loved anaesthetics – I just felt that I needed to stop looking around and develop a career.

We came back to Melbourne and I did a training rotation back here at RCH – and this time around I loved it. I remember being quite sick with a cold – in the past I might have justifiably had a day or two off but at RCH, I'd look at tomorrow's theatre list and think *that looks interesting*, and come to work. I remember one Friday night I got home and Fran said: "What's wrong with you, you're happy?" I had never come home happy before.

So I've come full circle and ended up back here as part of the furniture at the Royal Children's as a staff specialist anaesthetist. I did the end of my training here, stayed on as a fellow, stayed on another year as a fellow doing the rotations through intensive care, and then when I finally got my letters, I had a choice between a full-time consultant position at Monash Health, and a six-week locum[1] here. Monash had another wonderful anaesthetics department, but I took the RCH locum and they kept finding me more time covering for consultants on maternity and sabbatical leave, and before I knew it I had gone nine years without a formal contract. I never thought of leaving to find more job security – I felt part of the place and felt sure that my boss would keep finding a way to keep me on the books. There is something about here that just kind of clicks for me. As a registrar I remember working with one of the consultants who was really irreverent and showed that it was possible to clown around a bit with the children but still be a first rate professional, and I was thinking: *I think I fit here*. Also, I reckon I'm a little bit addicted to an intense emotional interaction and it's pretty easy to have that in a children's hospital! This is a good place to learn empathy, because you can feel it so much more readily for children who are stuck in hospital, with all the anxiety that goes with that, than for the fifty-year-old bloke who is having a day case colonoscopy, even though he's probably anxious too.

I've always had a tendency to look out for lost sheep and go out of my way to welcome newcomers in any setting – a legacy of my dad, along with his wide feet and white hair – and it felt natural to become involved with welcoming and supporting new anaesthesia trainees.

---

1   Short term, fill in jobs when doctors are on holidays / leave or where there is temporary understaffing.

I have now been the supervisor of specialist training here at the Royal Children's for nearly twenty years. In early years I just tried to be nice, but now it's a bit clearer what I want people to get out of their RCH rotation: I want to see them progress from feeling like academics to feeling like compassionate doctors who take personal responsibility for patients in their care. Most anaesthesia registrars come to us in their third year of a five-year specialty training programme, and they are about to sit their exams.[2] At the start, they are in a real parent–child / teacher–student mode: "What's the right answer to this?" "What should I do here?" "But you just said that, and they said the opposite thing." Then after a while, they settle in and the hierarchy gets lost. That especially happens when trainees work closely with consultants after-hours, and you're so busy that everyone just needs to pitch in. It ends up moving from: "What's the right answer for the exam?" to "How can I look after these patients with my current skills and resources?" This is a great place to discover a sense of being part of a medical community.

I have a lot to do with the orientation of new anaesthesia trainees, and my experience and research in orientation is probably as good as anyone's. One of the biggest hurdles faced by new trainees is feeling afraid that something bad might happen to a child in their care, and I try to harness this emotion at the start of the term. On their very first morning their orientation starts at 8 am, but they meet me at 7:30 and we go outside and stand out front of the hospital. I say: "Close your eyes. Hand's up who's feeling anxious, even just a bit, about starting here?" And of course everyone puts their hand

---

2   Medical graduates in Australia must successfully complete at least one year of supervised practice, generally known as an internship with compulsory rotations through various medical disciplines. If successful, they then qualify for full registration with the Medical Board and are licensed to engage in independent medical practice. In general, most doctors spend two to three years practicing as a *Resident Medical Officer* (RMO) or *Hospital Medical Officer* (HMO) in a hospital before commencing specialist training. Most specialty training programmes take between three and six years to complete. Doctors who have commenced specialist training through a Medical College are referred to as *registrars*. Those successful in completing the requirements of their college programme become Fellows of that College and are then referred to as *specialists*. Specialists typically work in specialist private practice or as a *consultant* in a hospital, or sometimes both. From Wikipedia: https://en.wikipedia.org/wiki/Medical_education_in_Australia. Retrieved 17/09/17.

up. And I go on: "If you're feeling anxious, imagine what you would feel like if you're bringing your child here, about to hand him or her over to an anaesthetist you've only just met!" I tell them that the only standard I ask of them for the term is that they feel able to look the parents in the eye and say: "I will look after your child." I don't care whether they can do it without help, or if they need to make twenty-five phone calls to do it. But that's the transaction: "I'll look after your child." And then I take the them inside and say: "As someone who has never worked at the hospital before, you are in a good position to experience what it is like as a new family coming here, not knowing where to go. You are on your own – you need to take the yellow lifts to level 3 and find Reception J. Off you go." And they go: "I don't know where the yellow lifts are." And I say: "Neither do the families." They have to go and find reception and get directions. And on the way through the maze of the hospital I tell them to try and see the look in the parents' eyes. You'll see *I don't know what's going on here, and I'm so worried.* That first-day of being new, you capture that, and it empowers them and helps them be empathetic to families when they entrust their children to you. It's a really rich experience to capture those feelings on the first day.

Most doctors who are accepted into specialty training programmes are really high-powered, high-quality people who learn quickly. So, the main educational aim early on is to recognise that everything's just so new to them, and that they are often overwhelmed. I've kind of rejigged our orientation. It used to be a series of facts on PowerPoint, delivered by hospital administration, and now it's all just how to function here to become effective. The main thing to recognise and address is that being new, everyone feels ineffective. In their previous job they had learned to juggle five balls; and then all of a sudden here they find they can only juggle three balls, and if I talk to them while they're doing it, they might drop them all. So, if you try to teach too early it's like; "hang on a second here, I'm just trying to calculate this drug formula, don't interrupt me." You just have to let them get that out of the way. So, the orientation is really basic, just ticking off: "Can you find the toilets?" "Can you find the coffee shop?" "Can you get paid?" "Do you know where to park your car?" "Can you log onto the computer system?" They just need to free up some hard-drive and then we can get started on the real training.

Most doctors in training programmes are used to becoming better, and more important, and more independent with each rotation as they grow into their professional role. Often they come back down to earth with a bit of a thud here, when they have to go back to being the student again after they have chosen their specialty path. This may be to do with procedures that they thought they had already mastered – they become difficult again, both technically and emotionally. There is a temptation to not only struggle with it, but to heap on a whole lot of stuff like: "I'm stupid, I'm hopeless, I'm useless, I'm worse than everyone else." So we need to create a safe space where they can share that, and realise that it's not them, it's the situation.

You've got to pace the training, and the support for where they are at. There are huge pressures around establishing a career, passing exams, and then getting a job at the end of it all. Your whole life is on hold until you've passed the exams, you can't really think of anything else. Conversations about finding meaning in your work probably come a little bit afterwards, when people are hitting a bit of a lull. That's probably the peak time for thinking: "Why am I here again?" It's probably nice to get them to write a little note to themselves at the start of their training about what their reason is for starting the journey. Because it's pretty easy to get lost on the way; it's so stressful. When I went through it, I knew I'd get a job – it was more a question of which job, whereas these days no one's sure they're going to have a job at the end of their training. The number of trainees has trebled per year. That makes things really competitive. It's tough.

This level of competitiveness and the anxiety it provokes has certainly changed the feeling of the training programme over recent years. We get the registrars to meet once a week with the idea of being collegial, building community, and making sure they're not feeling isolated. We want to open up those conversations about how tough it can be. As registrars (year 3) their opposition is the exam, whereas for the fellows (year 5) it's a different dynamic – they're kind of in competition with each other for references and for jobs, which can make it tricky to have the same sense of collegiality.

Our training programmes are sadly littered with people who have gone to a dark place and taken their own life either through misadventure or through quite deliberately doing it. They may well have stuff going on for them beneath the surface but we would often never know because they're putting on a very effective persona at work. They're under big pressure to not really reveal too many weaknesses, because they want to be the one to get the job. Anaesthetists and psychiatrists are the two most likely professions to commit suicide. It might have a little bit to do with the sorts of people who go into those specialties, but as an anaesthetist, you've obviously got access to chemicals that make you stop breathing. Heaven knows how one sets up strategies to prevent it. I imagine feeling isolated is part of it, so that's why we try and do our small things in the training programme – really just building community.

We have an end-of-term debrief. People have often lost a few layers of their protective coating by then. We'll sit down in the debrief room and I'll give them feedback which is almost always good – if there is anything bad, I address it at the time, I don't bring it up on the last day. And what I find is that more often than not, these junior doctors haven't had anyone sit down with them one on one and deliver positive feedback. Often there are tears – there's always a tissue box. It's a great privilege to be walking alongside them as they go through their training.

My emotional connection to my work is definitely not on a constant setting. The one thing that I can't stand doing is MRI[3] scans for acute squints; because you know what you're looking for – which is a brain tumor – but the parents don't know. And I'm not the one reporting, so if I see something, I can't say anything. That's an awful feeling. You know,

---

3   Magnetic Resonance Imaging.

in my twenty years here, I'm not one per cent closer to working out how one deals with that.

I used to do the burns list which involved a whole lot of dressing changes. I had this kid once, let's call her Cassie, who was about ten when she got leukemia and after her very first dose of chemo her immune system fell apart and a tiny little pimple on her bottom turned into this giant weeping lesion, and her heart stopped working. So, she was on a heart pump device with this huge open wound, and twice a week I used to wheel her around from intensive care to theatre to get her dressings changed. She was such a miserable little emaciated stick, and I found that very hard. I remember one night late, I was in that sort of dazed, tired, stupid state and was on my way to Maccas[4] from surgery – there was a corridor under the hospital so you could sneak from theatres down to Maccas and back without being seen in public. Anyway, I was down there and I found myself thinking about her and thinking: *I'd cut off one of my fingers if I could fix her.* I remember I was kind of looking at my hands as if I was on the way to the appointment to get it done. I was thinking: *Maybe that finger.* But then I thought *I could probably could think of nine other kids I would do that for, and then I wouldn't have any fingers left.* That was a big moment for me; realising that I've just got to just do my little bit. I can't do everything. She stopped coming and I eventually forgot about her, and then one day I walked past her and she goes: "Peter! What are you doing walking past me without saying hello?" It was four or five years later and there she was this healthy, in-your-face teenager. She did end up having a couple of relapses and was in and out of hospital again, although I think she's OK now. I remember one year at Christmas, we were driving to my in-laws and I knew Cassie was back in hospital, so I came in with a card and a present, and she goes: "What are you doing here, you big suck?" So that's been a nice connection. But then there are other days at work when there is some huge emotional experience and I'm not

---

4   McDonald's Restaurant.

feeling connected at all, and sometimes I find that almost more worrying than the times when I get a bit attached.

I was invited to write an editorial for the *Pediatric Anesthesia Journal*, which is a big deal, and I'm no academic. I was asked to write about professionalism, and what it means to be professional. The editor, who works in our department said: "This'll be right up your alley Mr Touchy-Feely –

Professionalism is doing the right thing when no one is looking.

have a crack at this." That was a fun project. I was pondering this topic of professionalism and around that time, I was due to meet a family from interstate whose child was scheduled for complex surgery, and I was to be their anaesthetist. I knew I would be stuck in theatre when they arrived in Melbourne, and as I already had spoken to them by phone and had all the medical information I needed, all I needed to do was say hello, so I arranged to meet them at lunchtime. I found them in the back of the relatively crowded Dumpling Bar in the food court, as it turned out. So I'm sitting on the floor of the Dumpling Bar, trying to engage this two-year-old who wouldn't have a bar of me, and thinking: *I suspect this doesn't look very professional.* And at that moment the little one's mum goes: "You know, you're the most professional anaesthetist that we've ever had." And I said, 'Sarah, hold that thought! What does professionalism mean to you?" She replied, "Most of our other anaesthetists have told us how dangerous our daughter's surgery is going to be, and then just whisked her away! But with you, I feel that you'll look after her when I can't be there to look after her." And that became the editorial. So, to define professionalism? In a nutshell, I think professionalism is doing the right thing when no one is looking.

We had this big pompous idiot come and do a grand round with us on professional demeanour once, and he was talking all about the importance of wearing a suit and tie and white coat, so that people know who is who. I held my tongue until he had finished and invited questions, and then from the back of the room I ripped into everything he had said. I said: "Give us one bit of evidence, other than your one subjective story about one experience; tell me one other reason why a child will trust me more if I wear a tie?" Not a very professional outburst, and I'm half embarrassed by it, but I also think I spoke for everyone in the audience. To me, the way I present myself to a family is vitally important, but the nature of my attire is almost irrelevant. Sure, it's nice not to be dishevelled, but it's vastly more important to be engaged, not preoccupied, not checking my phone during a consult, listening to people, remembering the parents' names. A big part of an anaesthetist's job is to build trust and connect with the family and the child in a short period of time. It may well be that the three-piece suit helps with that, or doesn't help. It might be part of your thing, it might not be part of your thing. I like the fact that at RCH, our dress code and hospital culture is pretty relaxed. I like to be serious, but not formal. It suits me here where I get to wear my green froggie headscarf in theatre, and walk around in my scrubs. Often I show patients my video of Ginger the dog, chewing up toilet paper: "Do you know what sort of dog Ginger is? She's a Farting Dog." And I sing the kids a song: "Ginger, the farting dog – the smelliest dog you know." So, that kind of stuff – like it's just nice to be that mixture of clown and professional. Hopefully people see that you're interested in, and there for their child. I think I would be crushed working at a different hospital. I remember one occasion when I was wearing my cookie monster headscarf while performing an eye block for cataract surgery on an elderly gentleman in an adult hospital. He said: "I hope that flippant hat isn't a reflection of a flippant attitude." I felt like saying: "Ooops, how did that get there? I'm sure it was a picture of the Queen this morning?!" Perhaps better that I stay at RCH.

I don't know too many people outside medicine who love their job. In fact, I don't think any of my old friends really love their jobs the way I love mine. I've just been so lucky to find somewhere that suits me well. Plus, it's well paid and it's twenty minutes' walk from where I live. I just want to stay here till they boot me out. In twenty years' time, you'll see fingernail marks on the walls as they drag me away!

If you're in a place that lifts your energy, it's easy to do your job well. But we can be an angel in one place and totally different in a place that doesn't lift our energy. For example, you know, trying to get your kids into good habits. My son never, ever takes his cereal bowl to the kitchen in the morning – not one of the world's great crimes; but in parenting it's easy to over-react when you've asked for the one hundredth time. So, that is not something that lifts my energy, and I look at myself responding in that situation and think: *What sort of person are you, behaving like this? Setting your own children up to behave the same way as you sometime?* Whereas here, at work, it just falls into place a bit like all the pieces of a jig-saw puzzle. I find it easy in this situation to be the kind of person that I like being. If you work for Telstra customer service and you've got me on the phone after twenty minutes on hold, I might not be so professional! So, professionalism, or empathy, is not a consistent personality trait, it's an admirable habit, like eating well and exercising regularly. Aristotle and I agree on that.

One of my most formative moments was a time years ago. I hadn't realised that I was 'on call' and I had just spoken to my kids who were littlies, and they were asking: "What time are you going to be home Dad?" I had said: "Soon, I'll be home in time to read to you at bed time." Then I got a call about a liver transplant and I said: "It's not me," and they said: "Yes, it is you." Not only was I on-call, but it was a case that was going to take all night. I had to ring up the kids and say: "Sorry, I'm not going to be home tonight." I walked out to pre-op to see this child, with this big dark cloud hanging over me, feeling sorry for myself that I was looking after all these other people's kids and not my own. And then something happened, it felt like there was something bigger than me in there. I saw this poor little kid and her family, and imagined what it would be like if that happened to our family. I almost watched myself walk around and speak to them, while part of me was still in this dark place, and yet without really thinking, I found the words I needed to find. I said: "We will put this day in the calendar, because this is the day that Sally gets fixed. We will celebrate this date every year, because it is a fantastic day." This child's illness had just arrived in the last two weeks. She had gone from healthy – to this fulminant, terrible disease requiring a liver transplant – in two weeks. I don't know how the planet works, but something happened that day. There is something for me in this lifetime about making peace with children. It just seems to be what fits my weird shape.

Sometimes I don't meet a family until they're in pre-op hold[5], and I'm supposed to meet them in one breath, and in the next breath say: "So, there's this terrible risk of death" – or whatever the risks are – and "we're going to have to use this 'doodidooda' and that 'schanana'." And the parents are thinking: *I don't care which one you use, I just want to know that you'll look after my child because I can't be there.* So that's a conversation I don't take lightly. Yep, I do the details and the consent stuff, but mostly the message is: "I'll look after your child then hand them back in one piece." That is a transaction I don't think you get in many places, and that really feeds my soul.

My story is no recipe for other people. This is just my own life journey. I think hope, heart and healing have to be internal goals. You can't put them on others. You can radiate them I suppose, or you can have bold thinking, but at the end of the day you can't rescue people. I've had recent experience of that. Both my parents got very ill this year. My dad died ten weeks ago, and for a while he didn't have hope. He would say: "Why would I bother changing my shoes, I'm going to die in this room aren't I?" It was really awful seeing that lack of hope, and no one else could give it to him. Fortunately, dad found peace in his final days, and it drew my sisters and me closer together. And my mum's now in a really difficult situation, and again, we display loyalty and give her love, but it's really hard to give her a sense of meaning and hope. I guess she has to find it herself.

The fortunate thing about this profession is that you really only have to turn up to work and be moderately nice to someone, and you've probably made a little step towards making someone's day or even life a little better. So there is a nice opportunity as doctors to feel that you

---

5   Preparation for surgery.

might have made the world a slightly better place. How's that for a nice note to finish on? Or should we finish with the rest of the lyrics to 'Ginger the Farting Dog' instead?

17 | CLOWNING, CURIOSITY AND A LOVE OF PEOPLE

DR JOHN BARTON

Retired General Practitioner, Psychotherapist &
Balint Practitioner.

Australia and New Zealand

For me, the essence of being a doctor is relationship. It is about being in a community, and being part of it in a very privileged way, which has all sorts of value. It is about connections with other human beings. This is very personal: it is not the only essence of being a good doctor. Some don't see it that way and that doesn't make them bad doctors at all.

I went into medicine because I liked people. Nothing about wanting to cure the world or about curing individuals – it was really just about what I liked doing. It took me a while to get there though. I did a PhD in chemistry before I studied medicine. I was very involved during that time in the anti-Vietnam war movement and anti-apartheid. I even joined women's lib for about two years until I realised it wasn't really the place for a man – that women had to do it! A group of us formed an organisation and put ads in the paper to facilitate abortion services. A few years later the group became New Zealand's first abortion clinic. At this point medicine still hadn't entered my mind. It was the time of long hair, rock and roll, and radical thinking – it was an amazing, wonderful time to be alive.

I was at the time extremely arrogant – I absolutely knew the way things had to be. It was all about changing the world, according to my opinions, because my opinions were right. Eventually it dawned on me that my street protesting hadn't done much, but my talking to people had made a difference. That struck me as profound. I joined a youth telephone counselling volunteer service and in the first training lecture, the concept of unconditional positive regard, was an 'aha' moment – a coming home. I thought: *This is brilliant.* After a couple of years, I thought I was good at counselling (later I realised I wasn't), and I wasn't enjoying chemistry so I was looking for a change. I flirted with being a social worker, but I decided on medicine.

I could see the power of doctors – the good guy doctors. Our abortion clinic, for example, hadn't taken off until a doctor came along and supported it. So I went to medical school with a political aim: that doctors have power, and that my aim would be to give it away, give the power to my patients and make them equal to me. I thought I would be a country GP and I never wanted to do anything else. Many of my friends thought I was going to do psychiatry but I knew I wouldn't. I'm interested in all people exploring themselves through growth and self-awareness.

In the years before I started med school, I had started my own personal therapy journey – encounter, psychodrama and gestalt therapy.[1] I had grown through those, and all these things were influencing my perspective on medicine. I saw a couple of things occur in the context of some of these groups which I could only describe as a miracle – the scientist in me couldn't understand or explain them. The man running those workshops, Max Clayton who was the father of Australasian psychodrama, is one of the biggest influences of my life. He was a genius. I was seeing magical and magnificent psychotherapy just before I entered medical school.

---

1   These are all forms of experiential, humanist, group psychotherapy emphasising the therapist – client relationship, self-awareness and self-responsibility.

Medical school was so full on that by the time I got through, all the activist, self-empowerment, arrogant self – all those things fell away. My focus and energy just became getting through med school. I was ten years older than all my classmates. When I first got in, I looked around and – at that time only really, really bright people could get into medicine – I was really worried, and worked very hard to try and keep up with them. By the end of med school, I had perfected the art of just passing exams. So, it was a grind, and my house surgeon (intern) years were terrible. These were my dark times, and they coincided with personal dark times. Looking back, I felt out of my depth in my house surgeon years.

Medical school had not been a good education for me, and being spat out into the hospital system was frightening and too much responsibility.

Medical school had not been a good education for me, and being spat out into the hospital system was frightening and too much responsibility. I didn't feel up to it, I felt I wasn't good at it and there wasn't a lot of support. I had learned stoicism from my family – I was conceived within days of my father coming back from having been in a prison camp in Germany for most of the war. He just lived through difficulties. So I got through it.

And then I went to a little country town in New Zealand and opened my own practice. There were two other doctors in town. That's when I learned medicine. Looking back, I can see that I made many mistakes. Not many that really endangered patients, but a few. But really, it is a job you have to learn on the job. And it was fantastic. I really loved being a small-town GP. I'd love it when people came to me with their troubles and I could do something about it. If I'm honest, there was definitely a bit of me that was fulfilled by being an important person in their lives. Being a doctor in a small country town – everybody loves you. I used to love walking downtown to buy the bread and the milk and know everyone to stop and chat.

As a final year medical student, I did a couple of clown workshops for pleasure. The essence of clowning is that the clown has to say yes to everything that is going on, whatever situation you are put into – the ringmaster is the boss. I really discovered the power of saying 'yes' in life, as a first principle. It is a great way of living your life. After about five years of being a country GP though (and saying yes to everything), I realised that I was becoming overwhelmed. Then I had to learn to say no, which I didn't find easy. I was on-call one night in three, but even on my nights off, if one of my patients rang me, I would go and see them. I was getting exhausted and my wife was getting distressed. We lived in a little house overlooking the railway yards in the centre of town. One night she went out and started yelling over the town how she hated everyone who had more of me than she did. It was very good for her to do that, I think. She said: "I'm trapped here – everybody loves you so much, you would never drag yourself away, which means I'm trapped here forever." When I realised how she felt, I said: "No if you want to go, we go." Hearing that meant she could bear it for a few more years, although we did eventually leave.

Then one of the other doctors in town upped and left with two weeks' notice. My practice doubled in size overnight and I now had a one in two call. The day he told me he was leaving, I put my practice on the market. It took me a year to sell. That year was terrible; on several occasions I was so exhausted I could not speak or think. The effort required to call the base hospital a hundred miles away and ask for someone to come and relieve me was all I could manage. I moved to another small NZ town, nearer to a big city and extended family. Then in 1997 I moved to Melbourne and became an inner-city GP.

To survive that time, I gave myself a 'no' rule. For two years, if anyone asked me anything as a doctor outside of my working and on call hours, my automatic answer would be to say 'no', right down the line. I had to do it really rigidly for those two years before I then took the rule off myself. Now I'm much better at saying "no" in a more flexible way. I had to take choice away from myself. Strangely enough, people didn't stop loving me, stop liking me, when I put the boundaries up.

Clowning could be really potent training for GPs, especially if there is a tension between what we are taught at medical school, and dealing with the person in front of you. I am capable of saying yes to things that are not kosher medicine – all sorts of things. I'm willing to take risks. I don't mean risks with my patients' lives, I mean risks in terms of what is a 'proper doctor' and what is not. When I started, I used to hug all my patients. Oh, God! Slowly it dawned on me that a lot of that came from my arrogance – I liked to hug, but I was totally ignoring whether people liked to be hugged or not. It was abusing the doctor's power – they would allow me to hug them because I was the doctor, they were not in a position to say no. So now I will hug the people who offer me a hug and if I also think it's OK and alright for me to hug them. There are people who want a hug but not for the best reasons. So I have a better understanding of those boundaries now too.

Twenty years ago, I realised that being a GP five hours a day is enough for me. I am intense; I'm intensely engaged with my patients. People who don't like it don't come to me. I reorganised my practice so that I would stop at five hours. I didn't make much money, however I worked well, and enjoyed my work.

In my time as a GP, I went back to attending psychodrama workshops for my own personal growth and pleasure and also to learn psychotherapy. I began running personal growth workshops with my wife, to which many of my patients came, and made real changes in their life. I continued my psychotherapy training, I'm an inveterate learner – I love learning. When we moved to Australia I started a therapy practice in my home for two days a week, and worked as a GP three days a week.

I had cancer in 2001. I didn't know if I would live or die for two years, and the treatment made me very sick. Being a patient was a fascinating experience. I learned so much from that time – I value it and think of it as a good experience. I did *believe* I'd survive, but I didn't *know* I was going to survive. As a result of the illness and uncertainty, I became more selfish, more able to put my needs first.

In my work life I was feeling pressured and was worried that I wasn't keeping up to date, or doing either General Practice or psychotherapy justice. Having two different ways of working was too much. I didn't want to give up General Practice, I really loved it, although there were things that drove me crazy like the red tape and the paperwork and the occasional patient. In the end, I was more excited about psychotherapy. So I thought I'd see if I could make a go of it full time. Within three months I felt like I was practicing so much better than I had been, and I realised what a difference it had made to the quality of my practice to be doing it full time. I haven't looked back.

I'm not sure how much of this journey into the heart of medicine is teachable or transferable.

I now work with GPs by running Balint groups. This is a process developed by psychotherapist and doctor Michael Balint and his wife Enid, which focuses on the doctor's personal journey and experience with their work, in a supportive, safe, collegial setting. I love being with GPs. For me, as a GP, I knew I wanted that kind of collegial support. As a country doctor, I could never get that. It's very personal for me – it was what I needed to be thinking about, and it's a way of connecting with my colleagues that is very special. In some ways Balint groups bring out what I think is the essence of General Practice. It is so good for us to be talking to each other about the essence of what we do. I believe there are lots of GPs who would benefit from Balint work, as I have done.

I'm not sure how much of this journey into the heart of medicine is teachable or transferable. I think some of it is down to personality, some down to people who are prepared to, or find it important to do the personal growth work to enhance their practice. I've done a lot of personal therapy. There are many things about my basic personality, however, which I received from my parents, for which I am hugely grateful. My parents were very left-wing egalitarian, lacking in racial prejudice. My mother always worked, one way or another, so there was a modelling of equality in their relationship which wasn't all that common at that time. Also, even more than that, my parents had just come out of the war – they knew the horrors of the war and were determined to create a better future for their children. They dedicated themselves to giving us a good childhood with the result that I have a happy, positive outlook on life. So the sense that I'm good, that the world is a good place, and that people are essentially good – that's a given in me, and I don't know how you can teach that to people. It might be a trap to think that we can transfer that, or that there is a particular way to help others find ways to be whole and loving. They can, there are ways, but sometimes trauma can really crush you and be difficult to rise out of.

For many patients in many situations, the heart stuff is what is both wanted and needed, and so, in terms of the overall job that a GP does, that is more important, in my opinion, than the technical stuff. There are a lot of GPs who just don't do it and don't see the need for it. Particular patients choose them but don't get what, from my perspective, they require from a GP. A GP who has no sense of the importance of the emotional quality of the relationship is missing something, I believe. The technical elements are of course utterly important. Nevertheless, to do General Practice well, for most patients, requires the ability to connect with them. Can I justify that with evidence base? No. However I believe that if it was measurable it would be clear. Our current ability to measure and need for evidence base is way too narrow.

I love people. I like their stories, and I do like being able to help people in the medical sense. As a therapist you don't help people in the same way, the patient does the work. In medicine, it is more about problem solving, and there are often good solutions. If someone comes in sick and worried, you can most likely make a diagnosis, and sort things to help them. It's a good job. It's a bloody good job. The bureaucracy is painful – exceedingly painful, utterly unnecessary in my opinion. Nevertheless the bulk of day-to-day medicine is a very joyful thing.

18 | ISLANDS OF REBELLION – ISLANDS OF EMPOWERMENT

PROFESSOR VIKRAM PATEL

Psychiatrist. Professor Patel is head of the International Mental Health Innovation Network, Researcher and Fellow of a number of universities and foundations around the world. His work is on the burden of mental disorders, their association with poverty and social disadvantage, and the use of community resources for their prevention and treatment. Professor Patel's work has been widely recognised by a number of prestigious international awards.*

United States of America, and India

Health is too important to be left to doctors alone. The problem that I see facing healthcare around the world is the over-medicalisation of health problems, to the extent that we have effectively disempowered the entire world, except for those who are doctors and nurses. We've disempowered people from acquiring the skills and the knowledge to oversee and maintain their own health.

There are clearly islands of rebellion now, including from the medical profession, but they are just small islands. The tide is very much one of heavy professionalisation, a very close coterie between medicine and big business, particularly technology, biomedical equipment and the pharmaceutical industry. What you see now is not only the disempowerment of the community, but also the conversion of health care from a social and public good to, essentially, a business enterprise.

At times I think doctors have themselves to blame. Doctors are facing burnout because they are controlling and wanting to remain the fountain-head of knowledge, so that even the most trivial things are seen by the doctor. And some of the most important health interventions are not being delivered because doctors neither have the time or the interest to deliver them. These interventions are about personal responsibility and personal empowerment around healthy lifestyle – which is at the root of most of the non-communicable diseases that are burdening the health systems of all countries, but particularly rich countries.

I wish I could say that becoming a doctor was some kind of a calling for me but actually, it was just the most prized professional choice in India at the time. The only barrier to being a doctor was about the grades you got. If you got the grades, there were two or three choices which Indian parents would allow you to pursue. I actually wished then, and have done many times since, that I could have got my real choice, and that was to become a chef. It wasn't the glamour job then that it is now, you were just a simple cook. It wasn't the kind of profession that a top-ranking student would ever choose.

So, my move into psychiatry was almost a rebellion, I think, against my parents – it wasn't the most prestigious choice in medicine, but I had spent five and a half years studying, and it was time to go my own way. Also, I found the narrow biomedical focus of most of medicine just bored me. I just wasn't cut out for it. Psychiatry felt to me like the more human end of medicine, although it wasn't humane by any means. Looking back, the training in psychiatry appalled me. People were tied to their beds, there were five patients in one small room, the door was locked at night, the psych ward in the hospital I was in was right next to the morgue, the staff were poorly trained, people were only treated with medicines, and when they were discharged back into the community, they left with nothing, no supports. It absolutely wasn't the kind of mental health care that is anywhere near how I practice today, although some of those things still go on today. But I recognised that my teachers at least made an effort to find out about the person they were treating, and their life. I thought: *Hey this is far more interesting than feeling someone's body and knocking them here or there with a hammer and then asking for some tests.*

I am a firm believer in universal health care.

At that time my definition of humane was very different to what it is now. Now it is to provide care in a setting that is preferred by the person who has the health problem, cared for by a person who they feel safe receiving care from, and at no cost. I am a firm believer in universal health care.

I love the idea of what we call collaborative care – I think it is the essence of what I espouse, which is that, by and large, health care is a collaboration between people with the professional knowledge, and people who are supposedly the beneficiaries of that knowledge. Everyone has knowledge. And, I think, especially in the mental health arena, probably more than any other area of medicine, there is an enormous repository of, not only knowledge which has not been harnessed, but also of capability. And so it seems to me, that in our organised health care system – the health care practitioner's role is simply to do what they are best trained to do – to carry out the diagnosis and treatment of disorders, especially those which actually need medical intervention. I don't think there is a sharp line where you can say: "This is where medicine ends and this is where community care begins."

I'll give you an example from my field – depression. Everyone talks about depression as if it is one condition. Actually, it is a very heterogeneous condition, with a very, very wide range of severity as well as aetiology. It is very clear from the guidelines that more than half of people who are diagnosed with depression will get better of their own accord over time without any medical interventions, yet this particular fact is not communicated to the general public, nor do the medical profession acknowledge it.

So, when we hear that, say five per cent of the population suffer from depression, we don't hear that only thirty per cent of them need medication. The other seventy per cent don't. Depression doesn't always self-heal, but in the majority, low-level depression will. With more extreme versions, there are some medical interventions that appropriately trained professionals need to administer. Some of depression, though, is adaptive. If you consider, especially the depression that occurs in the context of extreme life events, such as threatening life events, and if you think of some of the reactions to that, which may include withdrawing into your shell – although that may look pathological, you could look at it also as being entirely functional and adaptive because you don't want to go head-on into a threatening situation. There's a very tantalising possibility that many of the behavioural disorders that we deal with are actually, in their milder form, adaptive. But it's when they continue beyond this point and they become maladaptive, either through their intensity, or their duration, or they begin to impair your ability to function in day-to-day life, then I think they cross over into a health condition. This is a very challenging idea, but one which is increasingly being talked about by evolutionary biologists.

> *I think the therapeutic exchange is the most important part of the effect of virtually every health intervention, including medical interventions. In medicine we love to dismiss that by calling it the placebo effect.*

I think the therapeutic exchange is the most important part of the effect of virtually every health intervention, including medical interventions. In medicine we love to dismiss that by calling it the placebo effect. It strikes me as amazing that potentially the most powerful of all the medical interventions we have, which is the therapeutic alliance, is controlled for, in trials, as if it is some sort of invalid thing which is all in the patient's head. Actually, I think the really challenging part is that we don't completely understand the biology of the healing power of providing a space which enables people to heal themselves. I believe that this enabling will prove to be one of the greatest skills of the health practitioner. This is a talent, which I think traditional, complementary and spiritual healers have been able to invoke with great success, and this is now a skill which doctors and nurses are increasingly being taught to control. But because they are so biomedically, biologically focused, they really want to just strip away all the personality of the physician so that you are really focusing on the pill, or the surgery or the technical intervention. I think it is at the heart of everything that medicine does, and the more we try and 'control' for it in our testing of outcomes, the more we lose an opportunity to actually enhance a person's own healing capacity.

To invoke hope in a person should be seen as a central role in any medical intervention because hope in my view is at the heart of triggering healing.

A core element of the therapeutic alliance is compassion – empathy and unconditional positive regard for your patient. These to me are fundamental and I don't know why they are only ever taught in relation to mental health. I think what you would want to see is that this is integrated into every part of the training of the doctors – from the classroom to the clinic, in every specialty. It has to become a core skill upon which every doctor is evaluated. For example, if someone is being asked to examine a person's abdomen, you want to give equal marks to how the person is approached, how the person is touched, the body language, how they speak with the patient, as much as the technicalities. To invoke hope in a person should be seen as a central role in any medical intervention because hope in my view is at the heart of triggering healing.

The difficulty with producing an evidence base for this sort of thinking is that the biomedical model has such different epistemology. For example, with many complementary medicines, the healers themselves are the intervention, not the thing he or she is using. How can you randomise a healer? The theoretical framework is so different. And when you try and reduce complementary medicines down to the things that the practitioner does (rather than a blend of that and the person they are) so that it matches the biomedical approach, then you've actually lost the whole idea of what it is that these forms of medicine are actually practicing. I think, at the heart of complementary medicine is the idea that a good healer is able to invoke hope, and that hope is the psychological equivalent of the placebo effect. The hope to get better is actually the placebo effect, and it is actually invoking a range of physiological responses that trigger a variety of neurological changes and a whole variety of other changes – which we don't yet fully understand or know – that in turn heal. They heal the body from various sicknesses. Now of course they don't always work for all sicknesses. I would be a fool to say they work for everything. The point here is that they do work for many, and those are actually probably the ones you don't need medicine for.

What I would like to see is more honesty about the limits of the medical profession and equally, more honesty about the strengths of non-medical solutions.

Any change in ideology is, at the end of the day, more down to economics than ethics. The main reason why things are changing is because the cost of healthcare is far outstripping inflation and is far outstripping what countries can afford. Medicine has become such a gigantic industry – something's going to have to give. One of the things will be that states will have to have a good hard look at the spiralling costs of medical care. That is one side of the coin, and a bit of a cynical one. The other side of the coin I think is a growing disillusionment with purely medical approaches, especially the chronic diseases which afflict most of the world today. There's a sense that pills alone aren't a sufficient solution to a range of chronic and complex physical, psychological and physiological conditions.

What I would like to see is more honesty about the limits of the medical profession and equally, more honesty about the strengths of non-medical solutions. Solutions, for example, that are driven by the community. There are some computerised health interventions available, but also we could be empowering patients and lay people with additional skills and also recognising that they already have many skills, and we just haven't mobilised them.

Mental illnesses are amongst the leading causes of disability around the world and account for approximately fifteen per cent of the total burden of disease worldwide. Nearly 400–500 million people are affected by mental illness worldwide. The vast majority of these people do not receive the interventions required for their care (fifty per cent in wealthy countries and up to ninety per cent in developing countries). I am focussing on bridging the gulf of the great shortage of mental health professionals in the countries that need them most. There are more Indian psychiatrists in California than there are in India. For India to bring its population of psychiatrists in line with the proportion per head of population in the United Kingdom, India would need 150,000 psychiatrists. In 2012, there were 3000. That is approximately two per cent of the professional servicing available to citizens of wealthier nations.

So, there I was, trained in a model which required enormous resourcing from highly trained professionals, trying to implement my training in massively under-resourced developing nations. I wondered how I could help these people in the absence of these supports. I saw some studies about lay people having been successfully trained to deliver obstetric services and wondered whether a similar approach could work for the treatment of some mental health disorders. I call it 'task shifting'.

There have now been many successful experiments in task shifting in mental health care across the developing world. In rural Uganda, for example, Paul Bolton and his colleagues demonstrated that the villagers could be successfully trained to deliver inter-personal psychotherapy for patients with depression. Using a randomised controlled trial, they found that ninety per cent of the people receiving the intervention recovered, compared to forty per cent in the comparison villages. In Goa, India, my own studies showed that lay councillors could be trained to deliver psycho-social interventions for people with depression with a seventy per cent recovery rate, compared to a fifty per cent recovery rate.[1] I believe we need to simplify the message, unpack the treatment, deliver it where people are, using affordable human resources, and reallocate the scarce specialists to perform the tasks of training and supervision of these lay workers.

This is not just about accessibility and affordability, it is also about the democratisation of medical knowledge, and medical power.

These models are replicable to wealthier nations also, where healthcare costs are spiralling out of control. A significant part of this cost is human resource and yet medicine is becoming more and more specialised and isolated from the communities it serves. This is not just about accessibility and affordability, it is also about the democratisation of medical knowledge, and medical power. It is about empowering people and communities to become active agents in their own health and wellbeing.

*Professor Patel is Pershing Square Professor of Global Health and the Wellcome Trust; Principal Research Fellow, Department of Global Health and Social Medicine, Harvard Medical School; Professor, Department of Global Health and Population, Harvard T. H. Chan School of Public Health; Co-founder and member of Managing Committee, Sangath, Goa, India; Adjunct Professor and Joint Director, Centre for Chronic Conditions and Injuries, Public Health Foundation of India; and Honorary Professor, London School of Hygiene & Tropical Medicine,

1   For more information on these studies and the notion of mental health for all by involving all, see: https://www.ted.com/talks/vikram_patel_mental_health_for_all_by_involving_all. Retrieved 12/10/2017.

UK. His work is on the burden of mental disorders, their association with poverty and social disadvantage, and the use of community resources for their prevention and treatment. Professor Patel's work has been widely recognised by a number of prestigious international awards, including: the Chalmers Medal (Royal Society of Tropical Medicine and Hygiene, UK), the Sarnat Medal (US National Academy of Medicine), an Honorary Doctorate from Georgetown University, the Pardes Humanitarian Prize (the Brain & Behaviour Research Foundation), an Honorary OBE from the UK Government and the Posey Leadership Award (Austin College). He also works as a Professor at Harvard TH Chan School of Public Health, Adjunct Professor and Joint Director of the Centre for Chronic Conditions and Injuries at the Public Health Foundation of India, Honorary Professor at the London School of Hygiene & Tropical Medicine (where he co-founded the Centre for Global Mental Health in 2008), and is a Co-founder of Sangath, an Indian NGO which won the MacArthur Foundation's International Prize for Creative and Effective Institutions in 2008, and the WHO Public Health Champion of India award in 2016. He is a Fellow of the UK's Academy of Medical Sciences and has served on several WHO expert and Government of India committees. He also works in the areas of child development and adolescent health. He was listed in *TIME Magazine's* 100 most influential persons of the year in 2015.

19 | KORERO[1]

DR JENNY SIMPSON

General Practitioner in low socio-economic community care setting.

Wellington, New Zealand

The heart of medicine is such a lovely concept. I'm really interested in what it is that is actually healing about what we do – where does the real therapeutic work happen?

It is an old, wise concept – heart and healing. In a way, every generation has to re-find this one for itself. My generation of doctors rely so much less on really being aware of good physical examination, and good subtle science, than doctors one hundred years ago did. An older doctor would have a much better sense of assessing someone's demeanour, their pulse, their colour, smell – subtle things. These days we rely much more on technology – on ECGs, MRIs, and the like. I think the development of those scientific investigations means that to some extent, clinical medicine has lost its art. The other thing is that in the last fifty years there has been such a change in pharmacology, in all of medicine, and an expectation that everything is treatable. When things arise that can't be treated, or the treatment doesn't work, it is often seen as a failure. The impact of this new failure framework on doctors is huge, huge, huge. There is huge fear that you will miss a drug interaction,

The impact of this new failure framework on doctors is huge, huge, huge.

---

1   A Maori word for conversation, meeting, discussion and deep listening.

or that you haven't explained something properly, haven't received proper informed consent. I guess it is becoming more complex.

It's funny when you go through old paper notes on people. I remember once finding some old notes and the doctor had simply written, in his beautiful script: "Tonsilitis. Rx: penicillin." That was it. No extras about signs of fever, or rash, or anything else. One hundred years ago medicine was much more about people being with people as they faced life. But there was much early death too and so much has improved.

I initially worked in areas such as family planning, sexual health and youth health services, where people are basically well – mostly, not always – they just needed someone alongside them, to help make better decisions, or good choices for their lives.

My current clinic is a primary health practice that is particularly oriented towards low-income patients. The doctors and nurses do a lot of outreach. We go to soup kitchens, homelessness shelters, wherever people are, basically, who can't or won't access health services. We see the people who the system has failed – whether that be the health or criminal justice or youth and family, education. They have high rates of illiteracy. The key is to treat them with respect and dignity because they've often been treated poorly. We try and create a place here where people don't need to defend themselves straight off. If people aren't already defensive about why they are coming to see a doctor, if they can relax about that, then maybe one rigid barrier which they've had to put up to protect themselves, gets to come down, and maybe you can help create a shift. You can affirm, you can just be pleased to see them really, and then things happen.

The art of medicine is as much about humanity as it is about science.

I saw one man – he was in his mid-forties – he had a city council flat, and he hadn't paid his electricity, so they'd cut it off. He'd had no heat, no lights, no hot shower functioning in this place for twelve months. He couldn't get access to his children because child and family services said that his home was not a hygienic, appropriate place for children. He had high cholesterol and high blood pressure, but what on earth is the point of me giving him drugs for his cholesterol while he can't even wash himself, and he grieves for his children? You get a different perspective on stuff here. I think until you create a space where people don't need to be armed for an assault, then you're not going to provide any good health care. The art of medicine is as much about humanity as it is about science. The other side to that is, you can be very nice and all that sort of stuff, but if you don't know your medicine, that's no good either. It's a tough balance sometimes.

Something has to be done about health inequality. We know that people in lower socio-economic classes don't get the same level of care as the middle classes. It is as if the poorest are subsidising the middle / upper classes. It's just not just. I think part of it is a literacy-based issue. It is much easier for doctors to know, understand and hear people with the same level of literacy, same background – whether cultural, or ethnic background. It is hard for people with poor literacy skills, or an upbringing marked by poverty of any sort, and poor education, to advocate for themselves. They often don't have the verbal skills to express what's going on either in their head, or even physically. They just feel sick, or they feel tired, or they've got a headache, but they can't give you the finer details so sometimes people get short shrift because of this sort of thing. Their problems aren't heard.

I really think the world is abundant but a lot of it has been misappropriated by people with power. And that partly includes us too. It seems like there isn't enough to go around but there is enough. We just need to ensure that people get their fair share.

I have had my most memorable contacts with patients in General Practice when I was feeling most disenfranchised and disempowered by the management. I saw a man with debilitating poly-substance abuse, and a thirty-two-year-old, powerful looking man just out of prison, terrified of coping on the outside, spiralling down. With both

> *I often think medicine is best learned as an apprenticeship. If I could give advice to a young doctor or medical student, I would say: "Just listen to people. Just bite your tongue, even for thirty seconds, and you hear a lot."*

men, I could listen and keep *korero* with new eyes because I felt so alone too. As I went to shake hands with them at the end of the consults, they both softened and said: "Oh no," and gave me a warm hug. I think of them often.

I love working in this setting. The patients and staff are fantastic to work with. There are very few masks, and that is really lovely. What I really love about medicine is the people. I do enjoy the science of it as well – it is good to try and work something out to help somebody, to lighten their load. I wouldn't want to work somewhere where I was working alone. I like working as a team with the reception staff, nurses, other doctors and the social workers. There is no one person here whose skills are more important. I really think you shouldn't think that your skills and view are the one right one.

I often think medicine is best learned as an apprenticeship. If I could give advice to a young doctor or medical student, I would say: "Just listen to people. Just bite your tongue, even for thirty seconds, and you hear a lot." It's very hard when you are young and you are worried about getting the medicine bit right. But it can be very simple. Treat people as you'd like to be treated. Don't forget to greet them well. Remember cultural differences.

I have had plenty of experience being a patient, which helps. I have Multiple Sclerosis (MS). Recently I had kidney stones – it took me two months to get them out. It took a long time until I got seen in the public health system. They kept saying the kidney stones would pass, and they just didn't. Eventually I saw a private surgeon – I saw him at 9 am, and he had me in surgery by 2 pm on the same day. I suppose what I have learned from being a patient is that you should continue to advocate for yourself. If you think something's been missed, you have to keep advocating. That is what I try to do for my patients, who often can't really speak for themselves.

Disability enables connection with others. Having a visible disability or need allows people to be kind, and that is so cool. Traditional doctor-patient relationships have the power all with the doctor. And although I am not the archetypal power-over doctor, nonetheless there is an imbalance. But I have had two particular encounters which have made me thank God for my condition.

In 2010 when I was working in General Practice, I broke my ankle whilst shaking the doormat at home. Note to all: housework is dangerous! It was healed but I was limping due to my MS. I saw a patient who was depressed and battling alcohol and domestic violence, having had almost every bone in her body broken by her ex. She looked downhearted until she asked me why I had been away. I said that I had broken my ankle. She became instantly alert and, sitting upright, looked directly at me and asked: "Did your partner do it?" I told her no, that I had fallen. She said: "That's all right then," and the alertness went out. But for five seconds I felt firmly tucked under her wing. She would have gone out to make sure I was safe, would have forgotten her own needs if I had hesitated or shown any signs of being abused. It gave us a very human, simple connection.

When I was working at Addiction Services, I was leaving work for the day, walking with two sticks. Several people – all battling major drug addiction – were waiting to see someone, and I knew most of them a little. It was a time when there was bad press for anyone battling heroin or methadone. As I came into the hall, a man leapt up to open the two sets of double doors for me, saying a little bitterly that some people would say this was chauvinistic, sexist or patronising – or maybe chivalrous. I said: "Definitely chivalrous," then, "No, no. It is kind, it is truly kind." I tried to look at him as directly and clearly as I could, that we were together in this instant, and he was the helper. We both had major chronic conditions, but he actually had more chance of recovery.

I have been following the blog of an artist, Cathy Aten, who, because of MS, can no longer paint, so now she blogs. She reminded me that love is the reorganising principle. That being seen in the mess and not being turned away from is the key. This is being Jesus to one another. Jesus' healing over and over was the healing of the physical, but then the huge healing he created was reconnection with community.

When my MS was deteriorating, we had a brunch at my church. I needed to get to the toilet, made it up the long motorway of the aisle and up the huge mountainous flight of steps, and then the massive cliff corner to the loo – then caught my jacket on the dangerous outcrop of the door handle, lost concentration and my bladder gave out. Oh *MAN*. I lurched over to the hall, looked for my husband, couldn't see him, then looked for a plastic chair. No such luck. Then a friend rocked up and asked if I needed to sit down. So I said to him: "You are an adult man, I know you can cope with this – I have wet myself, I need a plastic chair – or a plastic bag." He raced and got one, I sat down, they all brought me lunch, and I had a great time. All because, instead of saying: "You poor thing, you will need to find your husband and go home," they just let me be – in the mess and not turned away from. It *is* that I am IN a mess, maybe even MADE the mess but I am NOT the mess – no-one ever is.

There's a lovely quote from Thomas Merton – he says that there is a spark of the divine within everyone, and if we could just see it, the world would be a mass of light. You do see it sometimes. Namaste is the Hindi way of saying this. It means the divine in me sees the divine in you. I think that is utterly true. I have kept a newspaper photograph of three men after the 2011 Christchurch earthquake. It is an extraordinary photo, taken of a critically injured, dying man pulled from rubble by a young chef and a young builder, all of them dust covered and shocked. And the rescuers were sitting with him, three hands near and over his heart, just waiting, being there. I look at it again and again. There are really four people in this photo – the three men, and the photographer. There was nothing they could do for the injured, dying man, but they held his hand and heart and stuck around – strangers thrown together in time. You may not be able to do anything much, but you stick around.

We see a lot of very broken people here – a lot of domestic violence, drug and alcohol, assault, mental health problems. There are some pretty ordinary times. I try not to be put off in the face of it all. To me, that Christchurch image captures the best of people. I just want to be like one of those young guys, stick around, hold on, and never give up, even if there is not much else I can do.

Postscript: Dr Jenny Simpson retired in 2014 due to increasing disability associated with Secondary Progressive Multiple Sclerosis.

20 | EAST MEETS WEST

DR JOAN CAMPBELL

General Practitioner and Traditional Chinese Medical Practitioner.

Auckland, New Zealand

I started my medical journey training to be a nurse and after graduating as a registered nurse, I continued by becoming a doctor. When I was accepted into medical school, I loved the intellectual challenge, and yet by the end of my second year I was thinking: *What am I doing? I used to look after the whole person and now I look after 'the bits'. I look after the myocardial infarction and the renal stenosis and the reflex oesophagitis. I don't actually look after people any more.* So I had a crisis about Western medicine in the early 1970s, and wondered if I would finish my medical degree. Then, in 1975, China intervened in my life and there I found a system of medicine, as old as time, which treated whole people, not just the presenting complaint – although that was treated too. In China I realised I could choose how I practiced medicine. I could still look after the whole person, and also 'the bits'.

If you look at the history of Chinese medicine you stand humbled by what they knew. As Western doctors, we think we are really clever. For example we try to 'physiologically manage' a woman's hormones – and yet the Chinese were tweaking hormones about 2000 years BC. They worked out that pregnant women had 'something' in their urine that improved the fertility of women unable to get pregnant. They used circular pots with three legs, made of marble or metal, and got pregnant women to pee into them. Then they put the pots in the sun to evaporate the urine and the powder that was left behind was HCG (human chorionic gonadotrophin). HCG is a hormone produced by cells from the implanting conceptus, which primes the corpus luteum to secrete progesterone, which in turn builds the lining of the womb to maintain the pregnancy until the placenta is formed during the first twelve weeks of pregnancy. The Chinese gave this white powder, mixed up with other herbs, to infertile women to help them get pregnant.

The Chinese are great observers of the real world. Modern physics, field theory, quantum mechanics and chaos theory – these concepts are all found in Chinese philosophy and medical theory dating back thousands of years. In Europe, up to the 1400s, farmers sowed by hand, while at the same time in China they were using wheels, ploughs, seed sowing machinery – not to mention using tissues, paper, silk, porcelain, money, and pasta. Marco Polo took noodles back to Italy with him, and also wheels and ploughs. The Chinese also had chemical warfare, gunpowder, and ghastly ways to kill you. They were clever, incredibly wise researchers, and used unbelievably cruel punishments for crimes publicly and in warfare. Their scientific knowledge, however, and their understanding of the real world are simply stunning. When you look at what they understood about the body and how to treat it with the resources they had, it's pretty mind blowing.

In Western medicine we frequently use technology to read the body. The first time I was in China in 1975 an old man took my pulses and through an interpreter correctly told me the story of my life, including a serious medical illness. I spoke no Chinese. He told me I had played the piano since I was a small child – he told me it was in the rhythm of my life and he felt that rhythm in my pulses. China is now sanitising and systematising its own medicine into the Western model because that's how it wants to package it to the Western world of evidence-based medicine. I find that really sad – eventually there won't be many people who can still read pulses as this old man did.

I am far more intellectually challenged in the Chinese model than I am in Western medicine, because every person has an individual diagnostic pattern and treatment in Chinese medicine. I still take a Western and Chinese history, do all the necessary investigations and make a separate diagnosis in each medical system. I don't choose to treat patients in the Western model unless it's a medical emergency and even then, I will assist with Chinese therapy alongside. In Chinese medicine everybody is different. Everybody with the diagnosis of hypertension is understood as having a different pattern, and the reasons why they have the illness are different too; so you treat the person. In Western medicine, the treatment is the same for everybody with the same diagnosis; while in Chinese medicine the treatment may be different for everybody with the same diagnosis. In Chinese medicine, you treat the patient's imbalances and work out their pattern – you don't put them into a diagnostic organ-system box; for example neurology, gastroenterology and so on.

A woman I saw yesterday couldn't easily be put into one diagnostic box – she'd visited lots of different specialists for different body systems, she'd had lots of surgery and taken lots of medicines. In our Western model, she had seven different diagnoses from seven different specialists, whereas in the Chinese model she has one pattern that wraps all seven diagnoses together. It is a complicated pattern, however, once you have put all of her life's events into the Chinese diagnostic framework, you can then see how the events connect. This way of working is an intellectual challenge for the practitioner, and for me this is much more satisfying than treating the bits. This is the way I choose to practice. It makes sense to me and it sure makes sense to the people who come for treatment under the Chinese medical model. Patients understand the connections between medical events in their lives, even when their health practitioners do not.

Western medicine treats symptoms, and usually suppresses them – so that people believe that the presenting condition, for example, rheumatoid arthritis, has been cured. Frequently, when people stop taking the drugs, the symptoms come back because the reason why they have the symptoms has never been addressed. Western medicine cannot ask or answer the question: "What is the root? What is the origin of the symptoms?", because it has no treatment methods for treating the origins of illness. If you are a Chinese medical doctor you fail your patient completely if you do not address the reason why they have something. It says in the Nei Jing, the world's oldest written medical textbook written centuries ago, that the 'superior' (a bit lost in translation) doctor prevents disease. This is accomplished by seeing the patient four times a year at the change of the seasons to take their pulses, look at their tongue, feel their abdomen if needed, ask questions about diet and lifestyle, and provide counsel about how to prevent disease. If the doctor doesn't do their job properly, they may end up having to treat people with disease, and in this situation the person does not pay. The 'superior' physician is the person who prevents disease, and is paid for that service. The inferior physician treats disease. So says the Nei Jing. Of course, Western medical doctors wouldn't appreciate being told they are inferior physicians!

While there are huge differences in the two forms of medicine, it doesn't mean they are incompatible. In 2005, when I broke my left wrist very badly and dislocated my elbow, I needed an orthopaedic surgeon. After each surgery, I had the morphine pump removed, and used decocted Chinese herbs boiled up from raw herbs provided by my Chinese medicine herbalist. The medical team thought I was mad. My response was: "These herbs are drugs, have been used for centuries, contain plants with opiate properties and are very powerful." I explained that they would give me pain relief by moving the stuck 'qi' (life force / energy) through my body and arm, and therefore treat the underlying cause of the pain. Post operatively, I didn't use any Western drugs through eight months of ongoing surgery, hand and arm therapy and recovery. The year I took out of my professional life taught me that what I know is a reality, and that Chinese herbal medicine is powerful stuff. The herbs combined with acupuncture, daily to begin with, and stubborn determination gave me back most of my function. I'm delighted that I can still practice and have a functioning arm and wrist that works, even if my left arm and hand look different to their right-side counterpart.

The thing that fascinates me about the drugs we use in the West is that we pluck an idea from an indigenous culture, such as a tribe which has been using a particular plant for healing, and which is known to have an effect on, for example, an aspect of heart disease. So, the plant is collected, and then scientists work to extract the exact molecule which is largely responsible for the effect observed, instead of looking at how the molecules work together in the plant to produce the healing effect. Nature has myriads of molecules that work synergistically together, and yet scientists

We take a single molecule for a single condition and we hope that it's going to give us a single outcome. Nature doesn't work like that. Nature never works with single molecules.

identify and then chemically synthesise the one that is most likely to assist with heart failure. We take a single molecule for a single condition and we hope that it's going to give us a single outcome. Nature doesn't work like that. Nature never works with single molecules. In our wisdom, we have taken one molecule without its supporting crew and we wonder why some drugs have side effects or adverse reactions.

In Chinese herbal medicine, they never take a single molecule for a single purpose and expect to get a single outcome. By repeated practice and observation of the outcomes, they learned centuries ago that single plants, identified for their medicinal properties, sometimes induced other symptoms called side effects. Some of these side effects made people ill and are serious enough to be called adverse effects. So, the Chinese learned, very early, that combining plants for a therapeutic effect was more sensible. Consequently in a herbal prescription they have a principal herb, known as the emperor – a drug, which is attended to by court officials: the ministers – and then there are adjuvant herbs that deal with side effects and augment the positive effects (of the emperor and ministers). So all the herbs are working synergistically together. In naturopathy, and Western herbal medicine, single herbs are still given. Nature doesn't work with single entities: everything is integrated and works together. Our bodies are the same. In the body, heart failure isn't a single symptom. When the heart is failing we know that the lungs are involved, the liver gets congested, the legs get swollen and so on; it is a whole-body response, even if we identify it as starting in the heart. Nevertheless, we often give a 'heart' drug, which may have adverse or side effects in the blood, kidneys, liver, brain or gut.

A Chinese medicine practitioner needs to know a lot about Western pharmacology because everything you put into the body, be it food, or drugs, changes the wrist pulses that are an essential part of Chinese medicine diagnosis. When you read the pulses for a person who is on five Western drugs, you have to figure out if you are reading the person's life, or reading their pharmacology?

From practice comes theory in Chinese medicine. Since the ancient Chinese did not have access to modern scanning techniques, they practised empirically by giving an acupuncture or herbal treatment, observing what happened, and documenting the results. When they failed to get the expected result from current knowledge, they changed the acupuncture prescription or herbal formula by adding or removing components and observing the outcome from the changes. In herbal medicine, they learned the functions of the individual herbs and they learned how to combine them. I believe it is the art of combining the herbs which is the extraordinary part of Chinese herbalism. It is using centuries of knowledge, observation and learning about the consequences of using specific herbal products in the body, and knowing how to moderate and modify prescriptions. So if you have a person with a wheezy cough, you take a history and attend to the pulses and tongue, the sounds of the breath and so on, and make a diagnosis. You prescribe a herbal formula, used for centuries, that will stop the wheeze and coughing and allow the lung qi to descend properly. There are many, many herbs that have those properties. The trick is taking the most appropriate principal herbs and adding in other herbs that will deal with secondary symptoms such as mucous, the inflammatory response etcetera. The Chinese refined their prescriptions over many centuries, and they had large numbers of people to try them out on. These people were not paid or pre-selected. Many of the formulae I studied in China were standardised by the 1400s and the basic prescriptions have not changed. The well-used and known formulae still stand, and you modify the grams of each herb according the individual person in front of you, and the weaving in of other herbal elements to support other personalised symptoms. In contrast, Western medicine has spent less than one hundred years working out modern pharmacology.

I spend my life observing in practice. I've never doubted my gut instincts and I've had some clinical experiences that allow me to know that there is another dimension to life and living, other than the purely anatomical or physical. There is another very powerful dimension which some Western medical thought has lost track of, even though Hippocrates understood the relevance of the personal.

I look after a very powerful Maori woman. She came for acupuncture treatment. The first time I needled her I had this strange 'cold' sensation and felt the skin on my arms had 'goose bumps' and the hairs were standing up too. I said nothing. She looked at me and smiled and said: "Ah, the whakapapa [ancestors] are here. Would you like me to introduce them?"

That's really personal, slightly scary stuff. It means I stand with reverence and awe at such an experience: at what the Chinese and other ancient cultures understood about us as being the microcosm, and our connections with the world around us, or macrocosm. The Chinese believe, and so do I, that the universal qi connects us and all beings, both within and without. And qi is what I work with all the time. I treat the physical, and I am privileged to treat the physiological, the personal and the spiritual. In Chinese medicine there is no division, like in Western medicine, into mind and body. There is only oneness. Chinese medicine is about observing the real world, the rhythms of nature, and then observing the same rhythms in the body. Chinese medicine is about understanding the relationships between the external rhythms and the internal rhythms, and how they affect each other. It is humbling beyond measure.

There's a living network (a channel system through which qi flows) in our body that connects us to the universal qi, and as an acupuncturist you can experience another person's qi, and your own. Western medicine demands evidence and has to be able to measure something to know that it exists. I know qi exists because of putting needles into people, and what I experience in my hands once the needle is inserted. I have also experienced qi in other ways. For example, I treat lots of people who are dying. The last gift I give to my patients is to step back to my nursing training and lay out the body after death. Sometimes the last few moments are not easy for the person dying or for the people sitting around the bed. I wash the body and have it looking beautiful for the family. As you wash the body you can still feel the person's qi around and above the body. Modern science has demonstrated that you can still measure lines of electrical conductivity on a dead body, or on an amputated limb, or a foetus at seventy-two hours after death. I didn't have a name for what I could feel until I did Chinese medicine. I just knew there was a presence, a so-called energy, warmth; a physical feeling that I could sense with my hands. I now call it qi.

> *I have to be really careful using the word 'compassion' because it has now become a sort of buzz-word.*

The Chinese medicine model is a compassionate model. I have to be really careful using the word 'compassion' because it has now become a sort of buzz-word. In 2009, when I was a member of The Compassion in Healthcare Trust[1], the Trust asked the Government of New Zealand to add the right to be treated with compassion to the Code of Consumer Rights (Health and Disability). Following consultation and a review, the government concluded that the Code already included the right to be treated with respect and with courtesy, and so the addition wasn't necessary. While the Trust did not succeed in having compassion added to the code it was able to have minuted in public discussion that compassion is not the same thing as respect and courtesy. Compassion is a virtue. When you look at what defines a virtue, like courage, there are a whole lot of different concepts embodied in it. We glibly say: "They really helped that person; gosh, that was compassionate management."

---

1   The Compassion in Healthcare Trust, New Zealand.

Compassion is more than that. It is actually about stepping into the other person's life and being their distress – you can never be their distress in reality, however, you can share; you can try to be in their position and be them for a short space of time in order to understand their distress. Compassion is at a completely different level to showing someone that you care.

Many medical students haven't had much of a life journey and when I trained most came from middle-class or upper-class homes full of opportunity. The 'personal journey', which is supposed to prepare you for this level of connection in this job, consists of six intensive years of study.

Many people start medicine young. In Australia you can start at graduate school, which is a much better idea. Many medical students haven't had much of a life journey and when I trained most came from middle-class or upper-class homes full of opportunity. The 'personal journey', which is supposed to prepare you for this level of connection in this job, consists of six intensive years of study.

And we wonder how they can empathise with an eighty-year-old woman who has broken her hip and is weeping because there's no one to look after her cat? Fortunately, doctors are part of a health care team – this is why I loved nursing before I became a doctor. Nurses stay at the bedside long enough to find out what's really troubling the patient. As doctors we attend the morning ward round usually over the top of the body in the bed, and move on. Sometimes we don't even hang around long enough to refer to them by name.

In my hospital internship, at hospital team meetings, the doctors would organise the caring to be 'done to' the patient. So doctors were head of the care giving team and while responsible for planning what happened to the patient, other people usually carried out the care. My nursing training never left me, and it meant making time and being available for patients and families.

Associate professor Dr Craig Hassed from Monash University is one of the people working to change attitudes in medical school training. He is teaching mindfulness to doctors and medical students – starting them early in their training on a journey of self-discovery so that at the end of their training, they actually know something about themselves, as well as medicine. This will make practicing medicine a whole lot easier.

When I decided to try and get into medicine in 1970, as my nursing training was coming to an end, the selection was entirely based on academic merit. I went for an interview in my last year of nursing to find out what I had to do. I had chosen not to do seventh form bursary in my final school year because I knew I would go nursing and nursing was hospital, not university, based. I thumbed my nose at my parents, who suggested bursary would be a good option anyway. I had won academic prizes in the seventh form, and nursing prizes every year of my training. That was not good enough to get into medical school though. I was told that nurses are dumb, that I had no outstanding academic record, and basically was asked what made me think I could get into medical school? I replied: "I am being reminded that I have no bursary academic record to present, but, I have won all sorts of academic prizes at school and in my nursing training to date, and I have really good marks and I think I can manage the academic challenge." The academic registrar said: "OK, you've got Latin, French, geography and history which are considered useless subjects, and no science subjects, so you'd better go to night school and do chemistry and physics and also get straight A's in nursing finals. Then we might consider your application." He knew I worked six days a week, on eight-hour shifts, day or night, but I said: "You're on, I'll do it." And so I did.

Fortunately, the Dean at the time was an enlightened man with a huge heart and was wise enough to see that capable people from different strands of life, who were prepared to work hard at the missing scientific disciplines, could make a contribution to the practice of medicine. So I made an appointment to see him and if it wasn't for him, I would probably never have got into medical school.

Once I started medical school in 1970, I realised that my rudimentary chemistry was insufficient to cope with the first-year requirements. The chemistry teacher, Mr White, was a wonderful and perceptive man – he used to look at the despair in my eyes during chemistry class and at the end of the session say: "Come and see me at lunch time. We'll go over it again." And physics might as well have been Greek to me – I didn't have a maths background. I used to say to the guys in our class: "If I wire up the equipment [thinking: *I hope I don't electrocute myself*], then will you do the stats on the results for me?" Thankfully I had a photographic memory. I used to put the physics textbook into my head and copy it out in the exam. I didn't have to be super intellectual to do medicine, I just had to have a good memory and be able to recall very large amounts of information.

> *I didn't have to be super intellectual to do medicine, I just had to have a good memory and be able to recall very large amounts of information.*

Mr White, who was a really inspirational hands-on, interactive teacher, was really concerned about the selection process for medical school – he believed it was very elitist, predominantly European, academically focused and privileged. He worked very hard to change the selection criteria over the next ten years to provide a more diverse ethnicity – for example Maori and Polynesian – and to create opportunities for people from less advantaged socio-economic backgrounds. It was all very controversial at the time: "How dare you bring in people of lesser academic record and standing?" The medical school was richer for the more diverse student mix.

I recently had a conversation about Western and Chinese medicine with some sixth year medical students. In response to my question about their philosophy of wellness, one young man in a class I ran stood up and said: "I'm going to be an orthopaedic surgeon and I'm going to be rich." I thought: *Well, nothing's really changed.* At least he was honest.

> *"You may think you have the answers for your patients, but it's not up to you to fix anything. If you spend your life thinking you have to fix it for the person who is having a conversation with you about their wellness, you will burn yourself out very quickly. Your responsibility is actually to be on their journey, not be their journey."*

Probably many of his classmates had the same opinion; but nobody else had the courage to say so. Currently we have a disease treatment model of health not a health system and we train doctors accordingly – to treat disease. I thought: *He actually feels really threatened and actually doesn't know why he is here.* If you are secure, you don't have to be threatened by someone with a different viewpoint. I say to all the students: "You may think you have the answers for your patients, but it's not up to you to fix anything. If you spend your life thinking you have to fix it for the person who is having a conversation with you about their wellness, you will burn yourself out very quickly. Your responsibility is actually to be on their journey, not be their journey."

It is important to be a sounding board for those who seek help about their own health and lives. If you do that, if you don't see yourself as having to fix it for everybody, then as a practitioner you will remain sane and can actually step out regularly and go on holiday! As health practitioners, we are enabling people to realise that they have amazing resources within, and that they can actually tap into them once they understand what the body has to offer. Being in practice is also about being respectful. When a person comes and tells you about their choices, it is important not to lecture them, belittle the choice, or tell them that what they want to do is wrong – providing the choice is not damaging or dangerous for their health. You can say: "Professionally I don't agree with this (for these reasons), but I respect your right to make your own choice." You just gently encourage people to learn and take responsibility for themselves, because otherwise you'd wear yourself out. I decided a long time ago that I don't want to keep putting bandaids on people and I don't want to keep running other people's lives. That's what exhausts you in practice.

Being empathetic, compassionate enough to momentarily be in another person's grief, distress, anger or whatever, doesn't burn you out if you understand that you don't have to fix their problem. You can listen and care and provide practical support, but you don't have to get it right for them. That's the bit that burns doctors out. The bit many doctors fail to understand is that they are giving therapy by listening. Sometimes they give therapy by doing nothing. They are also giving therapy by being empathetic enough to engage exclusively with the person in front of them. I mean listening with intention, not wandering off and answering the phone, or writing a prescription for someone else over there. I mean being fully committed to this conversation, with this person, in this moment.

Sometimes medical professionals are criticised for undermining allied health professionals who practise holistically. The same is true of some people who work in complementary medicine – they can be just as narrow minded as their medical counterparts. I'm a big fan of people having mutual respect for different ways of doing things and not belittling health professions, such as indigenous medicine, that may be poorly understood. Increasingly, evidence is being provided for indigenous medical models and their place in health systems is being promoted by the World Health Organisation (WHO). Chinese medicine is one example of an increasingly popular indigenous medicine that has been shown to be preventative in nature and sustainable within Western health systems, which are becoming increasingly expensive to maintain. Acupuncture is the most widely used and best evidenced modality of Chinese medicine currently used in the Western world. I believe that Chinese medicine empowers people to run their own lives and have insight into and responsibility for their own health and wellness.

By needling or giving herbal prescriptions, you change the rhythms in the body. For example when you reinforce the Chinese concept of blood, which underpins our stability, our physical standing, and our ability to know who we are – when you change that physiological rhythm, people then have the capacity to make changes for themselves.

Last week I saw a young anorexic patient who told me: "Whatever you did last week changed my ..." – and the word she used was – "intention." I had nourished her Chinese concept of kidney function. She told me that she had reduced her daily intake of drugs – she'd been an addict for many years and is on high doses of Diazepam or Valium. She said: "My psychiatrist said I had to stay on 120 mgs for three months, before I can cut down, but I've cut myself down to 90 mgs per day, and I feel OK." I reminded her that we are trying to get her off this drug slowly! She replied: "No, you didn't listen to me: I felt that something changed after the acupuncture and I knew I could cut down safely because my intention told me that I didn't need the 120 mgs. Something shifted for me after you needled me last week." There was somebody taking ownership for what she is doing! Her psychiatrist may not agree with her decision, however she was very clear that she was OK, and that she was the person who was going to dictate what happened. She felt that the needling had changed her dependency and her need to have large amounts of the drug. She was telling me not to interfere with her intention; she'd got it sorted. What she wanted was my support to continue taking responsibility for her own life. It was nine months of trial and error until the process of weaning her off the Diazepam was successfully completed.

We can blame the system for its complex multilayered structure, we can discuss different philosophical ideas like critical theory and postmodernist thought, yet at the end of the day, it's about many doctors still wanting to be in charge of the health team, still wanting to be the experts, and still protecting their specialty or guild. It's about some groups having the power to exclude others. It is often not about the public's health.

I have a few issues with the integrative medicine scene and the lip service given to patient-centred care. Many doctors still think they are the leaders and directors of the integrative health teams. In recent years, as part of my doctoral research, I interviewed people from across the health system: policy boards and the Ministry of Health; District Health Boards; Primary Health Organisations; and General

Practice. One of the main stumbling blocks to changing the New Zealand health system is the attitudes and beliefs of the doctors.

It's about patch protection and power. Nothing more, nothing less. We can blame the system for its complex multilayered structure, we can discuss different philosophical ideas like critical theory and postmodernist thought, yet at the end of the day, it's about many doctors still wanting to be in charge of the health team, still wanting to be the experts, and still protecting their specialty or guild. It's about some groups having the power to exclude others. It is often not about the public's health. It's that simple. It makes you want to weep.

You can work with an open heart and mindset in the Western model; it just means you won't be rich and powerful. How do you charge for services that are essential and time-consuming? It creates immense difficulty. For example, when you visit a family where someone is dying – and end up spending half a day – how can you send a bill for that, and if you do, what do you charge? I don't charge. Instead, I take a bouquet of flowers and go to the funeral to support the family. What comes back to me from that family is something immeasurable in monetary terms.

I learned about generosity when I fell in 2005 and spent the next year trying to put my life and my wrist, elbow, and shoulder back together. My patients cooked for me, the house was always full of flowers, and people would turn up on the doorstep and say: "I know you have to go for treatment today, can I drive you?" I was constantly in therapy working on restoring some function and my patients fed us as a family, and drove me to appointments, day after day – my caring for them came back one hundred-fold. Relationships are a two-way scenario.

I've done a huge variety of things in my long life. I'm now in my late 60s, I am blessed that the brain still works, I still have good energy, and I still love going to work. Chinese medicine is my passion and it is also my professional work. I continue to teach about Chinese medicine at every opportunity and am currently involved with the Chinese medicine profession and its journey to national regulation in New

Zealand, under the Health Practitioners Competence Assurance Act 2003. While I specialised in acupuncture over thirty-five years ago, more recently I have just completed a four-year part-time training in Chinese herbalism and I'd love another thirty years to learn more and work with that modality deeply.

To be in practice properly is hard work. It's about the being and doing of my own life intertwined with the lives of others. It's is not about going to work every day and doing things to other people; it is about going to work every day and being in partnership and conversation with other people. When I'm in practice, regardless of what is going on in the rest of my life, my focus and care must be on the people that I go to serve. I try to honour that – it's not simple.

I used say to my university students: "Your greatest teachers will be your patients, not me. You have to be willing to learn from, and be open to listening to the people that you care for."

Some people who come and ask for my skills and my experience don't always listen to what I have to say, but that's OK too. It means we have conversations of equal status and standing; it is not about me being the expert. I'm privileged to be there, to share people's lives and to listen to their stories. Consultation to me is conversation between two people of equal importance.

I used say to my university students: "Your greatest teachers will be your patients, not me. You have to be willing to learn from, and be open to listening to the people that you care for."

People share the most amazing stuff and that actually helps us – as therapists grow. No-one has exclusive rights to the truth and none of us know everything.

If you just work at the superficial level, you never ever understand what true conversations and consultations are about, because you never get beyond the stuff that keeps us out there somewhere. We can talk about the weather and the grandchildren and never talk about the personal, the soul. It's like the person who brings their palpitations or low back pain. My patients don't do that anymore. They have learned to bring themselves and not to be fearful of that. They know that whatever they bring will be respected, listened to and treated to the best of my ability. They come and say: "I've got back pain." And then they go on to say: "It's awful at work, I have someone in my life who makes my stomach churn, and the pain in my low back is worse when I have to deal with them. I don't know what to do." This is the start of a meaningful conversation.

My practice is a safe, nurturing environment for all, and a place where we have fun too. Sometimes I think all we have to do is open our hearts and the physical door, and show that we actually care about others as human beings, and the healing starts in the doorway. It starts in the way my receptionist greets people, and the conversations she has with them. It doesn't start with me, or the first treatment.

I had one woman who cried hugely throughout our initial history taking. Before I got to the physical observations of her Chinese pattern, she looked at me with this beautiful smile and said: "Thank you, I don't actually need any needling, it's all sorted. I won't need to see you again," and she left.

The Chinese say the practitioner is the needle. You don't have to physically put a needle in, to care for people. It is so easy to smile and to open your heart and show people you are genuinely interested in them as people. I sometimes think that all we ever do here in this healing space is be ourselves. It doesn't require lots of technology and lots of specialist expertise. It just requires some human-ness.

21 | TIME TO CARE

DR LIZ HARDING

General Practitioner.

Auckland, New Zealand

"Solo doctor post for two years working in Nepal. Beautiful views. Minimal pay."

The advertisement on one of the laboratory forms jumped out at me. I sat and gazed out the window for a while, dreaming of snowy peaks, saving lives, doing something really worthwhile; then I sighed and tossed it in the bin. Next week the same advertisement appeared. I looked a little longingly at it, then again threw it away. That afternoon, I discovered it uncrumpled and placed on my desk with a note scribbled by my practice nurse, "This would be perfect for you, Liz." And I thought it would be too.[1]

Nepal was the kind of experience that you love once you've done it I think, rather than actually when you are there. A lot of the time we were kind of bored and lonely, and sometimes I think we hated it. But you look back and remember the exciting times. What I loved about it was that I was the only doctor there within about six days walk, so it was just me, and I found that really exciting. I keep wondering why I didn't find it scary but I didn't. I guess I just took the attitude that if I

---

1   Excerpt from: L Harding, *You are a brave man: A Kiwi odyssey in the Himalayas*, Random House, New Zealand, 1997.

wasn't there, people who were seriously ill would definitely die. Since I was there; well, they had a chance, and I just had to have a go and do my best. The challenge was one of the reasons I was there.

In fact, most of the things that I saw were fairly basic things – some were fairly serious but you just did your best. We treated Tibetan refugees for frost-bite – I had to amputate fingers and toes – and we delivered a few babies which was sometimes quite stressful. We treated people with altitude sickness and fortunately they were all fine. We had a twenty-year-old man die of measles – that was really upsetting. We walked around and did clinics at all the local villages.

It was my plan when we got back, that I would probably spend the rest of my life doing aid work, but my partner wasn't that keen and then we had the children. I thought we'd just put them on our backs and keep going around the world, but I don't think I had a very realistic idea of what it was going to be like to bring up children. Nepal was a really great experience and I'm so pleased that I did it.

When I came back to New Zealand I couldn't believe how stressed everybody was. Maybe people can't afford to be stressed in Nepal, they're just busy surviving. I moved to a really high-decile (income) clinic where, in amongst such privilege, the patients were worried about everything. I found that a real culture shock. I was probably a bit offhand and grumpy with people who were worried about all these, I thought, imagined things. For a while I thought we were worse off than the people of Nepal – they might not have much food and material things, but they seemed to be much happier than we were. It made me really think about our culture and our society.

I went through a period of time when I felt really flat about medicine. I was also feeling the real pressures of having to earn an income to support the family and I was kind of dragging my heels to work and thinking: *Oh, it's just a job. I just have to do it.* That made me feel really sad because I had had such a passion for medicine in the past.

I felt particularly disappointed because having done lots of locums[2], I had worked for people who were like that and I didn't want to be one of those people. That was part of why I did locums – to try and stay fresh.

It's a funny job: it's a job that if you do it badly, rushing people through, you can get paid very well for it; and if you do it well, you get paid less.

After a while, I started doing Balint work and that rejuvenated me. It gave me the interest and the passion back for medicine. It reminded me how much I love really listening to people. One problem though was that it did make me spend a lot more time with people, which was good – it made it more satisfying for me – but it meant that I ran behind. Since I was getting paid per patient that I saw, my income dropped significantly. But I felt so much more satisfied in my work.

It's a funny job: it's a job that if you do it badly, rushing people through, you can get paid very well for it; and if you do it well, you get paid less. It seems that people will pay to go and see a counsellor to listen to them, but people don't expect to have to pay more for their doctor to listen to them.

It makes me think of the Chinese system where doctors get paid for keeping people well. That probably wouldn't work very well here either, because you'd be tempted to only take on healthy patients and people who were chronically ill would get pushed onto other people. That could be a potential problem with the capitation system – the system in New Zealand where you get a certain amount of money per patient that comes through the practice, regardless of how many times you see them in a year. So, if you get, say imagine it's $1000 per year, if you only see that patient once a year, then that's easy money because you don't have to do anything much. If, however, the patient has lots

---

2   Short term, fill in jobs at clinics where doctors are on holidays / leave or where there is temporary understaffing.

of chronic health problems and you have to see them every month or every week, it's a lot of effort to get that $1000 per year for them. They do pay you each time they see you, but the hope is that the patient fee will reduce with time, and if they are in a high needs clinic it is not a high fee, so there's a tendency to want to have healthy patients on your books. If you have a large number of healthy patients, you can earn a lot of money for a smaller amount of work. I imagine it would be getting harder and harder for the high needs patients to find a doctor who will put them on their books.

Hopefully most doctors don't think too much about that, but you can understand why they might, if they've already got an enormous workload. They don't want to add to it for little gain. Especially if you've got a patient with really high health needs who has limited money, because either they get into debt with you, or the doctor feels that they can't charge them. It's hard because you want to help your patient, but not get to the point where you resent them coming in.

At one stage I was spending so long with patients, I'm not sure that I would have been financially viable if I'd been working as a regular GP. That's a real pity. Maybe the clinics I worked for then even lost money when I worked there. But hopefully they thought that was OK because they liked to have someone who was thorough and who cared about their patients – and they paid for that service for two weeks knowing that they could have a holiday knowing that their patients were well cared for. If it had been my own practice, I'd probably have had to change how I practiced because I just couldn't have kept the books afloat. I don't know how you'd have another system. Maybe GPs could be paid a salary system but they still need to get through the workload and see the patients who need to be seen, and would it be fair for someone who takes more time to earn as much as someone who's seeing more people?

When I was doing the Balint training, I was witnessing these stories from doctors which were so from the heart. They didn't want to let themselves go over the edge too much in caring, in case they fell apart. Sometimes I think that is one of my problems: that I can sometimes feel too much, that I'm not made of the right stuff. It can be hard to find the right space to feel empathy or compassion for someone, but still be able to protect yourself from vicarious trauma. Sometimes people's troubles feel too much and I want to put barriers up to protect myself from them; other times I feel able to show genuine feelings of concern with them. It's very hard because I think it's quite natural when someone has just found out that they've got cancer, or that their baby has died or something like that, to be upset. But in the doctor role, you need to stay in control. I understand that if you have to treat someone you can't let your emotions take over and you need to make clear, sensible decisions. You are not actually helping someone if you are so overwrought with emotion that you can't assist them, but it can be very challenging. I think there's an enormous price to pay in not allowing yourself to feel the genuine emotions that come with upsetting outcomes, and often we are expected to just get on with it – move on to the next consultation – without time to process. It seems such an unnatural position to be in. I think that the patients I've met who have had a doctor who has shown some real genuine emotion have really remembered that, and have really felt it quite deeply.

When I was at medical school, we were exposed to a form of systematic desensitisation.

When I was at medical school, we were exposed to a form of systematic desensitisation. I'm sure it's a necessary process of our training. I remember being shown slides of increasingly more gory things as time went on, and you gradually got used to them. Obviously it is not helpful to have a doctor shrieking, fainting and running away from, for example unpleasant looking injuries, so we needed to learn to not react, or not be really shocked by these things. But, there is that real blunting of affect that you learn, and a kind of black humour that stops you feeling for people. When I think of my hospital training days, I feel that I didn't really think of patients as real people. It was more about their conditions and how to treat them. It seemed to me that hospitals were full of medical practitioners who were like that.

I cringe at memories of myself as a person in my twenties, and my lack of understanding of parent's feelings about their children. I recall recommending a 'parentectomy' during a difficult procedure on a child while a vocal, anxious mother was present. I grew up in a medical family, so after years of dinnertime conversations, I feel I'd already been desensitised, with emotions blunted.

I remember one time working as a house surgeon and being so tired that I actually fell asleep onto the patient who was being operated on, while I was assisting, I was just so exhausted. I was shouted at, and told off.

The General Practice training programme was the first time that I had any sense that my patients were really people. Meeting and working with GPs, and seeing the relationships that they had with their patients; I saw that they really cared about their patients. I never really felt that sense with consultants during my earlier training and hospital years, and I didn't get that sense at medical school either. I found hospitals a toxic and strange working environment, for me, and I was happy to get out of there. Although now when I ring up the registrars they seem much nicer than they did thirty years ago, so I think the training is changing. I hope the training has changed because I found it pretty unsupportive.

I remember one time working as a house surgeon and being so tired that I actually fell asleep onto the patient who was being operated on, while I was assisting, I was just so exhausted. I was shouted at, and told off. There was no sense of anyone being concerned about my level of tiredness. The workload was hard, and I remember bursting into tears at times when extra patients were given to me, or being confused about whether it was day or night. There was no sense of caring from anybody really, through the whole training. I don't know – maybe if people were too soft and caring we all would have broken down, who knows? Some of the consultants were quite bullying to medical students, and also to patients. I hope that doesn't happen anymore. You just had to pretend to be strong all the time. I remember one guy got really bad depression and went off work and no one followed up to see if he was OK. They just got really angry with him because it meant that our already difficult shifts got worse. I look back on that and think how terrible that was because we were supposedly the caring profession. Anyway, working in the hospital didn't suit me, and I did my required two years and got out of it as soon as possible. General Practice has suited me much better.

I'd been in a practice for a couple of years when I became pregnant. After having twins, I developed a post-natal depression. I'd become depressed during the pregnancy and had stopped work at twenty weeks. My partner had stopped work to help look after me and was going to stay home to care for the children, so by the time the children were nine-weeks-old, we had run out of money and I needed to return to work. I was finding life a challenge. The babies seemed to cry all of the time whatever we did, and with me fully breastfeeding them, we were significantly sleep deprived. I had lost my confidence and found GP consultations challenging. The locum I had arranged to cover me while I was on maternity leave had been asked to stay on. She was rostered on at the same time as me and I found it hurtful and difficult when my patients preferred to see her. I wasn't coping well and was sitting in my room crying in between patients. After a while, I realised it just wasn't going to work out and I left the practice and stayed at home for a while. I became more unwell, developing unusual thoughts and suicidal ideation, and it took a while before I was well enough to get back to work. Since then I've done repeated short-term locums for a few familiar practices. We've also travelled as a family while I worked as a locum overseas or in other areas of New Zealand. It's been a great way to combine family and work life.

You get out of a job what you put into it. When I was struggling I realised that I was going along to work with this negative energy and I thought: *No, I need to change that, I need to look at every new consultation and ask myself, "What's interesting about this person? What other things might they have going on?"* I'd just give myself a kick and say: *"OK, let's see if you can get more engaged."* And then I'd start doing that, and I'd start finding things to be interested in, and I'd start connecting with people again.

Having depression, while I didn't enjoy being really low, I do think that having the experience of depression has been really valuable for me because it has given me an insight into other people who have similar experiences. Those experiences have also humbled me and made me listen a lot more to people.

When I got out of medical school I thought I was pretty 'all that,' probably a bit arrogant. I was thinking, although not consciously: *I'm the expert and I'm going to tell you what to do.* It knocked me down a few pegs to experience mental illness, and made me realise that I am no better than anyone else I am talking to, that we can learn from each other, and we can work as a partnership to work out which is the best way to go.

A close relative's GP hung himself recently. It was written up in the GP Magazine *that he 'died suddenly.' A friend who was an anaesthetist cut his throat and killed himself, and it was advertised as 'accidental death.' I think to myself:* How many of us are killing ourselves? *If I died like that, I'd want people to know that I had struggles.*

I think that's a nice way to practice medicine. It's changed the way I see people. That's been a good thing. I think I'm pretty good at helping people with mental health issues. In fact, I light up when they come in. It's quite funny, a patient with a heart problem will come in and I might write two paragraphs in the notes. If they have a mental health problem I've written about two pages, because that's my real passion. I feel a real affinity with people who have struggles in that area.

I've had periods when I've been suicidal, so I do feel that my life's kind of like a bonus. I feel like it's such a blessing to still be alive, and I feel like I've had a second chance. I've had to make myself learn strategies to look at the world positively and that is such a bonus in my life. It's such a nice, happy way to live.

I'm sharing my story because I would like to see a book about doctors showing genuine feelings. So much of that is so battered out of you throughout medical school, and through the medical career. To hear that other doctors actually have feelings and challenges – and that it's OK – is powerful. There is this kind of myth that everybody just copes well and we all just put on this kind of facade. People don't naturally go around telling everybody their challenges and their difficulties, so you assume that you're the only one who has problems. You hear all about the people who get awards for things, but a lot of the real stuff gets hidden. A close relative's GP hung himself recently. It was written up in the *GP Magazine* that he 'died suddenly.' A friend who was an anaesthetist cut his throat and killed himself, and it was advertised as 'accidental death.' I think to myself: *How many of us are killing ourselves?* If I died like that, I'd want people to know that I had struggles.

I'm still here, doing my work because it's my job but also because I like people and I enjoy interacting with them. Some days are ordinary. Some days are really good. Mostly I find people interesting. I love the opportunity to ask them about themselves. I like the little puzzles. I like that medicine is often changing and new. There are always new things to learn, new things to know about. I like that I can get away with being my own kind of person – I can just be me. I don't have to work for some agenda, wear a uniform, and whatever happens in that room happens in that room. Mostly, I love it. And sometimes I make people better and help them, which is also great! It's a great job and I feel privileged to be a doctor.

> *The delivery went well. A healthy baby and mum always leave me buzzing and feeling good about the world. I hope I never lose that specialness and wonder at new life. I*

wandered back to the flat at about 5 am, just as the sun was beginning to rise behind Tamserku, a beautiful mountain that faces the hospital. It was snowing lightly and the ground was covered in what looked like icing sugar. I'd never seen it snow before and, caught up in the moment, danced around the front area of the hospital, trying to catch the snowflakes on my hands and face. I spun around to see a very puzzled expression on our health worker's face. He must think he's got a mad woman to stay.[3]

3   Excerpt from: L Harding, *You are a brave man: A Kiwi odyssey in the Himalayas*, Random House, New Zealand, 1997.

22 | GET REAL AND FEEL

DR MELVYN POLON

Paediatrician.

Sydney, Australia

If I can't love my patients then I'm wasting my time going to work. It is an absolute honour to be invited into their life. It is very intimate. I think intimacy is just being real and being honest and being open and connected. I hug my patients. For me, my work is incredibly intimate. I don't know how to do it differently. I don't know how to have a relationship with somebody where I'm cut off from them, where I'm wearing a mask, playing a role.

I cry sometimes at work, and the patients cry with me. I don't go running with tissues to save them. If someone cries, I feel a measure of success because I didn't make them cry; I facilitated a process which enabled them to have the cry they needed. Crying is how we move towards that serenity of acceptance. When we are resisting, we are struggling and in pain. As soon as we stop resisting, no matter how painful and sad, we're relieving our suffering by accepting our reality rather than fighting it. A lot of my work is around normalising, and teaching people to accept.

We live in such a competitive world these days: if the kid's not doing very well at school, send them to the paediatrician; if their handwriting isn't perfect, they need an occupational therapist; if they have behavioural problems, there are reams of labels and specialists we could give them.

275

We live in such a competitive world these days: if the kid's not doing very well at school, send them to the paediatrician; if their handwriting isn't perfect, they need an occupational therapist; if they have behavioural problems, there are reams of labels and specialists we could give them. My job is to have some wisdom and say: "Hang on a second, your child falls under the umbrella of normality – at the top end is the child whose fine motor skills are going to make them a brain surgeon one day, and at the bottom of the spectrum is someone who won't be a brain surgeon but will have other talents. Just love him for who he is. Don't try and make him what he isn't. You've got to find the balance between helping him to be the best person he can, by telling him that he can do better, but not making him feel not good enough by telling him too much to do better." That's just love. And I'm telling the parents this with love. My heart is way open. I want their child to have the best life possible.

But it took me a long time to get here. In the beginning, when there were people who were difficult, I used to get sick because I thought it was my job to make them feel better. I was successful at sending the parents away thinking I had been successful some of the time, but there were people I couldn't help, and they would suck me dry. Nothing I could do would help, and I would feel myself getting desperate, not knowing how to get rid of this person and not knowing what to say.

I needed to understand myself first before I could understand my patients.

I was unconsciously driven to do good, or be seen to do good, and I would go home and get sick and not be able to go to work for two days. I think I just grew up a bit and I realised that I can't fix people. I can just be myself and if being myself helps people, then great. I think my need to fix people was neurotic. It was compensating for some unconscious need in me which was part of my childhood story. Now I feel comfortable about giving what I'm capable of giving, and if it's not enough, it's not my problem. I can just give my best.

My aim is that a patient who walks into my room feeling disempowered walks out again feeling more power than when he or she came in. I do feel that I am doing my job now the way I always thought I should and could. I needed to understand myself first before I could understand my patients.

When I read that Jung said: only the self can heal, that resonated with me powerfully and I had to find out what it meant. The journey has been long and hard and if I might say so, heroic. Finding out who I am has become my proudest accomplishment.

We all have an inner world just as we have an outer world, but our Western culture is all orientated towards the goal and achievement oriented outer world. A lot of people live their whole lives never having an inner world, never knowing what their inner world is, and not knowing that their inner world is what drives all their attitudes, actions, ideas and feelings. Our whole approach to life is driven by an engine on the inside that we often don't even know exists. So, if we don't know about our engine, it limits our choices about how and who we can be in the world. A lot of people live their whole lives and go: "What the hell was that all about?" when it's over. What it is really about is opening up to who I really am on the inside, then I can understand how I became who I became, and then I've got choices.

The ultimate journey is to the feminine. It is so simple. There's a very simple little prayer which goes: "God, give me the serenity to accept the things I cannot change, the courage to change the things I can, and the wisdom to know the difference."[1] The courage is the masculine dimension and the serenity is the feminine dimension, which is in both man and woman. Wisdom is integration of the two. We're all trying to find balance between the two. Men have had authority over women and have run the world in their masculine way, and now we're in a new age where men are finding their female essence, and women are having opportunities to conquer, achieve, change and have courage.

---

1   Serenity Prayer, written by the American theologian Reinhold Niebuhr (1892–1971).

This won't ring true for everybody because different people have different personality types. If you are a very intellectual person, then you're not going to see the world through the lens of your emotions and you have to find your path some other way. I am speaking my truth, not necessarily the truth of others. But still, I can be myself and offer my way of seeing things and if someone relates to it, that's great, and if somebody doesn't relate to it, that's OK too.

I just want to be real and I want to know who I am so that I can speak my truth cleanly and clearly without contamination, without fear, and with humility. It makes no difference whether I am doing that with my wife, with my child, with my dog or with my patient – it is the same.

That to me is what applies in my work. As far as I'm concerned, there is no difference between who I am at work and who I am right now. I never ever felt that there was a difference. I remember once when I was a resident at the hospital and I was walking in the street at lunchtime eating a sandwich. The professor of paediatric surgery came up to me and said: "Melvyn, a man like you does not eat in public." And I thought to myself: *Bullshit. I don't want to put on a white coat and play a role. I just want to be completely real.*

My journey to try and be better doctor has been my journey to try and be a better person.

My journey to try and be better doctor has been my journey to try and be a better person.

The vast majority of people go to see a doctor because they are feeling vulnerable and scared. So if I apply the medical model, I'll take a history and do an examination and an investigation and make a differential diagnosis, and then an evidence-based diagnosis, and then a prognosis. Out of the vast number of all the people who are going to the doctor today, the number who fit neatly within that medical model is pretty small. Working from the medical model, more often than not, I'll say: "There's nothing wrong with your child," because within the medical model that is true. But how can I approach this person and find out the real reason why they came, from a different framework? How can I actually help them? One: by listening to them, listening to them properly. By shutting my mouth and my judgements and by just creating a silence around their talking, so that at least they are feeling heard, and then what needs to be named will be named. Two: I can demystify for them. Their child might be experiencing, say, a temperature, so I can explain that this is how the body works to fight infection, and that it is perfect that their body is doing that. I can say this is what is happening inside the body, this is why, and this is why we have this symptom. For example, I might say: "Your child is coughing a lot because you come from Iraq and his body is designed to breathe the dust in Iraq. This dust in this country is designed to be breathed by aboriginal people – it is safe here but your son's airways and his DNA are designed to breathe the air in your country." I can tell them when to worry: this is when your symptom is OK, and this is when the symptom represents a disease. And the third thing I can do to make them feel better is to connect with their child. I can look him in the eyes, play with him, talk to him and love him. I look into him, and I tell them that he's OK.

Thirty years ago, I would have cared what the medical model might have to say about my approach, but I believe that medicine requires people like me to teach people to have the guts to not worry about what medicine is going to think of you. I play the game. When I have medical students sitting beside me, I say to them that the first God we have to satisfy is the medical God who sits in that textbook over there, and the second God we have to satisfy is that child and their parents. We've got to send them out with more power than they came in with.

We are taught at medical school that the word psychosomatic has some sort of negative connotation – that it is just bullshit in your head that is making you feel what you are feeling, but that it is not really real. There is a very real connection between the psyche and the soma. A psychosomatic illness doesn't fit within the medical model, but if something is making a patient anxious, and it's giving them symptoms, then it becomes a medical issue. I'm quite comfortable with accepting that if I haven't got my shit together, it's going to have ramifications in my body. And it's not that I'm inadequate or a nutcase, or that I'm imagining for attention's sake, there is just somewhere where I'm not being true to myself that is going to give me symptoms. Me not looking at some deeper stuff is what made me sick in those early days as a doctor.

It is normal to feel sad, it is normal to feel scared and it is normal to feel not good enough. Whatever happens to you in your life, no matter how vulnerable you might feel, there will always be a part of you inside that is bigger than that feeling.

The word doctor means teacher in Latin. If the self can heal, then if I'm the doctor and if I can bring you more in tune with your own true self, the encounter will have been a healing encounter rather than one where you just walk away with a script. Many years ago we would have gone to the Shaman if we were sick. I like to think I'm a bit like a Shaman.

I had epigastric pain for about two months recently, and I had all these investigations. I went to see the hottest-shottest gastroenterologist and I told him that I wanted to wait a while before having another gastroscopy. I waited but the pain got worse. So I took myself off into the bush to see if I could help myself. I sat on the ground between two branches of a tree and I gave myself permission to feel my physical pain as well as my emotional pain. I surrendered to my sorrow of getting old and seeing my body deteriorating and losing capacity and I cried. Then I felt a lot better physically as well as emotionally.

My advice, if I could give it, to both patients and doctors alike would be simple: It is normal to feel sad, it is normal to feel scared and it is normal to feel not good enough. Whatever happens to you in your life, no matter how vulnerable you might feel, there will always be a part of you inside that is bigger than that feeling.

I would love to work with medical students around developing their listening skills and insight into their unconscious emotional dimension. Medical students do have to do communication courses when they start. The classic example case they get given is how to tell a patient that they are going to die. Then they have a go at responding and their response gets picked apart. It needs to go so much deeper than that – they need opportunities to practice listening in a whole, open way, and to get an experience of what it feels like to listen and be listened to in that way.

I would love to help people to understand that how they deal with people is a reflection of their self-awareness. If you wake up and become conscious you will interact with others in a more authentic way, and you will be healthier inside. You will heal yourself, and maybe you will become a better healer.

The magic is that you have to go to your own vulnerable place to be able to appreciate somebody else's, and in order to be real with them when they're vulnerable. And that's something that's missing in our training. We desensitise. That's great if you are training people to be orthopaedic surgeons or neurosurgeons where you don't have to deal with people's emotions, but so much of medicine is dealing with the *person* sitting there. There's *so* much behind the symptom. For a super specialist whose job is to rule out a diagnosis – that's where his work ends. And that is where our work starts. Our work, and the work of general practitioners, is the emotional dimension that is beyond the diagnosis. And we're not taught anything about that. In the old days there wasn't all the technology around so the doctor just patted people on the head and did their best, but now there's so much technology and information, there is no stopping. There is always another possible angle to explore. Patients want more information

> *Medicine will fly when doctors become more emotionally conscious. My advice, if I could give it, to both patients and doctors alike would be simple. Wake up.*

(or they come in with it already!) and then of course there's the litigious environment. Not a wonder doctors are stressed and disillusioned.

I do not blame systems for any challenges I have had in my work, it was my own unconscious emotional stuff that stopped me from being authentic and truthful in the past. Medicine will fly when doctors become more emotionally conscious. My advice, if I could give it, to both patients and doctors alike would be simple. Wake up.

23 | CRAZY SOCKS DOC

DR GEOFFREY TOOGOOD

Cardiologist, Doctors' Mental Health Advocate, creator of 'Crazy Socks4Docs Day' in support of doctors with mental illness, Writer and long-distance ocean swimmer.

Melbourne, Australia

I've worked at a number of different hospitals over the course of my career and I find it fascinating that, even if they are mere kilometres apart from each other, culturally, one hospital can be vastly different from another. It's a leadership thing. In one place, everyone will get along with each other: the nurses get on with the doctors and doctors get on with the nurses; there's limited hierarchy, and the consultants are good and very supportive. They're a bit like a small town; everyone takes the time to get to know everyone, they help each other out, and there's real mutual respect and teamwork. And then you could go down the road to another hospital; similar size, similar patient intakes, and you'll find a ridiculous hierarchy: nurses who are stuck up and rude, and consultants who are dysfunctional narcissists. In one hospital I worked at as a junior, they would scream and yell at us as younger doctors; whereas in other places I worked as a junior, I can't remember being yelled at once, even if it was probably deserved.

Often the people who work in hospitals are in this institutional bubble. It's like another world. You can try and change hospital cultures (although not as a junior), but it's a bit like walking into a footy club and changing that culture overnight. They're massive organisations and the cultural norms are often deeply embedded. They're not going to change much, or easily. It's changed a bit probably since my early years but there's still that arrogance and hierarchy in many places.

When I was a junior working in these environments, that made studying for the exams the most terrible time: you were so unsupported. That was when I first started to struggle a bit. I didn't have clinical symptoms but I was certainly more anxious at work, and probably a little bit burned out towards the end. There was always this fear that someone's going to yell at you. How can you perform well under those conditions? There were a couple of people who were downright bullies. I only realised later that what became my struggles with my mental health were really just accumulated stress. So earlier on in my career I suffered from quite significant anxiety around the end of my physician training, and at the start of being a consultant. I had to work a few things out for myself through cognitive behavioural therapy and medication.

I was well for quite a few years, and then slid into quite a severe depression. It wasn't just work related, there was also stuff going on for me personally. The major turning point was when a friend texted me that he was worried that I was a bit dark. I was still trying to work, and seek help, but I was getting hammered at work. Then I had a *transient global amnesia*[1], which is like a kind of stroke, and for twenty-four hours I had no idea where I was. It was a very scary thing. I don't know how, but I somehow managed to drive my car to work. I was apparently giving some vague responses, and then one of my secretaries asked me if I had been drinking or if I had taken any drugs. It was nine in the morning! I don't take any drugs, but it was kind of like I was seeing a kaleidoscope of

> *I think there's this expectation of 'presenteeism' in the medical profession. Ironically, we are least forgiving of ourselves and our own when we are unwell – you've just got to turn up and keep going, even if you're sick.*

---

1   A sudden, temporary episode of memory loss not attributable to epilepsy or stroke.

things; like seeing thirty-six images of the same thing. That's when I knew I was in a bit of trouble.

They called an ambulance and that was it. It was neurological and I still don't know exactly what is was, but it was undoubtedly caused by very severe stress. My workplace left me alone for a little while but not for long. I still kept getting emails and things like: "When are you coming back to work? We need to sort out the rosters." I just wanted it all to go away.

I think there's this expectation of 'presenteeism' in the medical profession. Ironically, we are least forgiving of ourselves and our own when we are unwell – you've just got to turn up and keep going, even if you're sick. You know, the old: "We went through it, we put up with it, we're strong, we're tough, get over it." But physical sickness is not the same as an emotional injury.

We've all gone through hard days but it's not the same as being mentally ill. They're totally different things and mental illness is still totally misunderstood, even from within the profession. There's also an inevitable misunderstanding from people who have never experienced mental illness themselves. Yes, you might be a bit down one day; you might be a bit anxious; you might feel a bit adrift, and you seem a bit flat – but you're feeling better the next day so you're not suffering from a mental health condition. It's a completely different problem. That's the one you can disregard for a day and you're alright.

I don't know why hospitals can be such unforgiving workplaces, and why we still don't 'get' mental illness. I can't work it out. I used to have a target on my back for raising these issues. It's much less so now. I think that's because my public profile has built a bit further, and these conversations are becoming more mainstream, so they are going to have to leave me alone. I'm involved with national mental health advocacy group Beyondblue[2] now. So I'm invited to forums and I sit at the same

---

2   Beyondblue is a high profile Australian support, information and advocacy organisation promoting the best possible mental health for all Australians. See: www.beyondblue.org.au

table as the Health Minister and a former Prime Minister, who want to have real conversations, and who have real concerns about this stuff. So your colleagues start leaving you alone, because you're making a difference.

It's interesting though that I bounce out and get all righteous, and get a seat at the table with all these extremely influential and powerful people – some of whom have led in the highest forms of management and power – and they turn to me and ask: "Well, what do you reckon, Geoff?" And then I go back to the hospital and no one really wants to know.

There are many elements of the profession who are genuinely engaged and concerned over the health of doctors. The pain in the profession has been ignored for a long time, but it is starting to surface and from the surface it can heal.

Part of the problem in working towards culture change in medicine is that there are so many disparate representative bodies and disjointed elements to pull together; there are specialty groups, political groups, government groups, hospitals, universities and colleges. Ambulance Victoria are doing some good work in this space but they're only dealing with one body, one union, with one representative group. The Australian Medical Association (AMA) is trying to do work in this area too. There are many elements of the profession who are genuinely engaged and concerned over the health of doctors. The pain in the profession has been ignored for a long time, but it is starting to surface and from the surface it can heal.

Things are changing rapidly in these conversations. In the last six months or so, I have seen more willingness to engage with these tough conversations about doctors' health than I've seen in the last ten to fifteen years. It just keeps coming. There are more stories in the press, and in the medical journals. I pitched a few of these stories to journals a few years ago and had no reply, and now they're chasing me for my story. So that's a significant change. For the better.

We have to fix ourselves up. I mean, it's a long career. It's a long training, and it's not an easy career to move from once you've done all that training. There is a lot riding on you making it work for yourself. Why should we have to do a dozen years of training only to throw our hands up in the air and walk away because it's too hard?

That's why I write about resilience. Because we can't just sit back and say doctors need to be more resilient. I mean people *do* need to be resilient, of course, but what I am trying to say is that people have started using the word as if lack of so called resilience is the failing of the individual. We've had to be resilient to get through medical school and a few years of residency.

We've got to take a look at the system around them and realise that doctors are struggling not because they're not resilient. Doctors are dying and we go: "Oh well, it's a tough job." They've *killed* themselves. They have started to fall down, but there was no-where for them to go. That's not *their* failing.

I've got millions of people from all around the world responding to the stuff I am writing. People are going: *For god's sake, yes!* We need to stop beating ourselves up for our weaknesses and let the health culture and the organisations take a look at what it means to be a sustainable, functional, supportive workplace. The time for corporate bullying and institutional blame-shifting is over.

Beyondblue's mantra is: hope, recovery and resilience. But they're not using the word resilience in the way the hospitals are, as a denial of systemic responsibility. They are using it with a sense of shared, group responsibility for resilience. A lot of your resilience comes from the support you have from the outside. If someone's struggled for a while, you need to build the resilience of the system around them: in the family, in the workplace, make them feel valued. You can't go and tell someone to do resilience training if you're treating them like rubbish at work, putting them on bad rosters, not valuing them, continually smashing them with long hours and endless lines of patients, and they're constantly sleep deprived, over worked and over tired. A lot of our supports come from outside of work but if we have no time to sleep, see family and friends and just live a bit and have fun, we're less equipped to deal with the demands at work. And it goes the other way too: if you're getting smashed around at work, you're bringing that load home, and it effects your relationships, and therefore your network of support. You can't be resilient if you've got three or four things smacking you down at once.

For a while you think it's all just you, that you're the one with the failings. And then you kind of realise: actually, it's not just me. A lot of it is to do with this circus around me. Realising that was a big step forward for me. When you have depression and anxiety, you feel like a failure, you feel like you deserve it; that's part of the illness. And then when you start to get better, you realise it's not all you. There are some things that are you, and you fix them up, but some things aren't.

In many ways one of the biggest failures in doctors is that we still really struggle to acknowledge and recognise when we are sick. And when we do, we need to be supported in that by workplaces that care.

The system just seems to be getting more, not less intense. We are constantly contactable, there is so much economic performance data that is imposed upon doctors, and we're expected to get through patients faster, justify and account for every thought and move, tick this box and that box. There is intensity on multiple levels. Some things, like having a mobile phone, have helped is some ways but there is no time and space where you can just switch off.

I reckon there's not one solution; it's got to be multiple solutions. It's about everybody doing a little bit every day. In many ways one of the biggest failures in doctors is that we still really struggle to acknowledge and recognise when we are sick. And when we do, we need to be supported in that by workplaces that care. That's the most crucial thing.

None of this is simple. Some of the cultural issues are difficult, if not impossible to resolve because some of these doctors and managers are narcissistic psychopaths with very limited insight into, or interest in their behaviour or impact on others. Often the 'chosen ones' in hospitals seem to be able to continue to get away with it, and the ones who survive, perpetuate the same behaviours.

I think the new generation of doctors coming through won't put up with it for much longer. They're millennials. They're not afraid to have tough conversations and they don't put up with crap. Also, I think, because there have been so many tragedies and deaths amongst young doctors, they have a strong voice.

I learned a lot when I was ill. Maybe I should go back and start training people to recognise and act on signs of stress before they get to the point that I got to. Schools are trying to teach this stuff; mindfulness and the like, and they're even teaching mindfulness in medical schools now too. But again, the personal self-care needs to be balanced with workplace care. There perhaps needs to be some planning so that teams and people who are working through periods with highly demanding workloads with high intensity consequences, have time to back off for a while after busy patches. They need to be allowed to slow down, to balance the intensity.

I would advise doctors to work across different clinical settings, just to see that their reality is not necessarily normal. And I want to say to other doctors who might be struggling: "It's not your fault, and you're not alone. It's OK to be ill." These are powerful messages. I've had junior residents come up to me who I don't even know, and they go: "You're my hero." I gave them hope about it being OK to be human, and be vulnerable. In fact, being vulnerable is important.

Doctors are by nature very anxious about making mistakes and this is reinforced with the litigious environment, and sometimes the work environment, as I've said. There are of course times where you just have to be prepared to knuckle down and work hard, say when you are studying, for a period of six to twelve months of stressful times.

But before too long you've got to make a decision before it is too late, to regroup and not become overwhelmed by stress. You can't keep continuing along those lines. Well, some do, because I loose work to them around here because they are continually available. I don't know what their life's like and if they ever see their children. I just can't do that anymore.

These days I don't take my work as seriously. It is not as important to me now that I have my life outside of work. Clearly when you are dealing with the patient you've got to concentrate on the patient, of course that is important. But I don't work myself into the ground any more like I used to. And I try and look after the people around me a bit, talk to them and see how they are going.

Doctors are falling over like flies at the moment. People are dying. Which is a pretty good catalyst for change.

On one occasion at work I was wearing odd socks because I didn't have any clean pairs at home. One of my colleagues asked me if I was OK. So I decided to make light of it and started 'Crazysocks4Docs' Day on 1st June this year to raise awareness of mental health issues in medical workplaces. It was a bit of fun to highlight a really serious issue. It went viral amongst doctors, medical students and other health professionals, and I'm hoping to make it an annual event.[3]

Doctors are falling over like flies at the moment. People are dying. Which is a pretty good catalyst for change. We're getting there. Any change in an organisation or culture needs a reason for change. It's early days but there is finally some momentum.

---

3   https://www.australiandoctor.com.au/news/latest-news/docs-go-crazy-for-odd-socks. Retrieved 17/09/2017.

24 "FIRST DO NO HARM"[1]

DR ROBIN KELLY

General Practitioner, Acupuncturist, Author and singer-songwriter.

Auckland, New Zealand

It is interesting the resistance to the words 'love' and 'healing' in our profession. And yet how many people have a problem because they can't experience love? And how many people get better when they're in a loving relationship? I can't tell you the number of people I've looked after who have struggled for years with chronic conditions, then they get into a loving relationship and their whole condition improves. This is the 'science' of love if you like. But it starts with self-love first, and usually if you open that up, the rest flows. It's like a flowering.

What profession would train for that long, to squeeze their expertise into six minutes of exchange? It is bizarre.

The 'powers that be' say that keeping medicine at arm's length is all about self-preservation, about not getting too close and allowing yourself to be too affected.

It's quite the opposite for me. If I were to see thirty-five patients a day and not go within, that's when I burn out. When people expect you to see them for fifteen minutes, they expect you to fix them in

---

1   This Maxim is one of the principal precepts of bioethics that all healthcare students are taught in, and is a fundamental health care principle throughout the world. From Wikipedia: https://en.wikipedia.org/wiki/Primum_non_nocere. Retrieved 28/09/2017.

fifteen minutes. They make it my problem. Here we are, being trained for up to fifteen years to become general practitioners, and then we are given fifteen minutes with the patient. In actual fact, the main work is squeezed into six minutes. What profession would train for that long, to squeeze their expertise into six minutes of exchange? It is bizarre.

It is all about communication. If you invest in that, where the person feels in charge, has ownership of their health, understands this from the start – the economic benefits would be huge, they are bound to be.

People still come in and see me with colds – as if doctors can do anything about colds – except further muck up the immune system. The thing that tires me out is telling this story time and time again: "We are an ecosystem of bacteria, viruses and bugs. We are actually attacking ourselves unnecessarily with antibiotics." That's why the antibiotic era is coming to an end. In the next twenty years, I would predict that we won't be able to use any antibiotics. We will start to see that we are stuffing up something quite serious. So I tell them that. I say: "All I can do is muck this up for you. Or I can reduce your temperature, but that is actually your body's clever way of fighting the infection. You're asking me to muck with the body's knowledge and make you worse." That's what drains me. But of course, if you take that away, a lot of places would say, well how will we survive without the coughs and the colds?

> *You can't go back, you can't unlearn this sort of awareness and go back to throwing drugs at people. Ethically I couldn't do that if I knew there were better ways.*

Soon after I started in General Practice in the 1980s, I trained to do acupuncture. A couple of other doctors did the training with me and together we became very impressed with how acupuncture could help people reduce their medication. I had a lot of older patients who were on huge doses of drugs (most of which have been withdrawn now as they were dangerous). Part of me was always interested in the philosophy behind Chinese medicine, not just the Western medical interpretation. So a number of us said: "Look, we need to take this seriously and honour the Chinese paradigm as it's been understood for millennia." So I studied Chinese medicine to the point of understanding its deeper implications, particularly the mind, body, spirit connections. We looked at why worry is going to affect someone's immunity, for example. That's what hooked me into it. And you could interpret it and use it in ways that people can really understand. The five elements and patterns of nature are also seen in the body.

But I had a young family and I was sole breadwinner. I had a busy practice in a system that was based on ten-minute consultations, and the Chinese model and acupuncture just didn't fit within that. So at the same time that I had this huge awareness, there was this conflict for me with the system. And yet you can't go back, you can't unlearn this sort of awareness and go back to throwing drugs at people. Ethically I couldn't do that if I knew there were better ways.

Especially in those days – the drugs were toxic. So as a doctor, following your Hippocratic oath to 'first do no harm', I took that to mean: 'don't poison them.' Although healing can happen in a moment, people need to be in a space where they are unwinding and unravelling – and that takes at least twenty minutes. So I started to lengthen my consultations.

I don't believe that effective mind–body medicine can be enacted with the system that we have set up. You need time. You need to not only know their medical condition, but also their philosophies, their spirituality, and you need to know whether they fear dying as much as the medical profession fears it. Many old people say: "Just give us a break, we're quite comfortable with this whole thing, we just don't want to be in a state of pain."

So in 1990, I sold my part of my General Practice and set up a clinic at home. I started off with twenty-minute consults. Over the years that wasn't enough, so I went to thirty minutes. I became very interested in the modern mind–body stuff, with the fusion of cosmology[2], quantum physics[3], and Ayurvedic medicine[4], which of course was all linked with Chinese medicine. It became more of what was happening around the world.

By the end of the 1990s I started to write. My first book was really my journey with mixing Chinese medicine and my understanding of non-material sciences with what I was doing every day.[5] The second book was about the science of intuition, global consciousness, how we are all linked, and introduced holographic concepts.[6] In the last decade, there has been so much science validating how quantum processes are being shown to occur within our bodies, it's been taken out of the laboratory of the very small, into living science. So, the old argument that this quantum stuff doesn't exists outside the laboratory is changing rapidly. Our understanding is changing so fast that I had to keep updating my drafts, so I wrote my most recent book with all the updated science.[7]

It is taking time for people to embrace this because it is a step that isn't actually intellectual. It is a step that requires the heart to open to it too. I write about the humanity of the scientific pioneers; what is happening in their lives for them to open up to this and to take the leap and start talking about compassion and love as being an integral, connective agent and force that binds us together. You look at research on non-locality and connections between people and it is so much more potent when those two people are in a state of compassion with each other.

---

2   Cosmology is a branch of astrology which explores the science behind the origins, properties and energies of the Universe.

3   Quantum physics explores atoms, subatomic particles and energy – it is sometimes known as the "science of the very small." From Wikipedia: https://en.wikipedia.org/wiki/Introduction_to_quantum_mechanics retrieved 1/10/2017.

4   Ayurvedic medicine is an ancient holistic Indian healing tradition, which aims to restore balance between mind, body and spirit.

5   R Kelly, *Healing ways: A doctor's guide to healing*, Penguin Books, 2000.

6   R Kelly, *The human antenna: Reading the language of the universe in the songs of our cells*, Hay House, 2010. Holographic concepts in this context relate to the organising principles of an electrodynamic field in relation to any biological system.

7   R Kelly, *The human hologram – Living your life in harmony with the unified field*, Energy Psychology Press, 2011.

Every day I see mothers and daughters come in, for example, with these instant non-local connections. The focus that I have is that knowing this, you reduce worry down because you trust your feelings and you trust your intuition and you begin to know that the cause of so many illnesses, such as depression and auto-immune conditions are often reduced down to connection. It is never just the emotions, mind you, but it is a big factor, and if we appreciate that, we can have an element of control over our illness. It can give us a certain amount of power and understanding. We can own it. If you are allergic to hay or wheat or something, you can try to avoid all those things and this gives you an ultimate control – you trust your first instinct – then you add your rationality.

They see compassion as all very fluffy and unnecessary, and they wonder how you can be compassionate and be able to resuscitate someone, for example. But of course you can, you don't forget how to do that stuff just because your heart opens. You don't become bonkers or gullible.

Feel first, then think. For example, if you meet someone you want to spend your life with, it is a feeling first – then you work out how it's going to happen. If you trust that – this whole idea of being in the zone – you reduce down worry and blame and shame. These are all the compounding emotions that are draining us and adding to our stress and illness.

I'm doing a comedy improvisation course at the moment. It's about how children play – without judgement. It's so funny, there's no winning or losing in it. If you stuff up, you really stuff up. It's very freeing. But it doesn't mean you're not going to think, you're actually freeing up your thinking – it's a bit like meditation.

I often get questioned by specialists and other colleagues who are threatened and confused by the mind–body approach I take to my work. They see compassion as all very fluffy and unnecessary, and they wonder how you can be compassionate and be able to resuscitate someone, for example. But of course you can, you don't forget how to do that stuff just because your heart opens. You don't become bonkers or gullible.

They argue the riskiness of inappropriate boundaries or transference. But life is transference – everything is interconnected. We have an emotional connection with everybody we meet, in everything we do. It is there all the time – we need to learn to live with it. Empathy can be as simple as asking yourself: "Who would I send myself or my wife or my child to if we needed a referral?" or "What would I want or need or do if I had this condition?"

Some say I'm simplifying things by just wanting to look at happy emotions, and ignoring nutrition, environmental toxins and other factors that affect our health. No, I'm not, because actually as part of this, when you start understanding that we're all connected, you have to start looking after the world, its environment and yourself. If you have love for yourself, it spreads to others. So, if you're caring about the environment, you're not going to cover the world with wheat and with milk cows. That's what's happened – exponential, easy consumerism that has tampered with our intuition, so that we have lost track of the connections and the bigger picture. That's why there's so much allergy: we've lost the balance. But it is extremely challenging now to get to the point where we can live without cow's milk. The only creatures who can't live without cow's milk are cows. It's an integrative approach. What I am saying is that there is a huge part of health and wellness which has been neglected by us because it's not scientific enough. But that doesn't wash anymore.

The science of placebo is the other thing that is misunderstood and dismissed as 'soft science.' Placebo is so scientific and we should be knowing about that. That's what I'm talking about – the science of compassion and self-compassion.[8]

I have people who come to me and say: "I feel awful, I've had all these tests and they all say there's nothing wrong with me." They show me a black and white 2D negative of their problem and I say: "Let's

---

8   There is evidence to support that there is a process that goes on between doctors (and other therapists) and patients that enhances the therapeutic outcomes. See, for example, a review of hundreds of studies into the placebo effect: Crow R, Gage H, Hampson S, Hart J, Kimber A. 'The role of expectancies in the placebo effect and their use in the delivery of health care: A systematic review', *Health Technol Assess*, 1999;3(3).

forget about the x-rays and the tests, they've just said you're not going to die tomorrow, so they've taken some worry away. But they're not actually getting at what's really going on, which will be something far more fundamental. Let's talk." I just allow them to unfold with their story because that computes back in. Once they start relaying their story in their own way, not in a linear way, it's probably the most powerful thing that I can do, just listen to that. And there are so many hints that come through that. Especially things like: "Oh, you wouldn't want to hear this" or "you'll think I'm crazy" – that's the one you want to hear. Then you are there as a gentle guide. Even with an hour you've got time constraints so I will chip in occasionally. We'll see a pattern emerging, and then we'll often go right back to their childhood, what's happening with their parents, their grandparents. Often it's about seeing themselves in context with past generations and future generations. This is particularly the case with mothers – they're often trapped between the two and they haven't had a chance to complete their full self-expression. Their immune system is often on hold until their guardianship role finishes, and that's when their illnesses all come out. It's a very typical pattern. You have to listen to all of the story to validate that and that helps reduce blame – which they know in their heart, but no one has ever heard or acknowledged it, often. Mostly, mothers have been doing it brilliantly for everyone else but the neglect has been for themselves. They will come to that themselves. The children can be forty before that happens, especially if they've seen a trait that they're protecting their child against. None of this involves guilt, you just listen and have compassion towards them. They leave feeling validated that they need to receive more. It can be the biggest issue for women – receiving.

For men – this is stereotyping a little bit – but if there is blood pressure it might be a blood line pressure to succeed in a certain way in life. This pressure seeded within themselves can manifest in the middle years. What do we do? We as doctors take their blood pressure and own it for them as an authority figure. If they own their own blood pressure machine, you give them ownership, talk about some of these issues, who they really are – you will see reduced blood pressure. The solutions to these things are simple, they are not arduous – we think it is all very heavy, taking responsibility for our health. But it's not.

I want to know their passions, their creativity. I gently question them when they say they are not creative. For example, they may have created all these kids who are creative, but think that they themselves are not. All human beings are creative. I try to be a slight agent for change in that – to encourage them. I encourage people to have massage, do Yoga, Tai Chi or Qi Gong[9], music, art, or for young guys, martial arts; whatever. To me that is all expression of who they are and a much closer connection to living healthily. That's what martial arts were designed for – focussing that innate aggression, going with it, not suppressing it. That's something that goes along with where their energies are. It's really as simple as that. We're in that lucky position of still being listened to as doctors, at the moment.

The power of this is the power of a relationship and therefore if you're doing well in a relationship, or you feel you are, there's nothing

To me it's a human right's issue that the power of compassion and relationship has been excluded from medicine. The power of true compassionate relationship is not to be underestimated. We can't dodge away from it any longer. That is the future.

more satisfying in the world as a doctor – if you feel you are helping people. What has been neglected in science is the power of the relationship – it's been relegated to placebo. With an empowering relationship, you do not have to prescribe so many pills, you do not have to submit people to unproven surgery, or unproven medicines. It doesn't negate those things, it just lessens the need for them. For example, if you need to use an antidepressant, you might be able to use lower doses.

9   Yoga, Tai Chi and Qi Gong, while very different in origin and practice, are all different variations of ancient and adapted exercises involving body and breath based energy movement, which are said to reduce stress and promote health and healing.

To me it's a human right's issue that the power of compassion and relationship has been excluded from medicine. The power of true compassionate relationship is not to be underestimated. We can't dodge away from it any longer. That is the future.

I am now writing books which question the so-called lack of science for much of this stuff, and ask: what science are we looking at? I have had a number of medical students email me recently. They were young people I have seen as patients, embarking on a career in medicine but determined not to lose this awareness that we are talking about, and wanted to know how to hold onto it. For the first couple of years there's so much information and they're so determined not to have this washed out of them. There is a brainwash going on. I've said to them: "You are aware of this and you may have to educate your professors."

I would hope that they are the generation that are going to be able to change it, rather than just drop out, which is what is happening at the moment. I would love people to do what I am doing early on in their career, rather than take the steps that I have. They'll have to take what might be seen as materialistic sacrifices but it is actually more difficult now to do this than it was thirty years ago. There has been a backlash from the profession. As the science becomes stronger, it is being withheld or disputed. People are ready but the profession may not be. There will be a tipping point with patients demanding this approach from medicine.

If we as a profession abrogate our responsibility by saying: "This stuff takes time; I haven't got time," we are expressing our total powerlessness. We can change it. The medical profession isn't totally powerless. But the status quo is boiling over with inefficiencies and it is not a system that is giving doctors satisfaction.

People of my age are just looking forward to retirement. Maybe more money is being thrown at them but there's no deep satisfaction. And how crazy is it that doctors, as they get wiser and wiser, leave the workforce. Look at all the wisdom we have – we should have, anyway. I just feel like I'm just starting.

The doctors who can't or won't do it anymore are burning out and blaming themselves. They are suffering from an inner disquiet, wondering: "Why do I feel so tired at the end of the day?" You've got blame and shame. There is sickness, addiction, cancers, and suicides in our profession. That is why this is such a human rights issue. If anyone is reading this and feeling this kind of discontent, I'd say to them: "You are not alone. Know that it can change. Be assured that it is the right way to do it. Don't fear losing income or credibility, because you will learn to live within your means because you get joy from other things. And lighten up. Laugh a lot." We need to stand together and help each other. I'm determined to work in a team, in a group, in a connected way. The more there are of us, the easier it's going to be. The time has come for us to speak our truth on this. What I do isn't some sort of cosy backlash to the mainstream; this is different. People just don't want to be churned through a big clinic set up that doesn't know them. And doctors don't want to work in that sort of environment either.

I would be paid more by our government agencies to spend two minutes injecting a steroid into a joint – giving it a state of bodily panic which dulls everything down – or injecting botox for fifteen minutes, than I would doing what I do in four hours, which sees lasting change and wellness.

If I do this work, I want to be in a place I love. You don't want a grumpy doctor, do you? I wouldn't want one. You definitely wouldn't want an angry acupuncturist! We should be creating new ways and new environments – it's a win-win in every way.

Unfortunately, the money is in quick consults still. I would be paid more by our government agencies to spend two minutes injecting a steroid into a joint – giving it a state of bodily panic which dulls everything down – or injecting botox for fifteen minutes, than I would doing what I do in four hours, which sees lasting change and wellness.

It's not all plain sailing. When you're an agent for change, there are so many overpowering and contradictory old messages out there that you seem to be sometimes combating with people, so it's got its challenges. But that's important as well; you've got to have challenges.

Before I changed the way I worked, I used to come back after a morning session just moribund really. I had to go to bed for a couple of hours before I could take on the afternoon session. I remember feeling very dark at that time and finding it very difficult; and yet it was also at a time where all this other awareness was coming. When I'm seeing people with chronic fatigue in that state, we always talk about what is emerging.

Chronic fatigue is actually about sensitivity – these people are open books to the world, they are the canaries in the mine – they are by nature open, creative souls, in general. The way to help them is not chemicals. There isn't a chemical way. The way is for them to appreciate who they are and gain energy from nature and from joyful relationships; because they're open to that, and that feeds them. And I encourage them to demand the right environment for them, because they want to live in the real world, they don't want to live in a bubble or be isolated. That's where principles from Qi Gong, Tai Chi and Yoga, come through.

Just like plants, we as people need to find the right environment in which to thrive. That has been my journey also, and that is what works for me – taking my time. If you are of service to people, if you are doing good, or being kind – not only does it expand your own consciousness but it also expands the world's consciousness, and that feeds back to you. It's the ultimate feedback system, and at the end of the day you're sustained by that. I think people are burning out because a part of them knows this, and a part of them is trapped – and not just in medicine but in every other job. So we're talking about sustainability.

The world is contriving to make sense of this – eating locally, appreciating what you've got around you, not trying to search for it externally in material things. The consciousness changes of the next decades will be internal changes. That is how the external world changes. And that is what we've got power over – our insides. We haven't got power over other people's journeys in that way. We can guide people but you have to set the example yourself.

Our political systems are based often on three and four-year terms and we're talking about future generations here. I think that the authorities should see the wisdom in backing this work, not excluding it, which is what has happened. It's not just health; it's education also. To me this approach should be integral to our education – from primary school onwards, in partnership with teachers and parents. I'm sure that's the way to go. Look what Jamie Oliver has done for food – it's cool now to cook and to eat consciously. Children get it. We're talking about spontaneity, play – this is their natural light. Basically, they're the teachers. Even working with the teenagers is easier than trying to shift it at the other end. This is a public health issue.

My dream for the future of medicine is that all the wonders of modern medicine will be combined with the compassionate approach that we understand that to be such an important part of health and healing, and that the focus will be on wellness: a level of wellness which isn't just not being sick – it is another level of wellness. I hope that the role of those involved in the profession, in all the healing professions, is acknowledged and supported. But ultimately, it's for the people, for everybody to gain ownership over their own health. We need to move away from the co-dependent model we have created. The children understand all of this. I hope that they are nurtured in such a way that we can evolve into levels of holistic wellbeing that we can only just dream of.

25 | DANCING DOCTOR

DR RICHARD MAYES

Rural General Practitioner Obstetrician, Medical Educator, dancer and dance instructor.

Castlemaine, Australia

I really struggle to put this story out there. My patients rely on me to be strong, invincible, perfect. None of them would have any idea that I've had some really dark moments through burnout. My family wouldn't even know.

I remember sitting at my desk for the first time and thinking: *Wow, this is me for the next forty years.* One part of me felt like I'd made it to where I wanted to be, but another part of me was thinking: *Jesus, is this it?* I was like: *Right, this is it, this is what I do.* I went into it all guns blazing – I was going to be the most helpful doctor, the most caring, most available doctor, see as many patients as I could. I did obstetrics as an add-on, and I said yes to everything. And I enjoyed it, the responsibility, being part of community, and suddenly and quickly being an intimate part of people's lives. I was doing the whole cradle to grave health care that I had always wanted to do.

But life was, without me realising it, getting harder and harder. In my first year as a GP, when we were new to our community, I had a baby who wasn't sleeping and a wife who didn't seem happy, despite me thinking I was doing everything right. The worse things got at home, the harder I tried to work, thinking that was the answer. Or maybe I was failing so dismally at home that I stuck at what I at least thought I was doing well at.

When I started to feel like I wasn't doing a good job as a doctor; that's when things started to really show up. I was getting angry at patients, who seemed to want more and more. It was a familiar pattern at home and at work of everybody needing more, and more was never enough.

I would get away from work thinking: *Oh, I need to breathe*, and I'd get home to a house where people were even more needy. I just couldn't figure out how I could do any more, and the more I tried, the more I felt like I was failing. I'd try and find things to make myself feel better. I exercised madly.

I remember one occasion early in my career at my parent's house. My father was an obstetrician and was my greatest mentor and teacher. He understood how tough it can be. We'd gone to visit them, about an hour from where we live. The children's delighted yells were coming from the lounge room and mum was busying herself in the kitchen making an awesome mum meal. There was laughter in the house. Going back home to mum and dad's was like putting on a comfy pair of slippers – it was always warm, the kids could have whatever they wanted, they were delighted and we were all scooped up. Just walking through the door, I would feel dad's welcoming smile, with mum standing behind him, and I knew that everything would be OK. It was a breath of warmth in amongst the horrors of that time.

We had just arrived and I was just settling in when my mobile phone rang. My whole body reacted. I went into another room to take the call so that I could be away from the family and didn't have to break the festivities. It was a midwife telling me that a first-time mum was in labour. There was an awful tearing in my heart: I so wanted to be there with that woman because I love being with women while they have their babies, and I hated the thought of letting them down after building that relationship for many months. But I also wanted, needed, to be a baby with my own mum. My mouth was saying: "I've just arrived in Ballarat, I could be there in an hour. Will she be OK to wait that long?" As I said those words I felt these huge hands come up over my shoulder and my neck, and dad whispered: "Don't make the same mistakes I did." I looked him in the eyes and nodded. He asked me who was on-call. It was the other 'always available' GP. I rang the hospital back and said: "Look, could you call the on-call doctor and keep me posted?" I still couldn't let go. I still felt I shouldn't be calling on the other doctor. I stood there torn, seeing how much fun my family were having, trying to work out how I could get back home and let my family stay and enjoy this moment. Then the phone rang and the on-call doctor said: "I'm a little anxious about her delivering here, I think I need to transfer her to a bigger hospital." I said: "That's fine by me." The other doctor got her day off, the woman had a lovely birth, and I got to have a beautiful day with my family. It was one of my first big lessons: do what's right in your heart and everything will work out right in the end.

When things got really bad we started flying to Queensland for personal / spiritual development courses which friends had recommended to us. The courses had us look at our 'essence,' our calling – at who we want to be in the world. It felt like I was opening up an old chest, an old toy box, and discovering all the toys that I used to play with; those things that bring me joy. In the first weekend away, I realised what I had become, and what I had let go of, and the dream was reignited. I saw myself again, and I remember the first time seeing patients again after that experience. I felt I was able to see people for the first time in years. I got back to what it was all about.

I think that was the first step to me relating more – opening up my heart. I just felt more present, even though that sounds very clichéd. I was able to see the joy in people that they couldn't see, that I'd lost sight of in myself, and then found again. I started pushing the boundaries around work–

I was always trying to please people. I hated letting people down. I felt completely responsible, 'Mr Fix It.'

life balance, even though I felt I was letting others down and making it harder for them. The feedback was that I was appearing happier. I realised that maybe putting family first was actually a way of getting through trauma. Practicing what we preach. The clinic became freer around letting me take the time off that I needed, and the other doctors became freer around seeking space themselves. The energy of the whole place changed.

I think trauma leads us to create patterns of behaviour that protect us from experiencing further trauma, which in the end become problematic in themselves. I'm not sure what it is that sits there in me, but something led me to behave in a way that I was always trying to please people. I hated letting people down. I felt completely responsible, 'Mr Fix It.'

We went on a two-month holiday once, and when I got back the receptionist said: "Gee it's funny, when you were away none of your patients came in." Then a patient said to me: "Richard, next time you go away you need to give me a general anaesthetic because I can't get by without you." Instead of feeling proud, I felt sick, suddenly realising the dependence I had created, not empowering them to become their own healers, to look after themselves. Somewhere in the past that dependence had fed a need in me to be liked and appreciated, but I suddenly saw it for what it really was. I realised I had set myself up to be the heroic, do everything doctor and it wasn't good for them or me.

We went to live in Queensland eventually because I was still really struggling to keep my boundaries in a small rural community. I started doing locums[1] which, for a time, I loved. There was no paperwork, no following up – just rock up, do your job and go home. I got to see how different practices manage workloads and I saw so much more of my family.

My frustration with the limitations of Western medicine and its use of medications as the first port of call came to a head that day that you mention in the book's introduction. I had more and more moments of questioning the way I was working and started to feel very alone in

---

1   Short term, fill in jobs at clinics where doctors are on holidays / leave or where there is temporary understaffing.

the way I was looking at things. We continued to do the courses, which were bringing me to a deeper understanding of the power of human connection, and I was starting to feel that there had to be a better way than the ten-minute medicine I was doing.

So I got carried away and set myself up as a solo GP in an integrative clinic – rather naively in hindsight – which was owned by a naturopath and had a whole lot of other complementary health therapists. I was really excited at first and had some wonderful interactions and outcomes with patients, and I was able to spend a lot more time with them. But it was expensive to run the place alone and I had to charge patients more than they were often able to pay. The naturopath was also sending me all these patients and asking me to tick boxes so that she could access some Medicare funding for them. She would say: "Don't worry about doing a history, I've already done that. Just tick these boxes and sign here. And please bulk bill them because they can't afford you." It became a bit about turf wars, and I felt there was no honouring of my own interest in, and responsibility to connect with patients. So, with that, and with the financial reality, I pulled out pretty quickly and, for a number of other reasons, including missing being close to family, we decided to move back to Victoria.

I sheepishly put my tail between my legs and asked for my old job back. A number of my friends said: "Why are you going back to that place that burned you out?" I said: "They didn't burn me out, my attitude did."

The shift in my thinking which I brought back was that working towards partnership and relationship with the patients was more sustainable in the long run because I was facilitating them to be their own healers. It took an enormous burden off me – I had been exhausting myself early in my career by thinking that I needed to take responsibility for them looking after themselves. When they got really unwell, I'd be really hard on myself and think: *Maybe if I work harder, get it right, learn more, I can make a difference.* I then turned to saying: "I'm here for you but you need to look at what's happening for you." If they didn't want to do that, that's fine but I wasn't going to wear it anymore when I went home. When the burden was lifted off, it gave me my compassion back, and the patients were getting better because they became more empowered to take more responsibility.

Medical training gave me no preparation for this really tough learning curve. It gave me a long list of all the possible things that can go wrong with human beings, and sent me out there to believe I was some kind of God who could fix everything.

> *Medical training gave me no preparation for this really tough learning curve. It gave me a long list of all the possible things that can go wrong with human beings, and sent me out there to believe I was some kind of God who could fix everything.*

I was so focussed on the illness in the early days, and the possible outcomes, that I could barely see the person in front of me. I thought a good outcome was to get patients better quickly and out the door, but many of my patients just kept getting sicker with that 'quick-fix' approach, and I was getting sick too. We and our patients just get caught up in the system, and underneath their ailments they're screaming out for understanding.

I have a patient who I always talk to quite spiritually. She always links symptoms with emotions and spiritual meaning. She came in one day and said: "Richard, I've talked to my spirit guides and they've told me that you're the one to fix me." My response was: "How funny, because I've just realised that I'm not here to fix anyone." We both laughed and then she said: "You're right, I can do it myself." But it became a bit of a misunderstanding because then she thought I didn't want her as a patient anymore, and she didn't come back for a year. When she came back we worked it out and she said: "I needed to come back to you because I need someone to walk with me." And instead of me apologising, we had a chat about what had happened for her in the last twelve months, and she talked about how she had got her power back.

Craig Hassed is someone I look up to. He was a GP and even in my day was running meditation sessions for us at university, which he still does. He writes books about mindfulness and medicine, and has embedded mindfulness firmly into the medical curriculum at Monash University. I am now a medical educator for the Monash Uni rural placement students based out of Bendigo, and I do a bit of mindfulness training with them. I was really excited the first time I ran the session, but I slumped a bit when I found that many of them weren't that interested; they just wanted to hear the facts. It is because they haven't yet experienced the day-to-day, they haven't yet walked the burnout tightrope. More and more people are specialising, so they're probably not thinking they'll have to deal with any of the messy, human stuff.

I sometimes introduce mindfulness, or body awareness into my consults. Different patients respond in different ways. Some really experience things in their body. For example, I had a patient who was a firefighter who was having workplace stress issues. He really experienced excitement or anxiety in a very physical way, so when he was talking about something I would get him to check in with what was happening in his body and see how he was feeling. He would say: "Yeah, I feel more aligned when I think about it that way, instead of just sinking into the blame game."

The pathway to mindfulness doesn't have to be meditation in my opinion. If you're struggling with demons and your mind is busy, meditation isn't necessarily a good way to fix that. For me, I needed to be doing something physical and monotonous, so sport – kayaking and running – is my meditation. When I get my body into a rhythm, I find the thoughts can release and transform, and funnily enough, that experience of grounding has helped me to meditate. I'm also doing Qi Gong now. A patient was telling me what he was doing for himself and I was looking for a body balancing art myself, so I went along. It comes from traditional Chinese medicine and uses movement to increase your energy.

Just recently I took up dance classes, run by a patient of mine who runs a youth hip-hop dance school. We had joked for a few years that the dancing I did as the mascot for our local fun run was getting lame, and I needed some schooling in the hip-hop arts. So she created a class for adults and it has absolutely taken off. We organised a 'flash mob'[2] at the local supermarket as part of our recent local arts festival, the Castlemaine Fringe Festival. People recorded it on their phones and it made its way onto social media and went viral. I was the only bloke dancing. There I was in my mullet wig, my headband and my eighties gear, and all of a sudden everyone's going: "Who's mullet man? Oh my goodness, it's the local doctor!"

Our ABC local radio station did a follow up story on their website on adults returning to dance and profiled me and a couple of others. Then we had a whole lot more enquiries about our dance class, and my now dance instructor colleague asked me if I would come on board as a dance instructor for a new therapeutic class we are piloting for older adults with mobility issues. I do the mindfulness stuff with them at the end of the class and we all just love it. It's been a great side passion to have and a funny, unexpected way to get a new name for myself as 'Mullet-Man, the Dancing Doctor.' Some people think I'm a bit weird, and my children pretend to be a bit embarrassed, but I have actually found it has been one of the most powerful things I could have demonstrated for my patients around self-care and wellbeing.

Having experienced the stress of burnout, however, I know first-hand how easy it is to become numb to the humanity of the person sitting before you, thirty patients a day, day in and day (and night) out.

It has had a huge ripple effect, which I totally wasn't expecting. I even heard that the video of me dancing in the supermarket was used by an American trainer at a professional

---

2   A popular form of group expression where people come together suddenly and seemingly unexpectedly in a public place to perform a pre-prepared dance or song routine, designed for fun, community building, and entertainment.

development day in front of hundreds of teachers, regarding the art of finding joy in a stressful world.

I find it very hard to articulate what it is that I do in my practice of medicine that might be considered noteworthy or 'different'. I know that in other countries there are whole organisations and movements dedicated to restoring compassion in medicine. That resonates very strongly for me, although it somehow feels that being compassionate towards patients should almost go without saying. Having experienced the stress of burnout, however, I know first-hand how easy it is to become numb to the humanity of the person sitting before you, thirty patients a day, day in and day (and night) out.

I used to have patients whom I considered to be 'heart sinkers'. They would take up lots of time and drain me of all my resources. These people would come back again and again, situations unchanged, to get their fix of me feeding their sinking hearts through listening to their endless sad stories. At the time, I thought it was compassionate for me to listen beyond judgement where others had given up listening and caring. But there is a duality there; I've come to see that sometimes I have to challenge these people to change their stories, to help them out of their sickness mentality. Instead of pandering to their victim story, it is more helpful for me to wake people up and to try to call their powerful being to come back. It is different for different people – there is compassion through pure understanding and love; and compassion through tough love – sometimes telling them a hard truth so that they can come to their own understanding. And there is also a need for self-compassion: for being OK with not being able to 'fix' everything and everyone, and even being OK with people sometimes not wanting to get better or make changes. It is also a fine line and I've had to learn not to go so strongly in with my perceptions and opinions – not arrogantly judging and traumatising people when my hunch was off par. Often it ended up being what I needed to face in myself. That was where the greatest therapy happened; when I realised there was a path we both need to walk in this therapeutic relationship.

Just as my label of 'heart sinker' became a self-fulfilling prophecy (and with a changed perspective, those patients became my greatest teachers), I have come to be very wary of diagnostic labels. A friend was telling me a while back about her experience of seeing auras which had been interpreted by doctors as part of an illness, in her case epilepsy. She had experienced out of body experiences all of her life, well before she was diagnosed with epilepsy, and they had been a source of great joy. The day she was told that she had epilepsy, she recounts that the doctors were almost euphoric, having 'solved her problems.' She was drugged, ostensibly 'fixed,' and she sank. The very next day I was gifted with a patient whose history I thankfully hadn't had a chance to read. She was keen to get off her antidepressant medication. Somehow the conversation turned to the auras she had been seeing. She described the same thing that my friend had described to me – I told her what a gift it was to be able to see such things. She had never seen it that way. It was a moment of true connection. She presented as anxious but otherwise psychologically normal. We then turned to discuss the drugs she was on – I turned to the computer and found that she had been diagnosed with schizophrenia. She was on antipsychotics and mood stabilisers and antidepressants. It suddenly became so clear to me why she might have become so shut down. Having someone see her and acknowledge her beyond her symptoms and labels meant an enormous amount to her and allowed her to take control again of her own healing.

I had another patient who had been diagnosed with schizophrenia, who on one occasion needed me to write a letter of advocacy, listing all of his psychiatric conditions and symptoms. What came to me as I started to list all these diagnoses was that they were just a lot of labels that had trapped him into a certain way of being. On his list were also schizoaffective disorder, acquired brain injury from toxic exposure, personality disorder – he had about seven different labels. He even enjoyed that process – he would research these labels and agree that that was exactly who he was, and that it explained everything. As I was trying to write the letter he was talking all about his passions. I realised that previously I'd seen his talkativeness as part of a diagnosis, as part of a mania. I mentioned that perhaps there were too many labels, that maybe, for example, he was simply talkative about things he was passionate about, and that we were making that wrong. He got it straight off, saying: "So what you're saying doc is that I have the disease but I'm not the disease." It didn't go much further, I wrote the letter but encouraged him to think a little differently about himself.

So often the limitations to wellness are what is going on in our patients' minds. We as doctors have even been trained to believe in these limitations.

He came back a few weeks later and confessed that he had left last time feeling pretty mad. He said: "I know what you were getting at, and thank-you, but I use my labels as they allow me to avoid what's really going on … I don't want to look at that, so thanks, but no thanks." There are times when I have to be OK with patients choosing not to want to make changes.

So often the limitations to wellness are what is going on in our patients' minds. We as doctors have even been trained to believe in these limitations. For example, I had a patient who presented with terrible lesions and sores on his hands, like a kind of severe dermatitis. He asked if it had anything to do with alcohol, and it turned out that he was an alcoholic. As part of my own journey I had come to realise that one of the best ways to bring about change is to engage people in talking about their dreams and passions, and what, if they could defy every limitation, they would love to be doing. So, instead of getting caught up discussing with this patient about how much he drank and how bad it is for his health, we talked about what he was missing out on in his life. He told me how he used to be a champion in his particular sport, and he came alive telling me about it. I ordered some standard tests. When he came back a week later he told me that he had stopped drinking, got back into his sport, and had met someone who was interested in herbal medicine and naturopathy who was helping him regain his fitness and to restore his body. His hands were one hundred per cent better. I nearly fell off my chair. It had only been a week. It demonstrated to me people's power to heal themselves when they are engaged in their truth. The simple act of hearing someone's dream had uncovered some of the obstacles, which often take weeks and months to come through with psychological theorem.

It is not surprising patients lack hope and motivation when doctors enter into a situation with such a belief system. For example, cycles of addiction and behaviour change theory would have us believe that people sometimes need to go through cycles of change seven times, that they need to wean slowly in order to go into successful remission – even the word remission suggests an expectation of relapse. I love giving people hope that they can turn things around as quickly as they like.

I have always had a knowing that there was a lot more available in the healing picture than what I had been taught. I started my career in the late 1990s when naturopathy and acupuncture and other alternative and complementary modalities were all fairly much mainstream, and I remember thinking that I would look into some of those things to have another tool in my belt so that I could have something else to offer. I could see that my role as a diagnostician was limited as it was often a diagnosis of exclusion. A lot of the pathology doesn't pick up the subtle changes, not to mention the spiritual and emotional levels of illness. So, if all the investigations come up showing no significant diagnosis, we are often left with labels such as chronic fatigue or irritable bowel syndrome – which explain the symptoms but don't address the causes, and don't look at the intricacies of imbalance in the system physically and emotionally.

By this stage, studies were showing that roughly the same numbers of people were seeing complementary therapists as were coming to conventional medical clinics. I started to talk to these therapists and found there was so much available: whole systems of healing which stand alone, and a lot of areas that I could see would help. So, instead of me having one additional tool in my belt, I realised I just need to know how to refer appropriately and help patients through the maze, and to find a modality that resonates with them. Once the patient realises that they can be in charge of their own wellbeing, they start becoming a partner in their health care.

We think that integrated medicine and mindfulness medicine are new areas but in fact they are a return to the old, when the only tools available to doctors were such things as herbal, nutritional, lifestyle and heart-based remedies. My father, a doctor during a particularly non-patient-centred era of care, was a huge mentor to me with regards to connection with, and understanding of people. My favourite story about him is that just before he finished work due to illness, during his last several months of work, he chose not to operate, just to consult with patients. He spoke to them about their conditions and what might or might not need surgery. He told me that he was amazed at how, without the option of offering to do surgery, by just talking to patients, they would often get better. He taught me meditation and visualisation for sport as a young man. He taught me about the power of the mind and how we can shift and change our mind, and that our capacities are only limited by our attitudes and mindsets. He had a down-to-earth common-sense spirituality, which taught me that medicine is a real privilege and a unique opportunity to truly connect with people. Like my dad, I believe that we are all connected, that we are all one. A medical relationship is a two-way flow – we all have gifts to bring, and our connections with each other will inevitably bring us alive if we can see that humanity in each other, and the lessons we have for each other. My father made his patients feel like the most important person in the world because, in that interaction, they were the most important person to him.

I think that's where I'm travelling now in medicine. If we come out of the small picture of medicine – charging through each patient, accumulating money and being up against time – and see that it is a great honour and privilege to be invited into another person's world, but also to help bring them home to their essence, to themselves, that's what brings me alive.

I do get caught up in the frustration when I'm not pulling that off. My job is not to save the world or solve everyone's hurts and problems: my job is to allow space and understanding for people to be where they are at, and to maintain the hope that they will come through. People need to connect with people who are hopeful and who believe in them. We all need connection with people who are willing to love us unconditionally.

My story is so organic. This is just my story today. I still struggle. I don't want to be held up as some kind of poster boy for conquering burnout or mastering compassion. I wish I had, but the reality for me is that it is a daily roller-coaster, which is (these days) mostly up. But who knows what is around the corner? I guess I just have to embrace that, and accept that part of my story is where I have come from, what I make of that, and what I made of things at the time. Someone wise once said: If you've got a clear idea of where you're heading in the future, it is probably somebody else's story you have mistaken for your own. If you are blissfully unaware, it is probably closer to the truth because it leaves you open to keep creating anew every day.

Putting our story out there, for all of us, is like revealing the dream that sits beneath us. The very act of telling your story reminds you that you have one, and of the worth of that story. To contemplate it, to look at it from different angles, to give voice to it, is to honour it.

CONTRIBUTOR PROFILES

DR JOHN BARTON

John Barton is now semi-retired and only takes on work that excites him. He is a registered psychotherapist (trained in psychodrama) and accredited Balint leader and trainer living in Auckland and working in Auckland and in Christchurch. He retired as a General Practitioner about ten years ago after fifteen years as a country GP in New Zealand followed by ten years in inner city Melbourne. His psychotherapy work is mainly as a supervisor of doctors, psychotherapists and other health professionals. He currently leads four Balint groups including one over the internet and supervises several other Balint leaders. He runs workshops teaching the use of small (toy) figures in counselling and psychotherapy; and occasionally teaches professional and clinical skills to second year medical students. He began learning bass guitar in 2011 and is currently rehearsing with two bands.

DR BRIAN BROOM

Dr Brian Broom is Consultant Physician in Clinical Immunology (Auckland City Hospital), a registered psychotherapist, and Adjunct Professor in the Department of Psychotherapy, and founder of the Post-Graduate MindBody Healthcare Diploma and Masters programme at Auckland University of Technology, New Zealand. He has been described as a 'philosopher physician', with a passion for 'whole person' approaches to health, un-wellness and disease. His mind–body approach has brought about healing change in many patients with chronic conditions. He has written several books and delivered lectures around the world on his approach (see 'Further Reading').

DR JOAN CAMPBELL

Dr Joan Campbell is an Integrative Health Professional and Registered Medical Practitioner specialising in acupuncture and Chinese medicine. She works in her own well-established practice in Auckland, New Zealand. Joan has worked in medicine and allied fields since 1966, including as a registered nurse, medical doctor, GP obstetrician, psychologist, Chinese acupuncturist, undergraduate teacher at the New Zealand College of Chinese Medicine (six years), and university teacher of post-graduate Chinese medicine / acupuncture programmes for health professionals at the Auckland University of Technology (1995–2014). She is currently a doctoral student at the University of Auckland and the Nanjing University of Chinese Medicine. Dr Campbell is Founder (in 2000) and immediate past Chairman of the New Zealand Acupuncture Standards Authority Inc., a voluntary regulatory authority for acupuncturists recognised by the New Zealand Government through the Accident Compensation legislation. Joan is working with the Chinese medicine profession on the national regulation of Chinese medicine under the Health Practitioners Competence Insurance Act 2003. After a long journey, the Minister of Health has agreed that Chinese medicine should be regulated and the process is now underway. Joan is a wife to Graeme, mother to Janette and grandmother to Zachary and Leonardo.

DR CATHERINE CROCK AM

Dr. Catherine Crock is a medical pioneer, producer of music and theatrics, humanitarian, mother and advocate for change. A Physician at The Royal Children's Hospital Melbourne, Australia, Catherine has successfully implemented a raft of positive changes to healthcare in the areas of organisational culture, services and patient-family support. She is the Chair and Founder of The Hush Foundation, a registered charity organisation working to transform healthcare by improving partnerships, culture and the environment to support health and wellbeing. Hush, in collaboration with some of Australia's finest musical talent, has commissioned fifteen albums of music specifically for application within healthcare. Dr Crock also founded and was Executive Director of the Australian Institute for Patient and Family Centred Care, which has now merged with The Hush Foundation.

DR GLENN COLQUHOUN

Dr Glenn Colquhoun is a General Practitioner and award-winning author and poet. His published works include: *The art of walking upright* (1999, Steele Roberts); *An explanation of poetry to my father* (2001, Steele Roberts); *Playing God* (2002, Steel Roberts); *How we fell* (2006, Steele Roberts); and *North South* (2009, Steele Roberts). His poetry and writing explores the places he has lived, the people he has loved, his work as a doctor, and Irish and Maori mythology. Glenn was convenor of the 2004 New Zealand Post Book Awards for Children and Young Adults and in 2004 he received the country's largest literary award: the Prize in Modern Letters. In 2010 Glenn was awarded a Fulbright scholarship to research medical storytelling programmes. He practices medicine on the Kapiti Coast. He lives in Waikawa Beach, New Zealand with his young daughter Olive.

DR MARK DAVIS

Dr Mark Davis is a Psychiatrist based in Lower Hutt, Wellington. He is married with four adult children and one grandson. Mark graduated from Otago Medical School in 1976 and completed his post-graduate psychiatric training (in the UK and NZ) in 1986. He worked as a Consultant Psychiatrist to Hutt Hospital (1986–1995), Victoria University Health Service (1986), Te Omanga Hospice, Lower Hutt (1998–2003) and has been in full-time private practice since 1995. His current work is predominantly third-party medico-legal assessments in the areas of chronic pain and post-injury psychological disorders, plus health issues for professional registration bodies. Mark is very interested in the area of professional education, health and wellbeing, and he wrote two chapters for the NZ DHAS book for doctors and health professionals – *In sickness and in health* (1998, 2nd Edition.) He has been on the NZ Medical Council Education Committee, and was part of a health advisory group to the New Zealand Veterinary Association. Mark is a certified Balint group leader and has run two Balint groups (for GPs, and one for therapists) over the past fourteen years. He is also a trained teacher of meditation and personal wellbeing, having undertaken such training over the past 25 years. Mark has facilitated a number of Health and Wellbeing workshops and retreats for doctors, health practitioners and their partners. His personal interests involve music (violin), reading, walking, golf (passionately), yoga and meditation, and time with family and friends.

DR LIZ HARDING

Dr Liz Harding is a Locum General Practitioner in Auckland, New Zealand. She has lived with her partner Diane for the past twenty-seven years. They have twenty-year-old twins, who are both finishing their last year of tertiary education. Their daughter is a singer-songwriter and their son is into computers. Liz gets a lot of joy from being a member of two community choirs, does spin classes at the gym in the mornings and attends Parkrun to keep fit.

DR PETER HOWE

Dr Peter Howe finished studying medicine in 1987, and has been a Specialist Anaesthetist at the Royal Children's Hospital in Melbourne, Australia since 2000. His other interests include playing the guitar (badly), surfing (very badly) and embarrassing his three teenage children in public. He is readily bribed by the promise of coffee or signed Hawthorn Football Club memorabilia.

DR ROBIN KELLY

Dr Robin Kelly is a General Practitioner and Medical Acupuncturist, author, speaker, and musician based in Auckland, New Zealand. His medical practice has evolved to embrace Eastern and modern mind–body philosophies. His focus is on integrating these holistic models into a modern, contemporary environment blending the best of the East with the best of the West, and where patients are seen as true partners. Together they devise 'Healing Plans' honouring each person's unique gifts. Robin is a sought-after conference speaker and workshop presenter. Dr Kelly is past and current Co-president of the Medical Acupuncture Society (NZ) and a Founding Trustee of New Zealand's MindBody Trust. He studied acupuncture and Chinese medicine in the 1980s, running teaching workshops for health professionals and doctors. Since the 1990s Dr Kelly's overriding interest has been in researching the roles consciousness and quantum theory play in the deep healing process, which is the topic of his books (see Further Reading).

ASSOCIATE PROFESSOR
VICKI KOTSIRILOS AM

Dr Vicki Kotsirilos is a well-known medical educator, speaker and respected Holistic GP at the Dunstan Dental and Medical Clinic in Melbourne. Dr Vicki integrates evidence-based natural therapies such as acupuncture, nutritional and herbal medicine with mainstream healthcare. She keeps up to date with the research in these areas and is co-author of the successful textbook *A guide to evidence-based integrative and complementary medicine*. Dr Vicki is a regular writer for *Medical Observer* and publishes a monthly column 'Integrative perspectives' widely circulated to most GPs in Australia. She holds three Adjunct Associate Professorial positions at the University of Western Sydney, Monash University and La Trobe University. Dr Vicki was awarded a Member (AM) in the General Division of the Order of Australia for four categories: *'Significant service to Integrative Medicine: to Health Practitioner Standards and Regulations, to Medical Education, and to the Environment'*. In 2017 Dr Vicki was again honoured to receive an Australia Day 'Environment Award.'

DR ELIZABETH LEWIS

Dr Elizabeth Lewis is a Psychiatrist based in Bendigo, Australia, specialising in bio-nutritional medicine. She graduated from Monash University in 1971 and has worked in psychiatry for almost forty-five years with twenty years in the public sector followed by twenty-five years in the private sector as a bulk-billing psychiatrist. Dr Lewis was an early activist for mental health rights and was one of the founding members of Mental Health Action, a successful human rights health advocacy collective.

DR RICHARD MAYES

Dr Richard Mayes is a General Practitioner Obstetrician in Castlemaine, Australia. He is also a Medical Educator and the Clinical Hub Co-ordinator for Monash University Medical School for the Bendigo region, and is a national instructor for the Advanced Life Support in Obstetrics and PROMPT training programmes, for which he was awarded 'Australian Trainer of the Year' in 2016. Richard also enjoys his role as 'The Bird' mascot for an annual local fun run which raises funds for the local hospital. He is also a Castlemaine Parkrun race director, and dance instructor 'in training'. In his down time he enjoys running, kayaking, participating in extreme sports events, practicing Qi Gong, dancing and hanging out with his two children, wife and dog.

DR KATIE MOORE

Dr Katie Moore is a Paediatrician, trained in London and Melbourne and now specialising in Paediatric Oncology. She has a Masters of Bioethics and is in the early stages of a Masters of Family Therapy. Katie is also a mother of four and wife to a wonderful man who works as a paediatric anaesthetist. As a professional, parent and patient she believes strongly in the vital importance of humanity and compassion in medicine.

DR VERONICA MOULE

Dr Veronica Moule is a rural General Practitioner Obstetrician, Homeopath and practitioner of anthroposophical medicine based in Castlemaine, Australia. After graduating from Monash University, she did her residency and early years of General Practice in the Geelong region. She and her family moved to Castlemaine when her oldest son was three. Her family has expanded to four children, and the babies whose births she first attended are now adults. She enjoys the depth of intensity and integrity that rural GP Obstetrics offers. Dr Moule's permanent on-call status means she searches for sanctuary in her home, paddling on the lake, cooking outside with an open fire and breathing in the wonders of nature.

PROFESSOR VIKRAM PATEL

Professor Patel is a Psychiatrist whose work is on the burden of mental disorders, their association with poverty and social disadvantage, and the use of community resources for their prevention and treatment. He is a Co-founder of Sangath, an Indian Non-government Organisation, which won the 'MacArthur Foundation's International Prize for Creative and Effective Institutions' in 2008, and the World Health Organisation's (WHO) 'Public Health Champion of India' award in 2016. He is a Fellow of the UK's Academy of Medical Sciences and has served on several WHO expert and Government of India committees. He also works in the areas of child development and adolescent health. He was listed in *TIME Magazine's* 100 most influential persons of the year in 2015. His academic appointments include: Pershing Square Professor of Global Health and the Wellcome Trust; Principal Research Fellow, Department of Global Health and Social Medicine, Harvard Medical School; Professor, Department of Global Health and Population, Harvard T. H. Chan School of Public Health; Co-founder and Member of Managing Committee, Sangath, Goa, India; Adjunct Professor and Joint Director, Centre for Chronic Conditions and Injuries, Public Health Foundation of India; and Honorary Professor, London School of Hygiene & Tropical Medicine,

UK. Professor Patel's work has been widely recognised by a number of prestigious international awards, including: the Chalmers Medal (Royal Society of Tropical Medicine and Hygiene, UK), the Sarnat Medal (US National Academy of Medicine), an Honorary Doctorate from Georgetown University, the Pardes Humanitarian Prize (the Brain & Behaviour Research Foundation), an Honorary OBE from the UK Government and the Posey Leadership Award (Austin College). He also works as a Professor at Harvard TH Chan School of Public Health, Adjunct Professor and Joint Director of the Centre for Chronic Conditions and Injuries at the Public Health Foundation of India, Honorary Professor at the London School of Hygiene & Tropical Medicine (where he co-founded the Centre for Global Mental Health in 2008).

DR SHARAD PAUL

Dr Paul is a Skin Cancer Surgeon, General Practitioner, and Evolutionary Biologist with a Masters in Medical Law and Ethics, and is currently completing a PhD in cutaneous / dermatological surgery. In 2007, Dr Paul invented the first new skin graft technique that reduces costs, pain and healing time for patients, and he has presented this new technique at international conferences. He is also a lecturer, student, author (fiction and non-fiction) and social enterprise owner (bookshop and literacy charity). Dr Paul is Adjunct Professor in the Faculty of Health, and Faculty of Creative Technologies at the Auckland University of Technology; Senior Lecturer, Skin Cancer, at the University of Queensland; and Hon. Senior Lecturer, Faculty of Surgery, at Auckland University. He was awarded New Zealand Medical Association's highest honour, 'The Chair's Award' in 2012 and the same year was a finalist for the 'New Zealander of the Year Award'. In 2015, he was awarded the 'Ko Awatea International Excellence Award for Leading Health Improvement on a Global Scale' at the Asia Pacific American Coalition Forum, the largest medical gathering in this region. Outside of medicine Dr Paul runs an award-winning café and bookstore called the Baci Lounge, in Newmarket, New Zealand. Proceeds are used to fund literacy programmes in low-decile Auckland schools, with the aim of helping children to "dream with their eyes wide open." When he is home, he teaches creative writing to disadvantaged children (by visiting schools personally once a week, and funding school libraries). He has also served on the National Commission of UNESCO (United Nations Educational, Scientific and Cultural Organisation). Dr Paul has been described by the New Zealand Medical Association as "one of the most inspiring, intelligent and compassionate men you are likely to meet." *TIME magazine*, in 2008, called him "Open Heart Surgeon" (*TIME*, July 17, 2008). Dr Paul's popular books include: Fiction: *Cool cut* (Picador, 2007); *To kill a snow dragonfly* (4th Estate, 2012); *The kite flyers* (Harper Collins, 2015); Non-Fiction: *The genetics of health* (Beyond Word / Simon and Schuster, 2017); *Skin, a biography* (4th Estate, 2013); *Dermocracy* (Collins, 2015); Poetry: *De nature melanoma* (Middle Island Press, 2015).

DR MELVYN POLON

Dr Melvyn Polon is a Paediatrician in Sydney, Australia. He describes himself as an introvert feeling personality type. He believes that a large number of our thoughts, attitudes and behaviours are driven by subconscious emotional forces. He also believes that the unconscious emotional dimension affects our health to a large extent. He has worked as a paediatrician for the past thirty years spending a lot of time telling children that the scared feeling, the sad feeling and the small feeling are all normal. Sometimes we can do something to make ourselves feel better and sometimes we just have to feel the feeling and wait for it to pass.

DR DAVID REILLY

Dr David Reilly is a General Practitioner, Homeopath, Integrative Medical Practitioner and early practitioner of MindBody medicine. He was one of the founding practitioners of the National Centre for Integrative Care in Glasgow, Scotland. Dr Reilly's work was credited by the Public Health Institute of Scotland with seeding the 'Fifth Wave' of Public Health, seminal in tackling the rising epidemics of modern living. Dr Reilly has long been a healthcare reform advocate, emphasising the study of the human healing response and its catalysis through therapeutic relationship, and evolving self-care, as a necessary foundation for better care and health. He used this focus as the basis of his leadership of the National Health Service National Centre for Integrative Care in Scotland, and led the creation of its new award-winning building as a model of a healing environment. As National Clinical Lead for Integrative Care for the Scottish Government he helped spread these ideas nationally. He has made extensive international contributions. He now directs TheWEL Organisation and its radical courses that have been shown to help patients and staff transform their own wellbeing and health, and so better help others.

DR NINA SAWICKI

Dr Sawicki is a General Practitioner, with an interest in qualitative research methods and congenital hearing loss. In her spare time, she loves 'tramping' (hill walking, mountain climbing and bushwalking), and writing. She lives and works in Wellington, New Zealand

DR JENNY SIMPSON

Dr Jenny Simpson was born in Scotland, coming with family to Dunedin in New Zealand at the age of four. She studied medicine at Otago, and Wellington, practicing in greater Wellington in family planning, sexual health, youth health services, General Practice and addiction medicine. She is now retired.

DR MEABURN STANILAND

Dr Meaburn Staniland is a General Practitioner with an interest in transformational men's work, rites of passage for his sons and teenage boys, meditation and Balint psychotherapeutic group work. He is based in Wellington, New Zealand.

DR TRALEE SUGRUE

Dr Tralee Sugrue is a General Practitioner and Homeopath based in Wellington, New Zealand.

DR GEOFFREY TOOGOOD

Dr Geoffrey Toogood is a Cardiologist, doctors' mental health advocate, creator of 'Crazy Socks4Docs Day,' writer and long-distance ocean swimmer. He is based in Melbourne, Australia

DR MARK WENITONG

Dr Mark Wenitong is a Kabi Kabi man from South Queensland. He is one of the founders of the Australian Indigenous Doctors Association and works in clinical practice research and policy in Far North Queensland and Cape York, and is trying to retire and just play music with his grandkids. His main musical interests are reggae and jazz, though he can't really play jazz. Dr Wenitong is one of Australia's first Aboriginal Doctors; Senior Medical Advisor, Apunipima Cape York Health Council, Cairns; past President and founder of the Australian Indigenous Doctors' Association and a member of numerous health advisory committees, including the Australian Government's General Practice Training Advisory Committee. He is based in Cairns, Australia.

DR ROBIN YOUNGSON

Dr Robin Youngson is an Anaesthetic Specialist in New Zealand, internationally renowned for his work on compassion in healthcare. A founding member of the national Quality Improvement Committee in

New Zealand, Robin was the New Zealand representative on the WHO International Steering Committee for Patient Safety Solutions. Current positions include: Honorary Senior Lecturer at Auckland University; Editorial Board of the Journal of Compassionate Healthcare; Global Compassion Council of the international Charter for Compassion. Robin is the author of the acclaimed book *TIME TO CARE – How to love your patients and your job* and has just published his second book *From HERO to HEALER – Awakening the inner activist*. Robin is the Co-founder of Hearts in Healthcare, taking his work on compassionate healthcare to fifteen countries around the world. For further information see: www.heartsinhealthcare.com

FURTHER READING

A guide to evidence based integrative and complementary medicine, Kotsirilos, V., Sali, A. and Vitetta, L., Elsevier Health, 2011.

Dermocracy, Sharad Paul, Collins, UK, 2015.

Finding hope when facing serious disease: Inspiring stories, healing insights and health research, Steven J Sommer, www.drstevensommer.com, 2017.

From hero to healer: Awakening the inner activist, Robin Youngson, Rebelheart Publishing, Raglan, New Zealand, 2016. Available as a gift at: https://herotohealer.org/

Healing ways: A doctor's guide to healing, Robin Kelly, Penguin, New Zealand, 2000.

Illuminating wisdom: Works of wisdom, works of art, Craig Hassed, Exisle Publishing, Australia, 2017.

Kitchen table wisdom: Stories that heal, Rachel Naomi Remen, Riverhead Books, New York, 1996.

Meaning-full disease: How personal experience and meanings initiate and maintain physical illness. Brian Broom, Karnac Books, London, 2007.

Mindful learning: Reduce stress and improve brain performance for learning, Craig Hassed, Exisle Publishing, Australia, 2014.

New frontiers in medicine, Craig Hassed, Michelle Anderson Publishing, Melbourne, 2001.

Playing God, Glenn Colqhoun, Steele Roberts, Aotearoa, 2002.

Skin, a biography, Sharad Paul, 4th Estate, UK, 2013.

Somatic illness and the patient's other story: A practical integrative approach to disease for doctors and psychotherapists, Brian Broom, Free Association Books, New York / London, 1997.

Time to care: How to love your patients and your job, Robin Youngson, Rebelheart Publishers, Raglan, New Zealand, 2012.

The essence of health, Craig Hassed, Exisle Publishing, Australia, 2008.

The freedom trap: Reclaiming liberty and wellbeing, Craig Hassed, Exisle Publishing, Australia, 2017.

The Genetics of Health, Sharad Paul, Beyond Word / Simon and Schuster, Australia, 2017.

The human antenna: Reading the language of the Universe in the songs of our cells, Robin Kelly, Hay House, USA, 2010.

'*The human hologram: Living your life in harmony with the unified field'*, Dr Robin Kelly, Energy Psychology Press, USA, 2011.

The meaning of illness, George Groddeck, Hogarth Press / Institute of Psychoanalysis, London, 1977.

Transforming clinical practice using a mindbody approach: A radical integration, Brian Broom (Ed), Karnac Books, London, 2013.

You are a brave man: A Kiwi odyssey in the Himalayas, Dr Liz Harding, Random House, New Zealand, 1997.